LIFE HISTORIES
OF NORTH AMERICAN
JAYS, CROWS, AND TITMICE

by

Arthur Cleveland Bent

in two parts

PART II

Dover Publications, Inc.

New York

This Dover edition, first published in 1964, is an unabridged and unaltered republication of the work first published in 1946 by the United States Government Printing Office, as Smithsonian Institution United States National Museum *Bulletin 191*. This work, which was originally published in one volume, is now published in two separate volumes.

International Standard Book Number: 0-486-21223-8

Library of Congress Catalog Card Number: 64-14302

Manufactured in the United States of America

Dover Publications, Inc.
180 Varick Street
New York 14, N. Y.

CONTENTS.

Order PASSERIFORMES—Continued.

CONTENTS
V

CORVUS CRYPTOLEUCUS Couch

WHITE-NECKED RAVEN

PLATES 37, 38

HABITS

The white-necked raven is smaller than the American raven, but larger than any of the crows; it has a relatively shorter and deeper bill than the larger raven; and it derives its name from the fact that the feathers of the neck and upper breast are pure white for at least their basal half. The name *cryptoleucus* is well chosen, for the white bases are well hidden; they can be seen, with the specimen in hand, by lifting the feathers; but in life they are seldom seen, except when the wind ruffles the plumage or when the bird bends its neck far downward in feeding.

This raven is essentially a bird of the deserts and open plains of the Southwestern States and Mexico. It formerly occupied a wider range in Colorado, western Kansas, and western Nebraska, but, with changing conditions, it has practically disappeared from these regions. Aiken and Warren (1914) have this to say about the withdrawal of the white-necked raven from its range in Colorado, where it was formerly abundant:

Some strong incentive was necessary to have induced these birds to wander northward from their native range in western Texas and New Mexico. This was offered by the slaughter and extermination of the buffalo herds on the western plains which was going on during the late sixties and early seventies. Pioneer settlers were pushing ahead of the railroads; transportation was by teams, and travelers camped along the road and fed grain to their stock. The Ravens, probably first attracted by the buffalo carcasses that strewed the northern plains later followed along the routes of team travel and fed on scattered grain left by campers. By 1874 the buffalo were nearly gone; completed railroads had put the wagon freighters out of business; frequent houses along most roads provided shelter for travelers and camping became unnecessary; the food supply of the White-necked Raven was curtailed and the bird presently retired to its former habitat.

The same thing happened to a less extent in New Mexico, for Mrs. Bailey (1928) says that "before the buffalo disappeared the birds occurred much farther north. * * * In New Mexico, at the present time, they breed from the lowest, hottest valleys of the State up to about 5,000 feet, and less commonly a thousand feet higher to 6,000 feet at Silver City."

As we drove westward from the valley of the San Pedro River toward the Huachuca Mountains, in southern Arizona, we crossed a wide, unbroken plain, a steady, gradual rise of gently sloping land; for the first 10 miles it was covered with a scanty growth of mesquite, creosote bushes, yuccas, and various cacti, typical of the arid plains of that region; but, as we drew near the mountains, approaching 4,000 feet in altitude, the plain gradually changed to an open grassy prairie, broken only by the rows of scattered trees that grew along the washes extending outward from the canyons and by an occasional solitary mesquite of medium size. On the grassy prairie horned larks, meadowlarks, lark buntings, and lark sparrows were common; and everywhere the white-necked ravens were in evidence, and their bulky nests were conspicuous even in the most distant trees. Such an environment as this seems to be the typical habitat of this raven in other portions of its range.

Courtship.—The springtime activities of this raven are thus described by Herbert Brandt (1940) as observed by him in Texas: "During early April the raven begins in the broad mesquite area to make this his bridal bower, to engage in his courtship, and to select the site of his future home. The building process is carried on leisurely because at that season there are many social affairs and quick nest-building is unnecessary since egg-laying is a May urge. It is then that the community takes to the sky, and the male especially is wont to perform in the air—soaring, side-slipping, wheeling, and tumbling, thus distinguishing himself as an aerialist extraordinary. At that time his snowy-lined neck-piece becomes so enlarged that the feathers stand straight out like a fluffy boa, while those on his chin upturn at an acute angle, and the over-weening, black-bewhiskered rogue is then the picture, to his ebony admirer, no doubt, of a handsome, chivalrous swain."

Nesting.—We found it a simple matter to locate the nests of the white-necked raven on the open plains of southern Arizona as they were usually in solitary trees and conspicuous at a long distance. One of our nests was in a large sycamore along a wash, 30 feet from the ground. Another was 30 feet from the ground in an ash on the open plain. The other five nests examined were all in small mesquites on the open plain, 9 or 10 feet from the ground. Frank Willard's notes for the same region record one nest 40 feet up in a sycamore, one 10 feet up in a willow, and one 12 feet from the ground in a mesquite in a wash.

Major Bendire (1895) says that "the favorite nesting sites in southern Arizona are low, scrubby mesquite trees, next oak, ash, desert willow, and yucca, and in southern and western Texas ebony and hackberry bushes are likewise not infrequently used for this purpose.

"The nests are usually poorly constructed affairs, and are a trifle **larger than** those of the common Crow. Outwardly they are mainly composed of thorny twigs, while the inner parts are lined with cattle hair, rabbit fur, and frequently with pieces of rabbit skin, wool, dry cottonwood bark, grass, or tree moss, according to locality. This lining is frequently well quilted and again apparently thrown in loose. They are extremely filthy and smell horribly. Old nests are repaired from year to year, some of them being, as Lieutenant Benson expresses it, seven or eight stories high, showing use for as many years."

The nests that we examined were rather loosely built of large sticks externally, but the inner cup was deeply hollowed, compactly made, and smoothly lined with strips of inner bark, cow's hair, wool, and occasionally a few rags. A typical nest measured 20 inches in outside diameter, and the inner cavity was 8 inches in diameter and 5 inches deep.

In addition to the sites mentioned above, nests have been found in low mesquite bushes 4 feet from the ground, in walnut trees, cottonwoods, palo verdes, tall tree yuccas, and giant cactus, as well as on telegraph poles, or windmill towers, or on almost any structure that will hold them.

Mr. Brandt (1940) writes of their nest-building:

As nearly as we could ascertain, the female does all the carpentry, but her glossy mate escorts her back and forth, strutting, full-chested, about her, puffing out his throat and uttering purring croaks of encouragement. She seems to pay not the least bit of attention to him, but hurries on with her building, interlacing the sticks and then adding thereto, in the base, a binding mat of grasses, rootlets, pieces of rope, newspapers, or other handy trash. She proceeds then to elevate the outer wall with well chosen sticks and at the same time raises the soft inner lining until a deep cup is formed, usually finished with cow or horse hair, though rabbit fur likewise is favored. The bird molds the basin of the nest with her breast, pushing, prodding, and pounding with sharp movements, all the while snuggling down into the bowl. * * * In one case, in Arizona, a nest was found in the process of being colorfully decorated with the black and white fur of the skunk, and the very air was redolent of that fact. A few hundred feet away we came upon the odoriferous carcass of the former owner of that fur with its back cleanly plucked. In the More museum are three ravens' nests made entirely of rusty wire strands instead of sticks, and these have been wound into a rather neat, presentable, wire basket, proving the dexterity of this ingenious bird.

The white-necked raven is a late breeder. We found our first eggs on May 29, and some new nests were still empty at that date. Out of 66 records mentioned by Bendire (1895) the earliest is May 6. "Only twelve other sets were recorded for May, and these usually in the latter part of the month. All the remaining sets were taken in June, and fully half of these after the middle of that month. * * * I can only account for the remarkably late nesting of this species by the fact that insects and small reptiles, which probably furnish the larger portion of the food of these birds, are much more abundant in southern Arizona after the rainy season commences, about the last of May, than before, and these birds seemingly understand this and act accordingly."

Shaler E. Aldous (1942), in his report on this raven, says: "Activity around old nests begins in April, and sometimes the ravens stay constantly in the vicinity of chosen nests as if maintaining claim to them."

Eggs.—The white-necked raven lays three to seven eggs, rarely eight, but the commonest numbers are five, six, or seven. I cannot improve on Major Bendire's (1895) fine description of them, which is based on a series of 288 eggs in the United States National Museum, so I shall quote it here:

The eggs of the White-necked Raven are, in nearly every instance, readily distinguishable from those of the other species of the *Corvinae* found in North America, and this is due to the characteristic style of their markings. The ground color varies from pale green to grayish green, and only very rarely to a light bluish green. Two distinct types of markings are found among these eggs, the principal but usually not the most notable one consisting of a mass of longitudinal streaks and blotches of different shades of lilac, lavender grey, and drab, running from pole to pole of the egg, and these are again more or less hidden and partly obliterated by heavier and more regularly defined spots and blotches of different shades of brown. In not a few sets these lighter and more subdued shades are wanting, and are replaced by a more conspicuous brown; but almost all of the eggs show the peculiar longitudinal streaks and hair lines so prominently characteristic of the eggs of the genus *Myiarchus*. Besides the more regularly shaped markings common to the balance of the eggs of our *Corvinae*, they are on an average also decidedly lighter colored, and a few eggs are almost unspotted. Scarcely any two sets are exactly alike. The shell is strong and compact. In shape they are mostly ovate; a few are elliptical and elongate ovate.

The measurements of 288 eggs in the United States National Museum average 44.20 by 30.22 millimeters; the eggs showing the four extremes measure **48.8** by **33.8** and **38.1** by **27.9** millimeters.

Young.—According to Bendire (1895), "only one brood is raised in a season. Both sexes assist in incubation, which lasts about twenty-one days; this usually begins only after the set is completed; but young birds varying in size are sometimes found in the same nest." Young birds apparently remain in the nest about a month, though I have no definite information on this; they probably hatch late in June or early in July, and young birds of various ages have been found in the nests all through July. "Early in August the young birds begin leaving the nests, and when they have attained their growth young and old gather together in enormous flocks" (Swarth, 1904).

Plumages.—Nestlings are like other young ravens or crows, naked at first but soon scantily covered with brownish-gray down. They are fully fledged in the juvenal plumage before they leave the nest. The juvenal body plumage is dull black, without any of the purplish gloss of the adults; but the bases of the feathers of the neck, chest, and breast are pure white; the lanceolate feathers of the throat, so prominent in the adult, are lacking; the wings and tail are as in the adult; the basal half of the lower mandible is light colored, probably flesh-colored in life. Young birds that Mr. Swarth (1904) raised in captivity began to molt about the first of October and were in full winter plumage by the first of November, having renewed all the contour plumage, but not the wings and tail.

I have seen no molting adults, but probably their molts are similar to those of the young birds.

Food.—Ralph H. Imler (1939) has made a comparative study of the winter food of these ravens and crows in Oklahoma. He concluded that the crows were apparently more beneficial than the ravens, as they ate many more insects and weed seeds. The percentages of the different kinds of food found in the stomachs of 20 ravens killed in December were as follows: Beetles, 0.1; grasshoppers, 1.8; mammals, 4.5; sorghums, 29.8; corn, 17.3; melons and citron seeds, 3.0; hackberries, 37.5; sunflowers, 4.5; and debris, 1.5 percent.

It seems to be quite as omnivorous as other ravens and crows and quite as useful as a scavenger, picking up whatever scraps of food are thrown out from camps and kitchens and carrying off and hiding what it does not eat. Major Bendire (1895) saw one dig a trench and bury a salmon croquette in it, covering it up and marking it for future reference; the Major dug it up, and when the raven returned for it he was disappointed and flew away in disgust.

Mrs. Bailey (1928) lists its food as "principally animal matter, including carrion (as dead jack rabbits), cottontails and cotton rats, field mice, lizards, cicadas, alfalfa caterpillars and 'conchuela'; also cactus, wild fruit, and probably waste grain. Stomachs of five young about ten days old examined by Ligon contained three small nestlings, probably horned larks, birds' eggs, a small lizard, beetles, grasshoppers, and 'jar flies'."

Vernon Bailey (1903) says: "The abundant and juicy fruit of the cactus, Opuntia, Cereus, and Mammalaria, supplies part and probably a large part of their food during July, August, and September, enabling the ravens as well as some of the mammals and even men to make long journeys into waterless valleys with comparative comfort."

Since the above was written, an extensive research report on the white-necked raven has been published by the Fish and Wildlife Service (Aldous, 1942), in which some 35 pages are devoted to a study of the food of this species, to which the reader is referred for details. The summary contains the following general statement: "Laboratory examinations of 707 adult and 120 nestling stomachs of the white-necked raven and field examinations covering almost every month show the bird to be an omnivorous and resourceful feeder and demonstrate that its seasonal food is governed largely by the factor of availability. In all, 288 different items (214 of animal and 74 of vegetable origin) were identified (table 5, p. 47), and if all material found in the stomachs could have been specifically identified no doubt the number would have been increased. Although the animal items far outnumbered the vegetable, the total volumes of the two kinds of food were about equal in the adult diet. The nestlings, though, were almost entirely carnivorous."

Insects made up most of the bulk of the food; grasshoppers (51.21 percent) were the largest item, beetles being second in volume, and Lepidoptera (mostly cutworms and other injurious larvae) third. Hemiptera, such as stink bugs and leafhoppers, were consumed in small quantities, mainly by the nestlings.

Spiders, earthworms, myriapods, and snails were eaten sparingly.

"Mammalian food was important in the diet, ranking second in the animal food of the adults and third in quantity in the nestling food. Most of it consisted of carrion, which was obtained chiefly from carcasses of horses, cows, sheep, and rabbits. * * * Small rodents were eaten sparingly. * * * Birds, including domestic poultry, and their eggs were found in but a small proportion of the stomachs. * * * Reptiles and amphibians formed about 6 percent of the food of the nestlings but only slightly more than 2 percent of that of the adults. * * *

"Cultivated crops offer the greatest supply of food to the white-necked ravens and so are somewhat responsible for the sporadic concentrations of these birds. Grain sorghums were the most important plant food item found in the stomachs examined and made up more than a fourth of the adult birds' subsistence. * * * Cultivated crops of less importance that are attacked by the raven and may be severely damaged locally are corn, peanuts, melons, tomatoes, castor-beans, sunflower seeds, and pears. * * * Wheat, oats, barley, and rye are minor crops in the raven territory and were not fed on excessively by the birds examined.

"Wild fruits were consumed in large quantities during the summer and early fall and therefore played an important part in helping reduce the amount of feeding done in cultivated crops at that time."

Behavior.—In a general way the behavior of the white-necked raven is much like that of its smaller relative, the western crow, though its flight is rather more like that of the larger ravens. Mr. Swarth (1904) writes:

They are usually quite tame and unsuspicious, paying little or no attention to a man on horseback or a wagon passing by; but after being shot at a few times soon become very wary and hard to approach, and as they are usually out on the open prairie it is an easy matter for them to keep out of the way. On one occasion I approached a flock of thirty or forty busily engaged in catching grasshoppers, and as they began to leave long before I arrived within gunshot, I thought to try an experiment; wondering if an appeal to their curiosity might not be as successful as it usually was with jays. Tying a stone in the corner of a red bandana handkerchief, I tossed it high into the air, and the result far exceeded my expectations; for though standing in plain sight, they came headlong to see what it was that had fluttered to the ground, and from that time on I had no difficulty in securing White-necked Ravens. When one or more were shot out of a flock the remainder did not fly off and alight again, but usually circled about, keeping in rather a compact body and ascending higher and higher; not descending to the ground for a considerable length of time, and usually a long ways off. * * *

In the spring of 1903, I noticed a place on the plains some eight or ten miles from the mountains, where some species of bird was evidently roosting in large numbers. The plains are covered with brush at this point, mostly scrubby mesquite, and for a space some two hundred yards long and twenty-five or thirty yards wide the trees were almost destroyed by the use to which they had been put. The ground beneath was inches deep with excreta, and the trunks and branches of the trees were white with the same; while they were almost totally denuded of leaves, except at the extreme top where a little green still lingered. In many cases the limbs were broken down by the weight of the birds. From the appearance of the excreta it was evidently a large species of bird that was roosting there, and as on a careful examination none but raven feathers could be found lying about, I came to the conclusion that it was they that were using the place, though I never found them roosting in such large numbers in any one place before.

William Beebe (1905) thus describes the coming of a vast horde of these ravens to roost in a canyon in Mexico:

And now as the sun's disk silhouettes the upraised arms of an organ cactus on the opposite summit, scattered squads of another army of birds appear and focus to their nightly rendezvous—the White-necked Ravens of the whole world seem to be passing, so great are their numbers. As far as the eye can see, each side of the canyon gives up its complement of black forms; one straggling ahead uttering now and then a deep, hoarse-voiced croak. From all the neighbouring country they pour in, passing low before us, one and all disappearing in the black depths of a narrow, boulder-framed gorge. A raven comes circling down from above and instantly draws our eye to what we have not noticed before, a vast black cloud of the birds soaring above the *barranca* with all the grace of flight of vultures. The cloud descends, draws in upon itself, and, becoming funnel-shaped, sifts slowly through the twilight into the gorge where the great brotherhood of ravens is united and at rest.

Bradford Torrey (1904) writes amusingly of being "mobbed" by a flock of these ravens near Tucson, Ariz. As he approached a lonely ranch a flock of these birds "rose from the scrub not far in advance, with the invariable hoarse chorus of *quark, quark*." He continues:

I thought nothing of it, the sight being so much an every-day matter, till after a little I began to be aware that the whole flock seemed to be concentrating its attention upon my unsuspecting, inoffensive self. There must have been fifty of the big black birds. Round and round they went in circles, just above my head, moving forward as I moved, vociferating every one as he came near, "quark, quark."

At first I was amused; it was something new and interesting. * * * But before very long the novelty of the thing wore off; the persecution grew tiresome. Enough is as good as a feast; and I had had enough. "Quark, quark," they yelled, all the while settling nearer,—or so I fancied,—till it seemed as if they actually meant violence. They were doing precisely what a flock of crows does to an owl or a hawk; they were mobbing me. * * * The commotion lasted for at least half a mile. Then the birds wearied of it, and went off about their business. All but one of them, I mean to say. He had no such notion. For ten minutes longer he stayed by. His persistency was devilish. It became almost unbearable. The single voice was more exasperating than the chorus. * * * "Quark, quark!" the black villain cried, wagging his impish head, and swooping low to spit the insult into my ear.

On another occasion he watched the playful antics of a flock of ravens going to their roost, of which he says: "Again and again, in the course of their doublings and duckings, I saw the birds turn what looked to be a complete sidewise somersault. * * * Sure I am that more than once I saw a bird flat on his back in the air, * * * and to all appearance, as I say, he did not turn back, but came up like a flash on the other side." On subsequent occasions he concluded "that the birds turned but halfway over; that is to say, they lay on their backs for an instant, and then, as by the recoil of a spring, recovered themselves."

While the above play was going on, "another and a larger flock were sailing in mazy circles after the manner of sea-gulls. * * * More than once I have watched hundreds of the birds thus engaged, not all at the same elevation, be it understood, but circle above circle—* * * till the top ones were almost at heaven's gate."

Field marks.—"The field character that best distinguishes the white-necked raven from the crow, with which it intermingles on the north and east boundaries of its range in Texas and Oklahoma, is without question the raven's less open-throated and distinctly lower-pitched and guttural voice. Other distinguishing field characteristics are the raven's slightly larger size; its longer and coarser beak; its slightly more rounded tail silhouette when in flight; and its tendency to soar, at which time the tips of the primaries are separated and upturned. Occasionally, also, the white bases of its neck feathers can be seen when the plumage is ruffled by the wind." (Aldous, 1942).

Economic status.—Mr. Aldous (1942) says about this: "It is extremely difficult to arrive at a generally applicable verdict with respect to a bird with such varied habits and such an adaptable nature as the white-necked raven. The occurrence of ravens in large numbers makes them potentially capable of doing either severe damage or much good, and during the season their habits may vary from one extreme to the other. If the birds were evenly distributed throughout the year and did not congregate they probably would be more beneficial than detrimental. In judging the economic status of the ravens examined in this study their yearly food habits may be segregated roughly into beneficial, 37 percent; detrimental, 33 percent; and of neutral significance, 30 percent. * * *

"In order to obtain the farmer's point of view regarding the raven, a farm-to-farm canvass covering 100 farms was made in Howard County, Tex., in April 1936. * * *

"The 100 farmers interviewed estimated that they grew about 13,644 acres of sorghum each year, and every farmer but one considered that the greatest loss the ravens caused him was to this crop. The estimated annual loss per acre ranged from nothing to $3 and averaged $0.66. At this average rate the annual loss from the total acreage of grain sorghums grown in Howard County would be $49,500. * * *

"The following opinions comparing the ravens with other pests were volunteered. Six farmers considered small birds—including lark buntings, English sparrows, and blackbirds—more detrimental than ravens to the grain sorghum crop; two thought that rabbits were as bad as ravens and two thought them worse; two believed that ducks consumed more grain sorghums than ravens; and two said that coyotes were more destructive than ravens to their melons."

The ravens are, also, accused of spreading contagious diseases of livestock and poultry, such as hog cholera, blackleg and roup, through their carrion feeding habits; but this has not been proved.

In some treeless regions, the ravens have formed the habit of building their nests on the cross arms of telephone poles. As they often use old haywire and cast-off barbed wire in their nests, these cause short circuits; this has cost one telephone company $2,500 to $5,500 annually to patrol the line and keep it clear. "There have been as many as 202 instances of wire trouble that called for special investigation in a year (1934), and between 700 and 800 pounds of scrap wire have been removed annually from the nests and the ground beneath the lines. Shooting, poisoning, and trapping have accounted for 1,500 to 2,000 ravens yearly, but the trouble persists."

Various control measures, such as shooting to kill or frighten away the birds, catching them in steel traps, poisoning them, or destroying their nests, eggs and young, have been tried with varying success, but none of these is very satisfactory. "The most selective and safest means of reducing the numbers of white-necked ravens is by catching them alive in large cage traps of the type known as the Australian crow trap that have demonstrated their efficiency on various occasions (fig. 12). One trap that was operated for 12 days in November caught 512 white-necked ravens; and 4 traps, used at one place from September 1934 until the following spring, caught 10,000."

Enemies.—According to Mrs. Bailey (1928) this raven has some friends and some enemies among the agriculturalists in New Mexico. One man stated that every raven was worth a dollar to him, as without the ravens it would be impossible to raise a crop of alfalfa seed, for they are the only control they have for the "conchuela," an insect of the stink-bug family; any one of his hands found shooting a raven was fired then and there. In another place the ravens were reported as saving the hay crop by feeding on the alfalfa caterpillar. Still another man was down on the ravens because during the melon season they destroyed $25 worth of cantaloupes and truck crops a day. The chances are that after balancing all the evidence it will be found that the ravens do more good than harm and should not be molested, except in a few special cases. Vernon Bailey (1903) writes:

Out in one of the driest, hottest valleys of the Great Bend country of western Texas a pair of big Mexican ravens came beating over the valley ahead of our outfit one day, when they were suddenly attacked by two pair of the smaller, quicker, white-necked ravens. The attack was vigorous, not to say vicious, with quick repeated blows and pecks till the feathers flew. From start to finish the big birds sought only to escape, but this seemed impossible. They pounded the air in vain effort to out-fly their tormentors, dove to the ground but were forced to take wing again, circled and beat and tacked to no purpose, and finally began mounting steadily in big circles, taking their punishment as they went, the smaller birds keeping above and beating down on them in succession till all were specks in the sky, and finally lost to view. Such a drubbing I never saw a smaller bird inflict on a larger, before or since, and it was probably well deserved. The nests of the white-necked ravens are unprotected from above and eggs are said to be a delicacy to any raven.

Fall.—After the young birds are strong on the wing, these ravens gather in immense flocks and travel about over the country, visiting the most likely feeding places and gradually drifting southward. F. C. Willard (1912) witnessed a heavy migration early in November in Cochise County, Ariz.; this happened just before a very severe winter, during which these ravens were entirely absent from that section. They migrated in one immense flock, which "extended over a distance of nearly three miles along the foot hills of the Dragoon Mountains near Gleason in this county. There did not seem to be any regular flight, but a sort of general slow movement to the south. The birds were present in many thousands and it was two days before the last stragglers disappeared."

Winter.—In its winter resorts in Texas the white-necked ravens are highly gregarious. Mr. Brandt (1940) writes:

When the winds of winter roar down from the north this black clan then gathers into large communities and moves about the countryside in active, restless flocks, often numbering thousands of individuals. They may then be seen feeding forward on the ground in the great open pastures, the rear birds eddying over those ahead and alighting, imparting to the flock the effect of rolling along. They then visit the cities and villages of the region, making themselves perfectly at home, and are less afraid of man than ever. The encroachment of civilization seems to have little or no effect on their numbers and they may be found perched in the trees and on the roofs of the houses, and feeding in the streets and yards. * * * To tour over these bare high prairies in January would be bleak indeed were it not for the two typical lively objects of the region—the White-necked Raven and the tumbleweed.

DISTRIBUTION

Range.—Southwestern United States and northern Mexico; nonmigratory.

The range of the white-necked raven extends **north** to southern Arizona (Baboquivari Mountains, Papago Indian Reservation, and Oracle); New Mexico (Cactus Flat, Cutter, and Fort Summer); rarely east-central Colorado (Hugo); and Oklahoma (Arnett). **East** to western Oklahoma (Arnett); central Texas (Haskell, Albany, probably Turtle Creek, and probably Brownsville); and Tamaulipas (Charco Escondido). **South** to northern Tamaulipas (Charco Escondido); Nuevo León (Monterrey); Coahuila (Saltillo); Chihuahua (probably near Chihuahua City and San Pedro); and southern Sonora (Hermosillo). **West** to central Sonora (Hermosillo and Magdalena); and southeastern Arizona (Fort Huachuca and the Baboquivari Mountains). The range is said to extend south to the Mexican state of Guanajuato, but the supporting evidence is not known. Formerly the species was common along the foothills in eastern Colorado north to the Wyoming line.

Casual records.—It is probable that white-necked ravens formerly were not uncommon in western Kansas and Nebraska. In the latter State one was recorded from the Republican River region in April 1877, and it was noted near Sidney sometime prior to 1904. Several were noted at Wallace, Kans., October 12-16, 1833, and one was taken at Ellinwood on November 8, 1934. Recorded occurrences in California and Montana are not considered properly authenticated.

Egg dates.—Arizona: 94 records, May 6 to June 27; 48 records, June 6 to 17, indicating the height of the season.

Texas: 58 records, March 15 to June 16; 30 records, May 12 to 20.

CORVUS BRACHYRHYNCHOS BRACHYRHYNCHOS Brehm

EASTERN CROW

PLATES 39-42

CONTRIBUTED BY ALFRED OTTO GROSS

HABITS

It has been aptly stated that if a person knows only three birds one of them will be the crow. The crow, if we include all the five subspecies, is widely distributed over the greater part of the North American Continent. Throughout this area this familiar bird is instantly recognized by anyone who sees it. Because of its striking coal-black plumage, its large size, its unusual adaptability, its extreme cunning and apparent intelligence, its harsh garrulous notes, and its habit of frequently appearing in the open, it has become one of the best known of our American birds. The common name crow is universally applied, and I know of no English local synonyms for it. Even before white man came to America it was well known to the Indians and every tribe had its name for this bird, which was such a conspicuous creature of their environment.

Unfortunately the crow has a questionable record as far as his relations to human interests are concerned. No bird has been the subject of more heated controversy than the crow, and none of our birds have been more violently persecuted by man. In spite of incessant persecution the crow has been able to outwit his human adversaries by its unusual intelligence and instinct of self-preservation, to the extent that it has been able to maintain its existence in all parts of its wide and diversified range. For this the crow commands our admiration.

Spring.—A few crows winter in northern New England, but the majority of them are found farther south during the season of extreme cold weather. The first arrivals of the spring migration reach Maine during February, but it is not until the latter part of the month or the first week of March that they become common. Low (1934), in connection with banding operations at the Austin Ornithological Research Station on Cape Cod, Mass., has collected data that suggest that three populations of crows may be found there as follows—permanent residents, breeding birds that winter to the south, and northern breeders that either winter or migrate through the region.

Determinations of sex ratios at roosts by Hicks and Dambach (1935) indicate that the migration of the sexes may differ in range and extent. Certain of our populations of crows undergo a relatively short migration, but banding operations conducted in Oklahoma by Kalmbach and Aldous (1940) prove that many of the crows wintering in that State migrate to the Prairie Provinces of Alberta, Saskatchewan, and Manitoba, a flight of more than a thousand miles. One crow shot at Meadow Lake, Saskatchewan, at latitude 54° N. had traveled 1,480 miles and another at Camrose, Alberta, 1,435 miles from their winter home in Oklahoma. Out of 714 crows banded, 143 recoveries were obtained. Of 65 crows recovered during the nesting season, 49 were from the Prairie Provinces. It is obvious that many of the returns recorded in the States north of Oklahoma were on their way to or from the Canadian breeding grounds. The results obtained by Kalmbach and Aldous not only give us definite information concerning the extent of crow migration but are important in their relation to the value of the extensive control measures undertaken in Oklahoma.

Crows have been used for important experimental work concerned with different phases of migration. William Rowan, proceeding on the hypothesis that the migrating stimulus is a physiological one originating in the gonads or sexual organs, experimented on various birds, but chiefly the crow. The crows were confined in outdoor aviaries at Edmonton, Alberta, and exposed to temperatures as low as 44° F. below zero, but from the first of November until early January they were subjected to an ever-increasing amount of light, supplied by electric bulbs. In this way they were artificially subjected to light conditions that approximated those of spring. At the close of this period it was found that the gonads had actually attained the maximum development normally associated with the spring season. Control crows not subjected to the light treatment showed no development of the gonads. The birds, both the light-treated individuals and the controls, were marked, banded, and then liberated. By means of radio and other publicity, the cooperation of hunters was solicited for the return of the bands. While bands from eight of the experimental crows were returned from the north and northwest (two of them from a point 100 miles northwest of the point of liberation), an equal number were recovered from the south and southeast, thus to some extent nullifying the experiment. This work does indicate that the stimulus that initiates migration is a physiological one, and it is assumed to be a hormone produced by the interstitial tissue of the reproductive organs.

Courtship.—Edward J. Reimann in correspondence writes of the early courtship of crows he observed in the vicinity of Philadelphia, Pa. On March 8, 1940, he saw crows paired at most of the nesting localities along the Pennypack Creek. In some of these places two or three birds and at times four or five, what he supposed to be males, were seen chasing a female in courtship. Late in March the crows were rather noisy as he passed through each prospective territory. At some places courting was still going on where small groups of crows milled about the trees. Males chased the females, courting them while performing aerial gyrations of diving and wheeling. It was apparent to Reimann that the birds were pairing off, were claiming their nesting territory, and were about to drive their unwanted rivals from the scene.

Charles W. Townsend gave the subject of courtship of many birds serious and careful study, and no one is better qualified than he in the recording and interpretations of their performances. The following account is based on his observations of crows at Ipswich, Mass. His published account (1923) in part is as follows:

Courtship in birds is expressed in three ways, namely in display, dance and song. * * * The courtship song of the Crow consists of a rattle, a quick succession of sharp notes which have been likened to the gritting of teeth. That this is a courtship song and not merely one of the bizarre expressions of this versatile bird, is shown conclusively by its association with courtship display and dance. Like all bird songs it is commonest in the spring, but may occasionally, as in the case with many bird songs, be heard at other times, especially in the fall of the year, when it is explained by the "autumnal recrudescence of the amatory instinct." Although the song is generally given from a perch, it may also be given on the wing, constituting a flight song, although there is no other difference in the character of the two songs.

The whole courtship of the Crow varies somewhat, but the following description of this act, seen under favorable circumstances, is fairly typical. A Crow, presumably the male, perched on a limb of an oak tree, walked towards another and smaller Crow, presumably the female, that seemed to regard him with indifference. Facing the smaller one, the male bowed low, slightly spreading his wings and tail and puffing out his body feathers. After two bows, he sang his rattling song, beginning with his head up and finishing it with his head lower than his feet. The whole performance was repeated several times. The song, such as it was, issued forth during the lowering of the head. * * *

During the love season, fights by rival Crows are common. Each bird tries to rise above the other in the air, and, with noisy outcry, each attacks the rival. Sometimes their struggles are so violent that the birds come to the ground, where they continue their fight and sometimes roll over together in their efforts, all the time voicing their wrath.

On the other hand, one may sometimes chance upon the loving actions of affianced couples. More than once I have seen one of a pair that were sitting close together in a tree, caress the other with its beak and pick gently at its head. The mate would put up her head to be caressed, and I have been reminded of billing doves.

Later Townsend (1927) made further observations which he elaborated upon as follows:

Spending the nights in an open lean-to in my "forest," at Ipswich, I found myself listening every morning to the courtship song of the Crow close at hand, and, on May 3, 1926, I discovered from my bed that a pair had their nest in a white spruce twenty-five yards from me, so that I was able to watch them closely. At about four-thirty every morning I awoke to the rattling song of the Crow, and I often saw one flying about in irregular circles, singing and chasing another. Both alighted on trees, especially on a spruce, from time to time. The song was given in the air and from a perch, and once I heard it given as a whisper song. I also heard for the first time at the end of the rattle a pleasing sound which suggested the cooing of a Pigeon or the note of a cuckoo clock, but softer and more liquid. It was usually double—I wrote it down *coi-ou* or a single *cou*— and generally repeated several times, although sometimes given only once. These soft sounds, which I heard many times when the bird was near, generally followed the rattle, but were often given independently. When the bird was perched, he bowed and puffed out his feathers at the time of their delivery as during the rattling song. The cooing was also given in the air and on one occasion, I saw a bird drop slowly down with wings tilted up at an angle of forty-five degrees, singing as he fell. The rattle song was once given fifty-four times in succession, followed by a series of *cous*.

The female was at times very importunate, calling slowly *car car* like a young bird begging for food. If the male approached, the calling would become more and more rapid and end exactly as in the case of a young bird in a gurgle or gargle—*car, car, car, cowkle, cowkle, cowkle*. After mating the male would fly to the next tree and call loudly *caw-caw* several times. Occasionally the loud *wa-ha-ha-ha* was given. An examination of the nest made at this time showed three heavily incubated eggs.

Nesting.—In northern New England and the Maritime Provinces the vast majority of the crows nest in coniferous trees and those that I have examined have ranged 18 to 60 feet from the ground. Of 22 nests observed in Maine, 12 were in pines, 6 in spruces, 3 in firs, and only 1 in a hardwood tree, an oak. A nest containing six eggs found on May 20, 1936, near Brunswick, Maine, is typical. It was in a large pine located near the center of a 10-acre grove. The nest was built close to the trunk of the tree and was supported by three good-sized horizontal branches at a point 42 feet from the ground and approximately 30 feet from the top of the tree. The foundation of the nest was made up of branches and twigs of oak, beech, and pine, the largest ones were one-fourth to three-eighths of an inch in diameter and 10 to 16 inches in length. The nesting bowl was made up of smaller twigs interwoven with strands of bark. The soft compact lining was entirely of finely separated fibrils of bark, which apparently were shredded by the birds before being placed in position. The foundation of nesting materials measured 22 by 26 inches, the depth of the nest from the upper rim to the base was 9 inches, and the rim of the nest proper was 12 inches in diameter. The interior of the nesting cup occupied by the bird was 6 by 7 inches and its depth 4½ inches.

All the nests of the crow are substantial and well built; they are crude in general external appearance but always delicately and warmly lined. The main departure from the type described above is the nature of the materials used in lining the nesting bowl, a difference somewhat dependent on their availability. Different nests may be lined with moss, reed fibers, grass, feathers, twine, rags, wool, fur, hair, roots, seaweed, leaves, and similar materials.

The crow seems to prefer coniferous trees not only in the northern sections of its range but even in the south where such trees abound. In States where hardwood trees predominate, they are more frequently selected as nesting sites. T. E. McMullen, who has made extensive observations on the nesting sites of 227 crows in Pennsylvania, Delaware, and New Jersey, reports finding 112 nests in oak trees, 62 in other species of hardwood including 13 in maple, and 11 in beech trees. The remaining 43 were in coniferous trees, 24 in pine, 17 in cedars, and 2 in hemlocks. The above nests varied from 10 to 70 feet in height from the ground, but the majority exceeded 25 feet. Edmund J. Reimann writes that he has found nests in Pennsylvania that were built at a height of 100 feet from the ground.

In the agricultural areas of the Middle West, where there is a lack of large trees, crows resort to second-growth timber and shrubs of various kinds. In central Illinois favorite nesting sites are the Osage-orange fences. These hedges, abundantly armed with thorns, offer excellent protection, even against the prowling naturalist who may wish to examine the nests.

The crow is adaptable in the choice of its nesting site. In the western Canadian provinces there are numerous instances where the crow has nested on the ground either from choice or because of the lack of trees. Ferry (1910) found a crow's nest at Quill Lake, Saskatchewan, that was situated on the ground at the forks of the dead branches of a fallen and nearly burned up weather-bleached poplar tree. At Regina, Saskatchewan, Mitchell (1915) found a crow's nest on the ground between wild-rose bushes; others were placed on clusters of rose and low bushes just a few inches above the ground. On June 13, 1935, Aldous (1937) found two crow's nests built on the ground along the shore of Lake Manitoba. Another nest containing three eggs was found in the tules over the water, and a fourth nest was built on marshy ground among the reeds. In the latter two cases there were trees and brush in the vicinity, and apparently these situations were a matter of choice on the part of the birds.

Horning (1923) cites an unusual experience with a nest that he found at Luscar, Alberta. "We found a crow's nest in a willow thicket about ten feet from the ground, on May 28, 1922. The situation surprised us, as the Crow usually builds very high. and there were high trees within a few hundred yards. We thought that the presence of an abundant food supply, in the shape of a dead cow, within twenty-five yards may have been the reason for the choice of nesting site. We cut down the nest, which contained three eggs, newly laid, and photographed it, leaving it not more than two feet from the ground, and inclined at an angle of about 55 degrees. We removed the eggs. * * * Judge of our surprise, on re-visiting the nest on June 1 to find four new eggs. * * * It seemed to us very unusual for the Crows to re-occupy the nest especially when so close to the ground and at such an angle."

Occasionally crows select sites that are an extreme departure from the usual situations. Harold M. Holland in correspondence states that a pair nested in the hollow of an old stub located in a wooded tract in Knox County, Ill. They nested in this place for at least three seasons in preference to other numerous apparently suitable locations offered by the surrounding woods. Potter (1932) states that a pair of crows remodeled the top of a disused magpie habitation.

Bradshaw (1930) comments on unusual nesting sites he found in Saskatchewan as follows: "In many treeless sections of the prairie, such as Big Quill Lake, crows have been found nesting on the cross-arms of telephone poles. In such cases one usually finds nearby a marsh well-stocked with ducks, coots, rails, grebes, and other marsh-loving birds. Probably the easy available food supply is the principal factor for the crow locating in such areas. * * *

"The most unique nesting site of the crow encountered was one found on the top of a chimney of a country church, between the towns of Pense and Lumsden." On the same road a pair of crows built their nest in a chimney of an abandoned house. In both cases, however, there were plenty of trees that the crows might have chosen for their nests.

Dr. S. S. Dickey, who has made extensive observations of crows in Pennsylvania during the nesting season, contributes the following observations made of the procedure of nest-building: "The female descended into the underwoods or would move along branches of the trees to masses of twigs. She would take one of them into her beak, twist it loose from its fastenings, and hurry with it to the site she had chosen for her nest. At first she tended to drop sticks en route, or else would proceed awkwardly in placing them in a fork or crotch. She dropped many sticks, causing a veritable heap of rubbish near the base of the nesting tree. Finally after many trials she managed to arrange a loose array of sticks in the base of the fork. Most of the work was done in the morning hours between 7 and 11 o'clock. Thereafter she appeared to weary and would fly away in company with the male in search of food. Late in the afternoon and shortly before dusk she proceeded again to work on her nest. The walls grew consecutively from coarse sticks and twigs to finer materials. She added mud, strands of rope, rags, corn husks, mats of dry grass, roots, moss and weed stems, and strips of bark from various kinds of trees. The rim was nicely rounded off with strips of grapevine bark. The interior of the deep wide cup was tightly lined with inner bark fibers, pads of hair, fur, wool, and green moss. It required approximately 12 days to complete the nest after the first sticks had been placed.

"If bad weather conditions prevailed, several days would elapse before the first egg was deposited, although in one nest an egg had been laid in spite of the fact that the edge of the nest was encrusted in snow. During fair warm weather eggs were found in the nest a day or two after the nest had been completed."

Although not mentioned by Dr. Dickey, it has been noted by many observers that both male and female take an active part in the building of the nest as well as sharing in the incubation of the eggs.

Eggs.—The number in a complete set of crow eggs is usually four to six, but in some cases there are only three and in others as many as eight or nine. Macoun (1909) reports an unusual set of ten eggs. In the latter instances it is probable the large number of eggs are the product of two birds, as it has been observed that two females in addition to the male have shared a single nest. Bendire (1895) has given us an excellent description of the eggs of the crow based on a wide experience and the study of large numbers of specimens. His account is as follows:

"Crows' eggs are rather handsome, and vary greatly in shape, size, color, and markings; the majority may be called ovate, but both short and rounded ovates, and elliptical and elongated ovates are also found in a good series. The ground-color varies from malachite and pale bluish green to olive green, and occasionally to an olive buff. The markings usually consist of irregularly shaped blotches and spots of different shades of browns and grays. In some specimens these are large, and irregularly distributed over the egg, usually predominating about the larger end, leaving the ground color clearly visible. In others again the markings are fine, profuse, and evenly distributed, giving the egg a uniform dark olive-green color throughout."

Bendire gives the average measurements of 292 eggs in the United States National Museum as 41.40 by 29.13 millimeters or about 1.63 by 1.15 inches. The largest egg of the series was 46.74 by 30.78 millimeters, or 1.84 by 1.21 inches; the smallest 36.07 by 25.91 millimeters, or 1.42 by 1.02 inches.

Sometimes eggs of abnormal size have been found. G. Ralph Meyer collected a set of eggs in which one egg measured 2.00 by 1.25 (50.8 by 31.8 millimeters), much larger than the largest egg in the large National

Museum series. One or more eggs dwarfed in size have been found in sets in which the other eggs are normal, but these usually prove to be sterile.

There are a number of reported cases of erythristic crow eggs, in which there is present an excessive amount of red pigment. In correspondence William Rowan, of Edmonton, Alberta, informs me that he has two sets of erythristic eggs that he obtained from central Alberta. They were laid by the same bird in successive years, and he states further that this same type of egg has been found in the same nest for seven successive years. Mr. Rowan believed that these eggs were unique and represented the first recorded case of erythrism in crow's eggs. However, there are published descriptions of so-called abnormal red-colored eggs that are undoubtedly cases of erythrism. Following are a few that have come to my attention. Bendire (1895) states as follows: In an abnormal set of five eggs, presented by Dr. A. K. Fisher to the United States National Museum collection, four have a *pinkish* buff ground color, and are minutely speckled with fine dots of ecru drab resembling somewhat in general appearance a heavily marked egg of the American Coot. * * * In another specimen, presented by Dr. Louis B. Bishop, the ground color is salmon buff and this is blotched with pinkish vinaceous. The entire set of six eggs was similarly colored. Sage, Bishop, and Bliss (1913) mention six pinkish eggs of a set obtained near New Haven, Conn., on May 8, 1884. Jacobs (1935) describes a set of five eggs he found May 1, 1934, in a nest located in a willow tree near Waynesburg, Pa., as follows:

Throughout the whole set there is not the slightest suggestion of the usual greenish-drab shades. The shell, held to the light, appears a rich cream-white such as seen in the eggs of the Eastern Sparrow Hawk, and on the whole, resembles in coloration eggs of the latter collected on the same day. The smallest egg is less thickly marked and contain sparingly scattered hold patches of mauve and maroon purple, which tints are brought out by the brick-red laid over varying shades of lilac and lavender, the majority of them all on the smaller half of the shell. It is a beautifully spotted egg with *brick-red,* mauve and maroon purple about equally apportioned and equalling the amount of lilac and lavender shades which are untouched by the reddish pigment.

The ground color of the four eggs originally rich creamy-white with lavender blendings in paler underlays is heavily mottled over with brick-red giving the shells a uniform rich vinaceous appearance, over which are diffused blotches of strong vinaceous-cinnamon blending into the underlays. Thus we have, in these five crow eggs, specimens appearing like huge Cactus Wren eggs but the general red shade is really stronger than that of the wren's eggs.

Incubation.—The incubation period of the crow is 18 days. One brood is reared each year, but in the southern part of the nesting range two broods each season are not unusual. Both male and female may take part in incubation and both share in the care of the young. Macoun (1909) reports a nest in which both birds were sitting on the eggs at the same time. The cavity of the nest was much larger than usual. There were five nearly incubated eggs in the same stage of development, indicating that these birds were male and female rather than two females. Occasionally three crows may be seen about the nest, but because of lack of sexual differences of plumage it is difficult to determine whether they represent cases of polygamy or polyandry. There is indirect evidence, however, that two females may be concerned. There are a number of cases on record where two sets of eggs were found in a nest that hatched on different dates. Jung (1930) found a crow's nest on June 15, 1928, in Alberta, Canada, that contained three eggs and one young about a week old. When the nest was visited the next day a fourth egg had been added. Three crows were seen about the nest and it is apparent that two of them were females, both of which were contributing eggs to this communal nest. In other cases three crows were concerned with a single nest, which contained a normal set of eggs hatching on the same date. Here, it is probable, two males were involved.

Young.—The young when first hatched are pink or flesh color and scantily clad with tufts of grayish clove-brown on the head, back, and wings. At five days of age the eyes are open and the exposed parts of the skin have acquired a brownish-gray color. At 10 days the principal feather tracts are established by the rapidly growing feather papillae. At this stage they assert themselves by loud clamorings for food, and the presence of a nest may be revealed by their incessant calls, especially as they grow older. When the young crows reach the age of 20 days many of the contour feathers are unsheathed, presenting a dull black color. Tufts of down still cling to the tips of these juvenal feathers, especially in the region of the crown. The eyes are a dark blue-gray, the scales of tarsus and toes are grayish black, the upper mandible or maxilla is black, and the lower mandible is pale yellow or horn color streaked with gray. The lateral basal portions of the gape are yellowish orange. At this age tufts at the base of the bill are developed.

After four weeks most of the feathers are completely unsheathed. The young at this stage also show a marked change in behavior especially in regard to a human visitor. Before this time they were passive but now exhibit fear and offer resistance at being handled or lifted from the nest. At this time they may stand on the rim of the nest or even leave to nearby branches of the tree where they are fed by the adults. In the course of another week they are capable of leaving the nest and making their initial flight. If disturbed they may leave the nest before reaching the age of five weeks.

Plumages.—The young in the completed juvenal plumage are dark grayish black above, with the underparts somewhat duller in tone; the wings and tail are black with violet and greenish reflections; iris bluish and the bill and feet grayish black.

The first winter plumage is acquired by a partial postjuvenal molt, which involves the body plumage and wing coverts but not the rest of the wings or the tail. The young in this plumage are similar to the adults, but the feathers show less gloss and the majority of the specimens have a greenish hue. The underparts are of a duller black, the belly with a dull slaty cast. The first nuptial plumage is acquired by wear, the feathers becoming brownish and worn by the end of the breeding season. The adult winter plumage is acquired by a complete postnuptial molt. The sexes are alike in plumages and molts. All parts, including bill, legs, feet, and claws, are deep black. The plumage of the body has a distinct metallic gloss of violet, and the wings are glossed with bluish violet and greenish blue; iris brown.

Albinism is common in the crow, judged from the more than 25 reported cases that have come to my attention. Since an albino crow offers such a striking contrast to the normal plumage, and because crows are more readily observed than the more secretive species, there are many reports of albinism. A few of the more interesting cases are cited below.

In the Bowdoin College collection there is a female crow collected at Yarmouth, Maine, that is pure white, including the bill, feet, and claws. The iris of this specimen was pink and so the bird was a pure albinistic type. Two albino crows taken from a nest near Portland, Maine, in 1910 were mounted by J. A. Lord, a taxidermist in Portland. An albino crow was seen at South China, Maine, for a period of several weeks during August 1930. F. A. Stuhr, of Portland, Oreg., reported having four live crows that were taken from a nest in Lane County, Oreg. Three of them are almost entirely white, showing only slight black colorations on the primaries and secondaries and at the base of the bill. The iris of these birds is brown, but the feet and tarsus are nearly white. Fleming and Lloyd (1920) report that two albino crows were taken from a nest 9 miles north of Toronto on June 29, 1908. Both birds were grayish white, the eyes blue-gray, the feet lead black, and the beak horn color. Harry Piers (1898) reported a partial albino collected near Halifax, Nova Scotia. His description is as follows: "Its general color was brown, darker on the throat, cheeks and belly; scapulars and feathers of back margined obscurely with whitish; primaries mostly whitish; tertials white; tail feathers light reddish brown margined with whitish on outer edge; legs, bill and iris brown." Several crows similar in coloration to the one described by Piers but with certain variations have been reported by other observers.

Warne (1926) cites a very unusual case of a pet crow that after five years suddenly acquired white feathers in each of its wings; when the wings were spread, about half of the area was white. Previous to this time they were black. Albinism is a hereditary character, and why white feathers would replace black feathers after five years is difficult to explain.

Longevity.—We have relatively few records on the longevity of the crow. Banding of the birds has not been conducted in sufficient numbers or for a long enough time to yield definite results, but the following four banding returns are of interest: A crow banded as a nestling in Saskatchewan in July 1924 was shot five years later in July 1929 only a mile and a half from the place of banding; one banded at Garden Prairie, Ill., was shot five years later at Marengo, Ill., on March 25, 1934; one banded at Richmond, Ill., on May 28, 1927, was shot seven years later in Kenosha County, Wis., on March 13, 1934; and one banded at Lundar, Manitoba, on May 1, 1926, was shot seven years later in Grant County, S. Dak., on April 2, 1933.

Kalmbach and Aldous (1940) are of the opinion that relatively few crows in the plains area live more than four years. This supposition is based on the rapid decrease in the number of returns during the years following the release of the birds. Out of 143 returns of 714 crows banded, 76 were received the first year and 47, 12, and 8 (first six months) in the successive years. All were reported killed, which emphasizes the intense persecution the crow receives from the hands of the gunner. It is possible, state these authors, that the number of returns for the crows banded might have been greater were it not for the fact that, in their winter home, many are killed in bombings under conditions not conducive to the recovery of the bands.

Crows kept in captivity have lived spans of life exceeding 20 years, but it is doubtful if many individuals in nature ever approach that age.

Food.—Few ornithological problems have been of greater widespread controversy than the economic status of the crow. It is an omnivorous feeder and readily adapts its food habits to the changing seasons and available food supply. Its food varies so greatly that isolated observations may be very misleading unless the food habits are considered from the standpoint of the entire population through all seasons of the year. If one is biased it is relatively easy to find abundant evidence either for or against the crow. It is no great wonder that this bird has been the subject of heated debate between the conflicting interests of those who **wish to destroy and** those who would protect this species with no thought of control. The advocates of either side of this question are probably sincere, but what we need is a common-sense solution of the problem, combining the interests of both factions. Only the thoughtless short-sighted person desires to have the crow completely exterminated, and the overzealous conservationist should submit to a reasonable control of a species when large numbers prove destructive to man's best interests.

The resourcefulness of the crow is vividly indicated by the fact that the Biological Survey identified 650 different items in the food eaten by 2,118 crows collected in 40 States and several Canadian provinces. According to Kalmbach (1939), "about 28 per cent of the yearly food of the adult crow is animal matter and consists of insects, spider, milli-peds, crustaceans, snails, the remains of reptiles, amphibians, wild birds and their eggs, poultry and their eggs, small mammals and carrion." About two-thirds of the animal food consists of insects, chief among which are beetles and their larvae and Orthoptera (grasshoppers, locusts, and crickets), each group constituting more than 7 percent of the food of the crow, and comprises the essential beneficial feature of the food habits of the species.

The numbers of insects eaten vary with the season. For example, few May beetles are eaten early in spring, but by April they constitute 5 percent of the food and in May, at the peak of abundance of May beetles, they comprise nearly 21 percent of the bird's diet. Likewise, the monthly increase in grasshoppers from May to September is shown in the crow's food, in which these insects constitute respectively by month 4, 6, 14, 19, and 19 percent of the food taken.

At the time of outbreaks of such insect pests the crow becomes a valuable agent in their control and herein lies the chief benefit to the farmer. Examples of isolated cases revealed the presence of 85 May beetles in one stomach, 72 wireworms in another, 123 grasshoppers in another, and 438 small caterpillars in a single crow's stomach collected in Michigan. In central Illinois I have seen large flocks of crows follow-ing the plow, where they were devouring great numbers of grubs of the destructive May beetle. It is also a common experience to see them digging up the grubs in the pasturelands where these pests were abun-dant. Alexander (1930) states that in Kansas the early spring crows eat enormous numbers of grubs and cutworms, which are very destruc-tive to wheat in that State.

Nestling crows require even greater quantities of insect food than do the adults. One brood of four examined by the Biological Survey had eaten 418 grasshoppers and another brood of seven had eaten 585 of these insects; one individual had taken the record number of 143 grass-hoppers. Of 157 nestlings obtained in Kansas, 151 had been fed grasshoppers. Caterpillars, always a favorite source of food for nestling birds, were present in more than a third of the 778 nestling crow stomachs examined.

The insect food of the crow is one of the strongest points in its favor and should be given proper consideration in judging the economic status of the species. The crow is an enemy of gypsy and browntail moths, but it has been observed that new colonies of moths often form about the nests of crows, indicating that these birds may serve as an agent in the spread of these pests.

Unfortunately the food of the crow is by no means restricted to insects, and among the bird's less admirable traits is its destruction of eggs and young of other species of birds, a habit that has placed the crow on the black list of many both sportsmen and bird lovers. However, these depredations, in many instances, have been greatly and perhaps willfully exaggerated in articles advocating the destruction of the crow, which have appeared in many sporting columns of newspapers and magazines. The examinations by the U. S. Biological Survey reveal that only about a third of 1 percent of the animal food of the adults and 1.5 per cent of the food of nestlings is derived from wild birds and their eggs, and only about one in every 28 crows and one in every 11 nestlings had eaten such food.

The percentage of such food, as would be expected, runs higher in crows that inhabit the proximity of nesting waterfowl. Examinations of adult crows collected in such situations in the prairie provinces of Canada show that they had eaten four times the quantity of other birds and their eggs, and the young six times the quantity eaten by crows collected in the United States. On the basis of frequency of such predation in Canada the adult crow is ten times and the nestling crow six times as bad as their fellows in the United States. This pronounced record of bird and egg destruction in Canada was due primarily to the fact that the birds collected were taken in close proximity to nesting waterfowl, almost to the exclusion of any obtained in agricultural sections.

Observations on the Lower Souris Refuge in North Dakota in 1936 and 1937 showed that the crow is not an outstanding hazard to waterfowl there. Only 1.7 percent of the 351 nests studied in 1936 were destroyed by crows, while in 1937 the birds preyed upon 3.4 percent of the 566 nests under observation. Even with the latter rate of loss, the crow on this refuge is at present considered to be a minor hazard to waterfowl.

Many independent observers have reported the destruction of eggs and young of both game and song birds, and there is no doubt that the crow at times is guilty of serious depredations. Baker (1940) reports the destruction of a colony of 1,500 little blue herons and 3,000 snowy egrets nesting in an island of timber known as "Live Oaks" on the coastal prairie, 9 miles south of Waller, Tex., by about 40 crows that inhabited the section. On Great Duck Island, off the coast of Maine, where I studied a colony of black-crowned night herons for an entire season, the crows destroyed 27 of the 125 nests under observation. During the season of 1940 crows proved to be a serious menace to the eider ducks nesting on Kent Island, Bay of Fundy, where Bowdoin College has established a bird sanctuary and scientific station. On this island the crows had the habit of carrying their booty to certain convenient places to be devoured. At one such rendezvous I counted 37 eider-duck eggs and 24 herring-gull eggs and in another 22 eider-duck eggs and 28 of the gull eggs. Crows have been reported as carrying an entire egg in their beaks, but at Kent Island the egg was usually punctured by a thrust of the beak. On several occasions we observed them carrying off the downy nestlings. In August I found a place where there were more than a dozen juvenal gulls that had been killed and partially eaten, presumably by the crows. Certainly in sanctuaries such as "Live Oaks" and Kent Island, where a special effort is being made to preserve certain species of birds, the control of the crows is necessary, as it is when they become too abundant in the vicinity of nesting fowl, such as in the Prairie Provinces of Canada.

Depredations on poultry have been reported. For example, Mousley (1924) states that he saw 16 young chickens carried away by crows. Numerous reports have been published citing instances where crows have killed and eaten various species of small birds, and even birds as large as the partridge have been killed and eaten.

Such depredations, though they may call for certain measures of control, in no way warrant the total destruction of a species that has been shown to be beneficial to man's interests at other times. In the case of poultry means of protection can be readily improvised.

Of interest but of lesser economic importance is the consumption of small mammals, crustaceans, mollusks, amphibians, snakes, and carrion. Eifrig (1905) found the crop of a crow filled with earthworms. Along the seacoast, especially during the winter months, mollusks constitute a most important element of the food. It is a common practice of the crow to carry clams, scallops, mussels, or sea-urchins to a considerable height to let them fall on the rocks to be broken and thus enable them to secure the edible contents, a habit shared by other birds, notably the herring gull.

Along the New England coast, especially in Maine, I have seen groups of crows on the mud flats at low tide, where they were feeding on the myriads of invertebrates that abound there. I have also seen them feeding on dead fish left behind by the tide, and at one time seven crows were taking their turns at the carcass of a dead seal. It is not unusual to see them thrusting their beaks into the mud to secure what seemed to be a *Nereis*, a marine annelid worm, much after the fashion that robins retrieve earthworms from our lawns. F. H. Kennard (MS.) on July 15, 1923, saw a young crow foraging on his lawn for earthworms. For over an hour he and others observed the crow pulling up the worms. After they were pulled out the crow would stand on the worm and cleanse it with its bill before swallowing it. Brewster (1883) relates an experience of crows eating 20 good-sized trout that had been hidden in a spring. The farmers along the Maine coast complain that crows as well as gulls are a nuisance in removing fish placed on their fields as fertilizer. Ball (1938) reports similar damage in the Gaspé region, and other complaints have come from New Brunswick and Nova Scotia.

When hard pressed crows may resort to all manner of means to obtain food. For example, Isel (1912) has seen crows enter the business district of Wichita, Kans., to feed from garbage pails back of restaurants; Crook (1936) has observed crows feeding on car-killed animals, including dogs, cats, chickens, opossums, pigs, and even skunks; Guthrie (1932) states that crows prize a dead snake as much as a living one; Anderson (1907) reports that in Iowa crows frequent the slaughterhouses to feed upon the waste of slaughtered animals; Scott (1884) observed crows feeding on a carcass of a dog while the temperature registered 14° below zero. These cases serve to emphasize the role played by crows as scavengers. They also attest the omnivorous feeding of crows and their extreme resourcefulness in securing a livelihood under adverse conditions. Such adaptability insures the success of any species in spite of persecution.

According to Kalmbach (1920) vegetable matter forms nearly 72 percent of the adult crow's yearly food, and over half of it consists of corn. Of 1,340 adult crows collected in every month of the year, 824 (over 61 percent) had fed on corn. During April and May, when the corn is sprouting, corn constitutes about a third of the food, and at the harvest in October it supplies over half of the crow's diet. The damage by the crow is chiefly to sprouting corn, corn "in the milk," or when the ripened grain has been stacked in shocks. Of the three, the second seems to be the most serious. It is not so much the corn the crow actually eats at this time but the subsequent injury resulting from water entering the ears from which the husks have been partially torn that makes the loss so important.

In 1938 the United States Biological Survey made a special investigation of the crow damage to grain, sorghums, and Indian corn growing on 210 farms comprising 39,797 acres in Grady County, Okla. The results reveal that Oklahoma has a winter crow population of between three and four million. The damage to grain sorghums was appraised at 3.8 percent and to Indian corn 1.7 percent. The loss of these crops in Grady County alone for the year was estimated to be $18,370.

On the basis of this investigation the Biological Survey concluded that in southwestern Oklahoma there may be need of measures of control. This situation is now being met by the systematic bombing of the roosts. The case of the crow in Oklahoma is qualified by the statement that in some of the wheat-raising sections of Oklahoma the wintering crows are a benefit.

It was concluded that the crow problem, though serious to sorghums and corn in some counties, is not of sufficient magnitude in the State as a whole to demand combined State and Federal action for its solution. Kalmbach (1920) writes that in the Northwest States, where corn is not raised extensively, wheat replaces corn in the crow's diet. The damage is especially severe at the time wheat is sown or is sprouting. Oats and buckwheat are also occasionally eaten, but the larger part of these grains represents a waste product.

"Apples and almonds are less frequently injured; while the aggregate losses to beans, peas, figs, oranges, grapes and cherries are not important. Fruits of the various sumachs, poison-ivy and poison-oak, bayberry, dogwood, sour gum, wild cherries, grapes, Virginia creeper and pokeberry" are also common ingredients of the food. "The mere consumption of wild fruit by the crow involves nothing of economic importance," but the "digestive processes destroy practically none of the embryos of the seeds, and crows act as important distributors of certain plants, some of which, as poison-ivy and poison-oak, are particularly noxious."

The indigestible parts of the crow's food, such as bones, teeth, fur, and hard seeds, are regurgitated in the form of pellets as is customary with such birds as hawks and owls. An examination of these pellets gathered at crow roosts reveal interesting elements of the food eaten by any such crow population. Townsend (1918) collected several hundred pellets from a crow roost located in Essex County, Mass. These pellets amounted in bulk to 662 cubic centimeters of material after they were broken up into their composite parts. The examination of this material by E. R. Kalmbach, of the Biological Survey, revealed 13 kinds of insects and 7 other invertebrates including *Melampus, Nereis, Mytilus,* and *Littorina*. Among the vertebrates there were fish, bones and scales of a snake, shells of hen's eggs, four meadow mice, a star-nosed mole, two short-tailed shrews, and large fragments of bone. There were seeds and parts of no less than 20 plants, of which the following are of special interest—10,000 seeds of bayberry, 2,300 seeds of poison-ivy and species of sumac, 360 seeds of cranberry, and varying numbers of seeds of juniper, smilax, winterberry, grape, and nightshade. There were also very small quantities of wheat, barley, corn, buckwheat, and seeds of pumpkin or squash, apple, and pear. These results again emphasize the omnivorous feeding habits of the crow as well as its resourcefulness during adverse winter conditions.

It is important to know not only what the crow eats but also how much it eats to enable us to form a complete picture of the economic status of the species. Forbush (1907) made careful records of the food eaten by captive crows, which throw considerable light on this problem. He found that two well-grown crows fed 20 to 25 ounces of food a day just maintained their own weight, but less than that amount was not sufficient. When the quantity of food given the birds was largely reduced there was a corresponding reduction in their weight. He concluded that young crows, when fledged absolutely, require a daily quantity of food equal to about half their own weight and will consume much more than this to their advantage if they can get it. When this amount is multiplied by the number of crows in an entire population the results are impressive. Experiments on the time required for assimilation of food revealed that from the time of eating to that when the undigested parts of the food were emitted average 1½ hours. It is not only what they eat at a single time, but it must be remembered that the average crow gorges no less than eight to ten full meals a day. Hicks and Dambach (1935) found that the average weight of the filled stomachs of 75 adult crows was 36.6 grams and that their food contents averaged 11 grams.

The following interesting experience submitted in correspondence by R. Bruce Horsfall reveals how we may unwittingly condemn the crow when the facts are not clearly understood. Mr. Horsfall bought a farm near Redbank, N. J., where he planted five acres in corn and ten acres in asparagus. He noted that the lower end of his field, where the crows were present each day during the early morning hours, yielded no harvest. Mr. Horsfall immediately jumped to the conclusion from published accounts of crow depredations on farm crops that these birds were responsible for his loss. Without further investigation the crows were shot and the bodies left there as a warning to others. After a number of crows were killed an examination of the stomach contents revealed a mass of greenish liquid filled with cutworm heads, black beetles, and other undigested materials. On the following day a visit was made to the fields in the early morning hours at about the time the crows were accustomed to be present. Great numbers of cutworms were found before they dug into shelter for the day. Mr. Horsfall thereupon decided to welcome his much-maligned friends and he had reason to regret his past hasty judgment. He placed ears of corn on the ground and left the fields to the crows. They recognized the change of attitude, returned in numbers, cleared the field of cutworms, and rewarded the owner by giving him a full yield. Since this experience Mr. Horsfall has been a staunch friend of the crow.

Forbush (1927) relates a similar experience of Gardner Hammond, of Marthas Vineyard, Mass. "Mr. Hammond owned great pastures where many sheep grazed. He told me once that he had offered a bounty of fifty cents each for Crows, as the birds had already killed about 200 of his newly born lambs, and that the native hunters under the stimulus of this bounty had killed nearly all the crows about the Squibnocket region. Notwithstanding my objection he continued to offer the bounty, although he expressed some fear that the expense would leave him bankrupt. About three years later he hailed me one day to see if I could determine what had destroyed the grass in his pastures. The grass was dead, having been cut at the roots by white grubs which had increased so rapidly after the destruction of the crows that they had already ruined a large part of the pastures. The offer of a bounty was withdrawn and the pastures gradually recovered."

Charles P. Shoffner, associate editor of the *Farm Journal* of Philadelphia, sent a questionnaire regarding the economic status of the crow to the readers of the journal who are scattered all over the agricultural districts of the United States. The results of this questionnaire are interesting, since they present a cross section of public opinion of a group of citizens most vitally concerned in the problem. Some of the replies were copied directly from the reports of the Department of Agriculture or other sources, but 9,731 were selected as being apparently based on personal observation or opinion. Among these 1,801 were in favor of the crow and 7,829 against him. Of the latter, 7,573 replies charged damage to crops, 6,937 to poultry, 4,112 to young pigs, sheep, rabbits, etc., 6,796 to song birds, and 6,493 to game birds. As Mr. Shoffner truly says, due weight must be given to the fact that reports were solicited by mail and it would be natural for farmers who had suffered serious damage to write their disapproval, while those who had suffered little or no loss would not trouble to do so. The interesting point is that so many persons defended the crow.

The conclusions of the *Journal* were:

1. The Crow wherever found in large numbers is injurious to farmers from March to December.

2. Where Crows are numerous they should be reduced in numbers and this should be done under active cooperation of State or National Agricultural Authorities. The Crow need not be exterminated.

3. The good Crows do by eating insects does not compensate for the damage done by eating eggs and young of other birds.

4. In acting as scavengers, Crows carry disease; farmers should bury or burn at once all dead animals.

There is a great difference in local conditions. In the West crows are a serious menace, while in parts of the East they are neutral or actually beneficial. Of the conclusions arrived at by the *Farm Journal*, those who have studied the economic relations of the crow will take exception to conclusion No. 3.

(For further comment on this questionnaire, see The Auk, vol. 43, pp. 140-141, 1926.)

Behavior.—The crows return to their roosting place early in the afternoon. The flight then is high and quite direct. Various estimates have been made of their speed in flight. Crows have been known to keep up with trains running at the rate of 60 miles an hour, but the speed determined by Townsend and others indicates that under ordinary conditions it seldom exceeds 20 to 30 miles an hour. If this rate is correct then a crow during sustained flight of a 10-hour day would cover only about 250 miles. Ducks, according to Lincoln (1939), travel 400 to 500 miles in the same period.

Townsend (1905) in writing of his experiences with crows in winter at Ipswich, Mass., records some interesting incidents as follows: "Hearing a great outcry among a party of Crows one day at Ipswich, I saw several swooping down to within a few feet of a fox. Reynard seemed not a whit disturbed, and carried his brush straight out behind as he sauntered along. * * * I have heard them make a virtuous outcry over a couple of innocent hares that were running through the dunes.

"Tracks show that it is a common habit for Crows to drag their middle toe in walking and sometimes all three front toes are dragged. Again, tracks of the same or other Crows show that the toes are lifted up without any dragging. I have seen Crows hop, and have found evidence of that in the sand. In landing from the air, their tracks show it is often their habit, to bound or hop forward once with feet together, before beginning to walk."

Some observers have stated that the crow in flight carries its feet extended backward, but F. H. Kennard, in some unpublished notes, records an observation made under favorable conditions. He was very near a crow that was silhouetted against the snow as it took flight. It raised its legs, after dangling them straight, directly up under and flew off with the closed claws showing as two lumps barely projecting from the feathers of the lower breast.

The feet of the crow are not well adapted for grasping, and their appearance would not at all suggest that they are prehensile, yet these birds do at times carry fairly large objects by means of their feet. At Kent Island I saw a startled crow grasp an eider duckling in its claws and transport it to cover in a thick growth of spruces. Chamberlain (1884) observed crows carrying two young of a brood of robins in their claws, and Kneeland (1883) has seen crows carrying fish heads and other objects too large and too heavy to be conveniently carried in the bill yet too precious to be left behind when food is scarce, as it often is during the winter. Chamberlain also saw a pet crow seize a partially eaten ear of boiled corn in its claws and fly away with it when accosted by a barking dog. Fred J. Pierce (1923), in an article entitled "A Crow that Nearly Looped the Loop," presents the following interesting observation: "I noticed a Crow flying overhead carrying an article in his feet that looked like a mouse or something of that sort. This Crow wanted to transfer the morsel to his bill, and in trying to do so bent his head underneath him so far that he lost his balance and barely escaped overturning in the air. This must have surprised him considerably, but he was a determined Crow and shortly tried it again with no better success. He was continuing his vain efforts when lost to view, but as his unsteady flight had brought him very near the ground, he doubtless alighted, where his object was accomplished with much less danger to his equilibration."

The adult crow is very wary and suspicious of man, an instinctive behavior for self-preservation that has been acquired through generations of experience. Yet crows taken from the nest at the proper time have become pets that have exhibited the greatest confidence in their companionship with human beings. There are innumerable instances on record in which crows have proved to be interesting and entertaining pets.

Lorenz (1937) has pointed out that a young bird, when reared under artificial conditions, will invariably react to its human keeper in exactly the same way that it would have reacted, under natural conditions, to birds of its own species. He has also stated that the period of acquiring this imprinting is confined, in some species, to a very definite and often astonishingly brief period, and that certain actions of the bird for the remainder of its life depend on the imprinting during this crucial period.

Cruickshank (1939) in testing out the statements of Lorenz, contrasts the behavior of two crows that he kept as pets. The first was taken from the nest when it was only two weeks old. It was raised in his home with great attention and soon reacted to him and his wife as it would have to its own parents if left in the wild. The crow followed them about, fluttering its wings and excitably begging for food. After it had learned to fly it paid no attention to local wild crows or to other human beings about the camp, but would single out Mr. Cruickshank or his wife and follow them everywhere. The food-begging act was performed for them only. The appearance of either of them or the sound of their voices was sufficient to start its begging. In various other ways this pet crow showed that it had thoroughly accepted its human foster parents and rejected all others. The other crow, obtained a few years before, had been taken on the day it left the nest. Though kept in isolation for the ensuing two weeks this crow never accepted Mr. Cruickshank in any way. His appearance never released the begging act, and the bird was always interested in the calls of nearby crows. At the first opportunity it flew off into the woods and never returned. This individual evidently had been obtained at too late a period. The imprinting had already taken place, and even close attention and strict isolation did not initiate a reverse.

The above experience readily explains the varying success persons have had in attempting to make pets of crows. Many have written about their pet crows, but one of the most detailed accounts is presented by Norman Criddle (1927), who had four crows that he obtained near Treesbank, Manitoba, on June 19, 1926. These birds exhibited considerable fear when first obtained, and it was necessary to feed them by force, but after a day they strongly exhibited the begging reactions. They greeted his approach by enthusiastic cries for food and their fear of man had vanished. Later, when able to fly, they were allowed to roost among the trees, but in the morning they collected around the feeding cage and his approach was always greeted with enthusiasm. They would alight on his head and shoulders as readily as on any other perch. During the day the crows devoted much of their time collecting and hiding objects of various kinds. As they grew older, berries and other food were hidden with the definite object of using it later when hungry. One of the crows would alight on its foster parent's shoulder, pull out the pocket handkerchief, deposit a throatful of berries, and then carefully shove the hankerchief back into place on top of them. The love of destructiveness became a dominant trait. Newspapers and brightly colored flowers in the garden were pulled to small bits, and other objects were similarly treated. When a pan of water was provided they soon took to bathing, although they had never experienced water before. Bathing and playing in the water became a regular pastime. Sometimes, after flying to Mr. Criddle's shoulder, they would playfully pinch his ear or run their beaks through his hair. One of them repeatedly tried to dislodge the button from his cap. Each of the crows was different in its personality and details of behavior. Mr. Criddle presents a multitude of experiences indicating that these crows performed just as they might have done toward their own kind if left in nature.

Pet crows are known to possess unusual ability to articulate the words and imitate the sounds of the human voice. They readily master such simple words as "mama," "papa," "hello," "howdydo," and others, and human laughter is often imitated to perfection. This presents the question as to how the crow is able to articulate and imitate so well. We should not expect to find the tracheal syrinx and its controlling muscles to be well developed in a bird that is not recognized for its ability to sing. To the contrary, the crow has a complete set of voice muscles. It is these muscles that give parrots and certain passerine birds such a variety of vocal modulations, so that they can mimic other birds or even the human voice. Hence it is not at all surprising that crows exhibit this unusual ability of imitation.

Pet crows are known to be very adept at learning and to meet new and previously inexperienced conditions. Coburn (1914) has proved this ability experimentally. He found that crows learn very quickly to distinguish the correct exit door when placed in a dark box from which there were translucent and lighted exits, each of the same area and light intensity but of different shapes. In this way it was shown that they distinguished with very little practice between a circle, a triangle, a square, and a hexagon. In this and other tests the experimenter was convinced that the crow's reputation for brains is quite deserved, and that Henry Ward Beecher was correct when he said that if men could be feathered and provided with wings, very few would be clever enough to be crows!

Voice.—The crow does not excel in its musical ability, but it has a great versatility in its voice. It has an interesting repertoire of many calls and notes, which serves it well in its interrelations with its fellows. It also has superior imitative faculties, and captive crows have exhibited unusual aptitude in learning new calls. Even human laughter is imitated, at times so appropriately uttered that it is difficult to think of it as mere coincidence.

The calls and notes have been subject to diverse interpretations; hence several representative authors have been quoted to present a better-rounded concept of them. Hoffmann (1904) states: "Besides the ordinary *caw,* and the many modifications of which it is capable, the crow utters commonly two other striking notes. One is a high-pitched laugh, *hă-ă-ă-ă-ă-ă;* the other a more guttural sound like the gobble of a turkey, *căw căw căw.*" Knight (1908) interprets the various calls of the crow as portraying signals that have a distinct meaning to their fellows:

When a band of crows is feeding one or two are generally posted as sentinels and a *caw c-a-a-w* of warning from these is sufficient to make all seek safety. Their call *caw-caw* is uttered in varied tones and different accents so that it is capable of meaning a great many things from alarm to satisfaction, and one acquainted with their ways can usually tell just what they are saying in a general way. For instance I have never failed to correctly judge from their excited and confused cries that they had an owl penned up somewhere and were engaged in "mobbing" it to their satisfaction. The alarm *"caw"* uttered sharply and quickly, which means "look out" is well known to about everybody who has ever seen a Crow. Their prolonged cries of distress when their home is menaced should be easily recognizable. The prolonged *car-r——a——c——k* of a love sick individual in spring, uttered in various tones and drawn out into prolonged gurglings, though somewhat like the call of the young for food is still quite different.

Forbush (1927) writes:

Some Crows, if not all, are capable of producing unusual, tuneful or pleasing sounds. As an example of the unusual let me refer to an individual that I heard early one morning on Cape Cod repeating for over an hour syllables like *clockity-clock, clockity-clock;* while as showing the musical attainments of the species mention may be made of a Crow that I saw on the banks of the Musketaquid, August 10, 1906, which uttered a series of exceedingly melodious, soft, cooing notes unlike any others within my experience. In the same locality on July 14 a young Crow remarked very plainly *aaaou, cou, cou, cou, aaaou, coucoo.* On October 20, 1903, I heard and saw a Crow give an excellent imitation of a whine of a dog. * * * I have heard from Crows a varied assortment of notes, some of which apparently were imitations, such as the cry of a child, the squawk of a hen, or the crow of a young rooster. The cooing notes mentioned above were similar to sounds uttered by the male in courtship. At this season, also, the male has a peculiar cry which may be an attempt at song and has been represented by the syllables *hollow-ollo-ollo.*

Townsend (1923) gives the following account of the calls of the crow:

There are many other words in the Crow vocabulary than the simple *caw,* and I find a number of them recorded in my notes. Many are common and familiar sounds of the countryside, and their recognition is always a pleasure. First, one may consider the modifications of the *caw.* Of these, *orr, orr,* are common, as well as *ah, ah,* the latter delivered at times as with a great feeling of relief. Again, the note may sound like *gnaw, gnaw,* delivered with a nasal inflection and in a taunting manner.

On the other hand the notes may lose all semblance of the typical *caws,* and rapidly repeated and wailing *kaa, wha, wha, wha, kaa, wha, wha, wha,* may be heard, or, as I have written at other times, *ou, ahh, ahh, ahh.* Again, a loud and cheerful *ha, ha, ha,* may be heard, suggestive of one of the calls of the Herring Gull. A despairing *nevah, nevah,* is not uncommon. Occasionally one may hear a loud *cluck.* One of the most extraordinary combinations of Crow notes that I have ever heard was emitted near my house at Ipswich early one

April morning. The bird called *chuck-chuck, whoo-oo,* and then *cawed* in the ordinary manner, repeating the formula in this order several times. Its significance was hidden.

The conversational notes of a small group or family of Crows are always entertaining, and the observer is impressed with the extensiveness of their vocabulary and with the variations in their feelings. At times the notes are low and confidential, pleasant and almost melodious, if I may use that word here; again they are raucous and scolding, bursting at times into a veritable torrent of abuse. In the same way, in human conversations, one may, even without understanding the words, be able to interpret the meanings and motives involved. [See under Courtship for additional notes.]

Allen (1919) has called our attention to the time rhythm, which he attributes to a well-developed esthetic sense of the crow. He has noted that the *caw* notes are not only in triplets but at times they give four *caws* in groups of two (2-2); again he noted that the bird cawed 2-1 a large number of times in succession and on other occasions 2-1-1. The time was so regular that he could detect no variations. The length of the several notes and their pitch and quality were uniform, the rhythm being all that differentiated the phrase from other performances of the crow.

Allen does not believe the series of combination of calls represents a code of signals, nor does he believe them to be purely mechanical and involuntary, but he thinks the crow takes delight in the rhythm and variety of his utterances. He asks the question, "Is he not, in a limited way, a true artist, a composer as well as a performer?"

Wright (1912), in a study conducted at Jefferson Highlands in the White Mountains, N. H., determined the order and manner in which summer resident birds within range of hearing awoke and voiced themselves. According to Wright the crow is a comparatively late riser, as it ranks twenty-fourth among the common birds in time of voicing itself. Fourteen records show that the earliest times at which a crow was heard to call were 3:35 and 3:36 A.M. The average time of the first call was 3:44 A.M. The variations of the crow's awakening was only 21 minutes on 14 occasions, ranging in date from May 27 to July 9, and covering ten seasons. Wright concluded that the crow was one of the most regular in awakening of the common birds he observed.

Enemies.—The crow is recognized as an enemy of certain species of birds, especially in the destruction of their eggs and young, but it is itself in turn preyed upon by hawks and owls. Horned and snowy owls have been seen to capture and kill crows, and the remains have been found in the stomach contents of others. Likewise remains of crows have been found in the stomach contents of red-shouldered and red-tailed hawks and goshawks, and probably the crow falls a victim to other species of the larger hawks. Even the smaller species of hawks may sometimes exhibit a daring inclination to tackle a crow. White (1893) relates an experience in which the small sharp-shinned hawk was seen to attack successfully a crow on Mackinac Island, Mich. Sutton (1929) found the crop of a Cooper's hawk, killed near Shippensburg, Pa., packed with feathers and flesh of a crow. According to the observer a second Cooper's hawk was seen to fly up from the spot where the first was killed, and nearby among the weeds was a partly eaten and fairly well plucked crow, the flesh of which was still warm. Dr. Sutton, although admitting he is unable to prove the case, believes that one or both of the hawks killed the crow.

It is well known that even smaller birds, notably the kingbird, may harass a crow and make its existence very uncomfortable. Currier (1904) in an account of crows observed at Leech Lake, Minn., writes: "One pair in particular had our sympathy. They had a nest full of young in a scrub oak standing alone out on the marsh, where several pairs of Kingbirds, and thousands of Redwings were breeding. Every time a Crow made a move it was pounced upon by from two to a dozen of the smaller birds and forced to light for a time. The Yellow-heads would also join in at times, but they were not so persistent. The Red-wings seemed to be the worst."

I have seen crows that have chanced to enter sea-bird colonies viciously and violently attacked by terns.

That crows are never on good terms with predaceous birds, especially owls, is evidenced by the great commotion aroused among the crows whenever an owl is discovered. Fortified by numbers, they exhibit great audacity and may harass an owl for hours at a time. In fact, the presence of an owl may frequently be revealed by the cawing and behavior of the crows at such times. Their antipathy for owls is so great that they may be lured by a stuffed owl placed by a gunner who wishes to destroy them. For the past 15 years I have had several live horned owls in a large flight cage in the backyard of my home in Brunswick, Maine. Almost every morning during the spring migration, flocks of crows ranging from a dozen to 25 or 30 alight in the surrounding trees and awaken the entire neighborhood by their haranguing calls. The crows alight on top of the cage but the least movement on the part of the owls sends them scampering to the tree tops under loud protests. Seeking renewed courage the crows descend again and again to repeat the performance. This goes on in spite of the fact that it is in the midst of a thickly settled portion of the town.

Crows, as well as other birds, fall as victims of flesh-eating mammals. Errington (1935) in his study of the food of midwest foxes, reports that crows are eaten by them.

Wilson (1923) reports a case in which a crow was attacked by a
large snake, but such instances are probably rare.

Among mammals, the crow's greatest enemy is man. Since the
economic status has been questioned thousands of crows have been
killed by poisoning, shooting, and especially by bombing the populous
roosts. A few are killed on the highways by automobiles.

No comprehensive study of the diseases of the crow has been made
to my knowledge, but as has been shown in the case of other species of
birds, disease is probably an important factor in the life of the species.

Mitchell (1929) reported an epidemic of tuberculosis in crows of
western Ontario, where he conducted experiments to see if infection is
likely to be carried to other animals. Eaton (1903) has given us a detailed report of an epidemic of roup in the Canandaigua crow roost in
Ontario County, N. Y., during the winter of 1901-2. Eaton estimates
that at least a thousand crows succumbed to the disease in that region
alone. Dr. Fox (1923) in a pathological examination of 16 crows, found
cases of tropidocerca, occasional intestinal cestodes, and a few filaria.

Dr. E. B. Cram (1927) lists five internal nematode parasites found
in the crow. Three of these are found in the proventriculus, the glan-
dular part of the stomach, and the other two in the trachea, or lungs.
The parasites are as follows: *Acuaria cordata* (Mueller), found in the
wall of the proventriculus; the males range from 10 to 11 and the
females 22.5 to 40 millimeters in length. *Microtetrameres helix* Cram,
found in the walls of the proventriculus; the males of this small worm
are 4.9 and the females 1.2 to 1.3 millimeters in length. *Tetrameres
inispina* (Diesing), known only from the female, which is 3 millimeters
in length; this parasite is found also in the proventriculus. *Syngamus
trachea* (Montague), occurring as adults in the trachea and bronchi
and as larvae in the lungs; immature worms have been found in the
peritracheal tissue and air sacs; the males are 2 to 6 and the females
5 to 20 millimeters in length. *Syngamus gracilis* Chapin, found only in
the trachea; the males are 3 to 3.3 and the females 8 to 11 millimeters
long.

Harold Peters (1936) lists three lice and one tick as common external parasites of the crow. The lice are *Degeeriella rotundata* (Osborn), *Myrsidea americana* (Kellogg), and *Philopterus corvi* (Osborn)
and the tick is *Haemaphysalis leporis-palustris* Packard. A different species of tick and two species of mites have been found on the southern
crow. The tick is *Amblyomma americanum* (Linnaeus), found in a crow
from South Carolina, and the mites are *Liponyssus sylviarum* (Canes-
trini and Fanzago) and *Trouessartia corvina* (Koch), found on crows
collected in South Carolina and Florida, respectively.

But by far the worst enemy of the crow is man. Where crows are numerous, especially in their winter roosts, enormous numbers are killed by bombing with dynamite. As one example of this, Dr. Walter P. Taylor (MS.) tells us that in Collingsworth County, Tex., on April 7, 1937, bombs were exposed in a shinnery clump to kill crows. There was one stick of dynamite to each bomb, and the bombs were connected with wires, so that they could be fired simultaneously. Sixty bombs were set off at the first discharge, at which it was estimated that 40,000 crows were killed; at the second shot, 120 bombs were set off, killing nearly as many more. Other bombing operations are mentioned under "Roosts."

Roosts.—During the summer crows associate only in pairs at their isolated breeding places, but in fall they exhibit a marked gregarious inclination, and birds from many miles of territory congregate in immense roosts comprising thousands, sometimes tens and even hundreds of thousands, of individuals. These roosts are not only made up of the birds breeding in the region but the flocks are augmented by birds that have migrated from nesting grounds located farther to the north. In New England there is a marked tendency for the crows to move from inland areas to roosts established near the coast. Food is the primary factor involved in this shift; whereas the feeding grounds in the interior become covered with snow and ice, the seacoast provides an uninterrupted food supply that is replenished with every flow of the tide. Even the severe winter weather does not drive the hardy members from the roosts established in the dense coniferous forests that fringe the coast. Most of the roosts in northern New England are comparatively small, however, and one must go farther to the southward before meeting with aggregations of unusual size.

Townsend (1918) has presented a vivid account of a crow roost that contained approximately 12,000 individuals, located in the thickets and hardwoods on Castle Hill near Ipswich beach, Mass. Following are extracts from Dr. Townsend's paper, which portray in detail scenes similar to those many others have experienced.

In the short winter afternoons the Crows begin their flight to the roost long before sunset. By three o'clock or even as early as one o'clock, especially in dark weather and in the short December days, this bed-time journey begins, while in the latter part of February the flight is postponed until half past four or a quarter of five. From every direction but the seaward side the Crows direct their course towards the roost. Three main streams of flight can be distinguished: one from the north, from the region of the Ipswich and Rowley "hundreds,"— the great stretches of salt marshes that extend to the Merrimac River,—a second from the west and a third,—apparently the largest of all, broad and deep and highly concentrated,—from the south.

It was the last of these rivers that on a cold December afternoon with a biting wind from the northwest I first studied. * * * It was an impressive sight. About 3 o'clock the Crows began to appear, singly and in small groups, beating their way in the teeth of the wind towards the north. In flying over the estuary of the Castle Neck River they kept close to the water as if to take advantage of the lee behind the waves; over the land they clung to the contour of the dunes. As we walked among these waves of sand the Crows often appeared suddenly and unexpectedly over the crest of a dune within a few feet of us. Silently for the most part, except for the silken rustle of their wings, they flew over in increasing numbers until it was evident that they were to be counted, not by hundreds, but by thousands. Many of them alighted on the dunes to the south of the roosting place; sand, bushes and stunted bare trees were alike black with them. Others assembled on the bare hillside to the east. About sunset a great tumult of corvine voices issued from the multitude,—a loud cawing with occasional wailing notes,— and a black cloud rose into the air and settled in the branches of the bare trees to the west of the roost. From here as it was growing dusk they glided into the evergreens for the night.

The last day of the year 1916, I spent with Dr. W. M. Tyler in the dunes. The wind was fresh from the northwest,—the temperature was 15° Far. at 6:30 A.M., 18° at noon and 20° at 6 P.M. As early as one o'clock in the afternoon a few Crows were seen struggling north over and close to the surface of the dunes. Others were noticed flying high and towards the south. This southerly flight came from over Castle Hill to the north, passed the roost and continued on over the dunes. At half-past three some of these birds, which were apparently turning their backs on their usual night's lodging place, met with a large company coming from the south and all settled together in the dunes about two miles south of the roost. Some of the birds coming from the north, however, settled in the bare fields by the roost, and their numbers here were augmented by a stream from the west. This concourse on the hillside set up a great tumult of cawings just before four o'clock. At five minutes after four the united multitude of northerners and southerners rose from their meeting place in the dunes and flew low to join their noisy brethren on the hillside. This river of black wings from the south was a continuous one and it was joined just before its debouch on the hillside by the stream from the west. The river from the north had split into two layers: the lower flying birds came to rest on the hill,—the higher flying ones favored by the strong northwest wind, continued on their way south, notwithstanding the great current that was sweeping north below them. They joined their comrades in the dunes and retraced their steps. No signs of starvation and impaired vigor in these unnecessary flights, or in the game of tag in which two or more of the birds at times indulge!

The pace is now fast and furious. The birds are anxious to get within touch of the roost before it is dark but none have yet entered it. At 4:15 P.M., 135 birds pass in a minute from the south alone on their way to join the concourse on the hillside. A little later this southern river becomes so choked with birds that it is impossible to count them. From our point of vantage in a spruce thicket on the hill we can see that this flock stretches for two miles into the dunes and it takes them four minutes to pass. The speed of flight, therefore, must be roughly about thirty miles an hour. At 4:15 P.M. the sun sets, but in the yellow glow of the cloudless sky the birds can be seen pouring by from the west and south. The bulk of the stream from the north now comes to rest on the hillside for only occasionally can a crow be seen flying to the south over the heads of the southern stream.

At 4:35 P.M. Dr. Tyler and I again counted the southern stream for a minute as they flew silently between us and the lighthouse. One of us counted 160 the other 157 birds, so it is probable that our counts are fairly accurate. This constant watching of the black stream from the south against the white light-house produced in both of us a peculiar optical illusion. The lighthouse and dunes seemed to be moving smoothly and swiftly from north to south!

At 4:37 P.M. a great cawing arose from the hillside and a black cloud of birds rose up, some to enter the roost, others to subside on the hillside. It was evident that the birds from time to time had been diving into the roost. At 4:40 P.M. it was rapidly growing dark and the tributary streams were evidently dwindling. Only 50 went by the lighthouse in a minute. Five minutes later it was nearly dark and only a few belated stragglers were hurrying to the concourse on the hill.

At 4:45 P.M. Dr. Tyler and I walked around to the north of the roost and al-though we could see nothing in the darkness we could hear the silken rustle of wings and feathers as the Crows were composing themselves for the night's rest among the branches of the trees. The babble of low conversational notes that went up from the company suggested the sounds of a Night Heronry although cawings and carrings were interspersed with the kis and uks and ahhs. * * *

In the dim light we could make out that the hillside field between the roost and the sea was still blackened with birds that were continually rising up and entering the trees. Some of them perched temporarily on the bare tops of the hard woods where they were visible against the sky. The noise and confusion were great. It would seem as if the roost was so crowded that the birds had to wait their time for a chance to get in and that a constant shifting of places and crowding was necessary before the Crows could settle in peace for the night. Hence the prolonged varied conversation; hence the profanity.

It was an intensely interesting experience, this observation of the return of the Crows to their night's lodgings, and one wished for eyes all about the head, well sharpened wits to interpret and a trained assistant to take down notes. * * *

At the full of the moon on the sixth of January I visited the roost at 9 P.M., a time when all well regulated Crows should, I had supposed, be sound asleep. As I approached the roost much to my surprise I heard distinct sleepy cries like those of young herons, and when I reached the edge of the roosting trees there was a tumultuous rush and bustle of Crows flying from tree to tree and overhead. Strain my eyes as I would only occasionally could I catch sight of a black form, although the air was brilliant with the moonlight and the reflection from the snow. I turned back at once as I had no desire to disturb the birds' slumbers but it was evident that many, even at this late hour, had not settled down for the night.

The morning flight from the roost takes less time than the evening return. As I approached it in the semi-darkness at 6:25 A.M. on January 7, a distant cawing could be heard and a minute later nine Crows were seen flying off to the south, and three minutes later, nine went off to the west. At half past six, after a great uproar of caws and uks, occasional rattles and wailing ahhhs, a broad stream boiled up from the roosting trees and spread off towards the west, ob-scurely seen in the dim light except when the birds stood out against the be-ginning red glow in the east or against the light of the setting moon in the west. As I stood concealed on the hillside among a grove of spruces, the Crows passed over my head, noiselessly except for the silken swish of their wings, fully a thousand strong. Then no more for over five minutes although the tumult in the roost continued in increasing volume. At 6:40 the roost boiled over again, but the birds spreading in all directions soon united into a black river that flowed over the dunes to the south. The settings of this black stream were the white sand dunes and the luminous glow in the east which had become a brilliant crimson fading to orange and yellow and cut by a broad band of pink haze that streamed up to the zenith. The morning star glowed brightly until almost broad daylight. The sun rose at 7:14. At 7 I entered the roost and hurried away the few hundred remaining birds some of whom were in the bare tops of the hardwoods ready to depart, while others were still dozing in the evergreens below.

Nuttall's Ornithology (1832) gives an account of two roosts on the Delaware River in Pennsylvania. One of them was on an island, near Newcastle, called the Pea Patch, a low flat alluvial spot, just elevated above high-water mark, and thickly covered with reeds. The crows took shelter in the reeds and at one time during the prevalence of a sudden and violent northeast storm accompanied by heavy rains, the Pea Patch Island was wholly inundated in the night. The crows apparently made no attempt to escape, and were drowned by thousands. The following day the shores for a distance of several miles were blackened by their bodies.

Stone (1899) states that the crows that inhabited Pea Patch and the neighboring Reedy Island were estimated at 500,000.

Another famous crow roost is one located in Brookland, near Washington, D. C., which accommodates practically all the crows that feed in the vicinity. Oberholser (1920) estimated that this roost contained 200,000 birds. A very large crow roost was located at Arlington, Va., across the Potomac from Washington. Dr. W. B. Barrows estimated that 150,000 to 200,000 crows came to it every night during the winter of 1886-87.

Widmann (1880), in connection with an account of a crow roost located on Arsenal Island opposite the southern part of St. Louis, writes: "As early as August they begin to flock in, first by hundreds, then by thousands, and in December hundreds of thousands sleep there every night. The roar they make in the morning and evening can be heard for miles around, and the sight of the influx of these multitudes in the evening is something really imposing." Later Widmann (1907) in writing about this roost stated: "All through fall and in moderately cold weather in winter, the Crows spent the nights perched ten to fifteen feet above the ground in the willow thicket of the island, but when the cold weather became intense they deserted the willows entirely and spent the nights on the snow-covered sand bank in front of the willow thicket and exposed to the fierce northwest and north wind. When they had gone in the early morning, every bird had left an imprint of its body in the form of a light depression in the snow with a hole in front made by the bill and a few heaps of excreta on the opposite side, showing the bird had spent all night in that position, always with the head turned toward the wind, letting the wind sweep over its back, but keeping the feet from freezing."

Although crows are very resourceful in combating the adverse weather conditions of winter, extreme subzero temperatures have been known to play havoc with them at the roosts. J. W. Preston wrote Bendire (1895) of a roost of 40,000 crows located near Baxter, Iowa, in which many of the birds died of starvation during the cold winter of 1891-92 because they were blinded from the freezing of the corneas of their eyes. Likewise, Ridgway in *Science,* February 10, 1893, p. 77, mentions the sufferings of the crows in a roost near Washington, D. C. He states that many had their eyes frozen, which was followed by the bursting of the organs and the consequent death of the birds from starvation.

Crows have probably evolved the habit of congregating in roosts for mutual protection, but in the present day, since the verdict concerning their relations to man's interests in certain States has been pronounced against them, thousands of individuals are killed by man at the very roosts where they sought refuge against danger. Imler (1939) states that 26,000 birds were killed by the bombing of a large crow roost near Dempsey, Okla., on December 10, 1937. The Game and Fish Commission bombed another roost at Binger, Okla., on December 6, 1938, killing 18,000 crows. Frank S. Davis, inspector for the Illinois State Department of Conservation, killed 328,000 crows in roosts near Rockford, Ill., with the use of festoons of dynamite bombs. This wholesale slaughter was given great publicity, appearing with photographs in the issue of *Life* for March 25, 1940. Numerous roosts throughout the winter range of the crow in the Middlewest and South have been dealt with in a similar manner. In addition to shooting and bombing, poisons also have been employed. This unprecedented destruction of bird life has been received with both commendation and violent criticism. Some of the larger roosts numbering hundreds of thousands of individuals provide us with one of the most spectacular scenes of bird life. It is indeed unfortunate that departments of conservation find it necessary to destroy them.

Winter.—Along the New England coast winter is one of the most interesting seasons for a study of crows. At this time they are more numerous than during summer, since the snow-bound conditions of the interior bring them to the tidal shores, where there is a more accessible and constant food supply. They may be seen leaving the roosts early in the morning, often before sunrise, in groups of two or three to a dozen or 20. At this season they seem to lead an aimless kind of existence, meandering here and there, flying low over the mud flats or open fields in a persistent search for food. Sometimes their wanderings take them long distances, going hither and thither until a carcass or other food supply is located. At all times they are alert and suspicious, always proceeding toward food with caution, often alighting on convenient vantage points to carefully inspect the surroundings and to make sure no harm is in store for them. Finally an individual more audacious, perhaps hungrier than the others, approaches to test out the situation. If he succeeds in escaping harm the others quickly join him in active competition to gorge themselves. At such times one bird may act as a sentinel to give warning in the event of approaching danger.

Edward J. Reimann in correspondence concerning crows seen in winter in the vicinity of Philadelphia, Pa., writes: "Crows in winter, especially when ice has formed in the waterways, will be found frequenting the low flats of streams and creeks left bare by the low tide. They can be seen congregated in immense flocks feeding on the seeds of arrow-arum *(Peltandra virginica)*. When the rivers are full of drift ice, crows seem to take a particular delight in perching on the cakes and traveling up and down stream with the tide. On some occasions crows were seen to be eating fish frozen in the ice."

DISTRIBUTION

Range.—Most of North America; migratory in the northern regions.

Breeding range.—The crow breeds **north** to Alaska (probably Kodiak Island, Seldonia, and Hinchinbrook Island); southern Mackenzie (Fort Simpson and Grandin River); southern Keewatin (50 miles south of Cape Eskimo); southern Quebec (Onigamis, Godbout, and Mingan Island); and Newfoundland (probably Port au Port and St. John's). The **eastern** limits of the range extend southward along the Atlantic coast from Newfoundland (St. John's) to southern Florida (Royal Palm Park and East Cape). The **southern** limits extend westward along the coast of the Gulf of Mexico from southern Florida (East Cape) to Texas (Houston and Kerrville); northern New Mexico (Glorieta, Santa Fe Canyon, and Santa Clara); central Arizona (White Mountains and the Salt River Bird Reservation); and probably northern Baja California (Guadalupe). **West** to probably Baja California (Guadalupe); California (San Diego, Buena Vista Lake, Stockton, and Red Bluff); Oregon (Warner Valley and Silver Lake); Washington (Camas, Westport, and Everett); British Columbia (Stanley Park, Gull Island, and Massett); and Alaska (Forrester Island, Sitka, and probably Kodiak Island). The crow is also resident in Bermuda.

The range as outlined is for the entire species, which is now separated into four geographical races. The eastern crow *(Corvus brachyrhynchos brachyrhynchos)* is found from Maryland, the northern parts of the Gulf States, and northern Texas north to Newfoundland, Quebec, northern Manitoba, and southwestern Mackenzie; the southern crow *(Corvus b. paulus)* occupies the southeastern part of the range (except Florida) west to eastern Texas; the Florida crow *(Corvus b. pascuus)* is found only in the Florida Peninsula; the western crow *(Corvus b. hesperis)* occupies the western part of the range north to southern Saskatchewan and central British Columbia.

Winter range.—Resident throughout the southern part of the breeding range and north to southern British Columbia (Comox, Chilliwack, and Okanagan Landing); southern Saskatchewan (East End); southern Manitoba (Portage la Prairie); southern Ontario (Sault Ste. Marie, North Bay, and Ottawa); northern Vermont (St. Johnsbury); Maine (Avon and Ellsworth); New Brunswick (Scotch Lake and Fredericton); Nova Scotia (Wolfville and Pictou); and southeastern Newfoundland (St. John's).

Migration.—Since in winter the crow is found in limited numbers, as far north as southern Canada, dates of arrival and departure do not convey a true picture of its migrations. Extensive migratory flight is, in fact, confined to the birds of the Great Plains region. In the files of the Fish and Wildlife Service there are several hundred instances of crows banded during the summer in Saskatchewan that were subsequently recovered during the following fall and winter at well-connected series of localities south through North and South Dakota, Nebraska, Kansas, Oklahoma, and Texas. Similarly, crows banded during winter in Oklahoma and Kansas were recovered during the following spring and summer north through Nebraska and the Dakotas, to Manitoba, Saskatchewan, and Alberta. Crows banded at northern points on the Atlantic coast show very little movement but are generally recovered within 100 miles of the point of banding.

Egg dates.—Alaska: 15 records, May 10 to June 11; 8 records, May 17 to June 6, indicating the height of the season.

Alberta: 21 records, May 2 to June 9; 10 records, May 13 to 24.

British Columbia: 10 records, April 17 to June 4.

California: 112 records, March 21 to June 12; 56 records, April 9 to 21.

Florida: 52 records, January 21 to May 27; 26 records, February 26 to April 2.

Illinois: 39 records, March 27 to May 22; 19 records, April 9 to 27.

Kansas: 22 records, March 3 to May 15; 11 records, April 3 to 19.

Maine: 60 records, April 16 to May 27; 30 records, April 28 to May 8.

New Jersey: 146 records, March 30 to June 12; 74 records, April 15 to May 7.

Ontario: 12 records, April 14 to July 5; 6 records, April 25 to 30.

Oregon: 17 records, April 16 to May 27; 9 records, April 29 to May 11.

Texas: 9 records, February 28 to April 26.

West Virginia: 27 records, April 5 to May 28; 13 records, April 12 to 19.

Washington: 6 records, April 22 to May 22.

CORVUS BRACHYRHYNCHOS PAULUS Howell

SOUTHERN CROW

HABITS

This southern race was named by Arthur H. Howell (1913) from a type collected in Alabama and described as "decidedly smaller than *Corvus b. brachyrhynchos,* with a much slenderer bill. Nearest to *Corvus b. hesperis* but with shorter wing and slightly larger bill." He says further: "Although the bird is nearest to *C. b. hesperis* in size, its range apparently is separated from the range of *hesperis* by a strip of country in central Texas in which no crows breed." He gives as its range "Alabama, Mississippi, Louisiana, southeastern Texas, Georgia (?), South Carolina, and north to the District of Columbia and southern Illinois." It evidently intergrades with *brachyrhynchos* at the northern and western limits of this range. He also says that it is decidedly smaller than the Florida crow, *pascuus,* which is rather remarkable, as Florida races of other birds are generally smaller than the more northern races.

I cannot find that the habits of the southern crow are materially different from those of the eastern crow on the one hand, or the Florida crow on the other hand, depending on the conditions in which it lives. It builds similar nests in many different kinds of trees and feeds on similar classes of food. It has some of the bad habits of the northern race but is nowhere so abundant as to do much damage, and it destroys so many injurious rodents and noxious insects that it probably does more good than harm and should not be molested.

M. G. Vaiden writes to me: "These birds are not so plentiful in the Yazoo-Mississippi Delta of the Mississippi as they are in the hill section lying some 70 miles to the east of the Mississippi River. However, large numbers are found during the latter part July and in August and September, feeding along the mud bars of the river and about the great number of barrow pits left from levee construction, where they feed along with the herons, wood ibises, egrets, and buzzards on the dead and dying small fry left as the pools dry up. They are destructive to other birds' nests, especially killdeers and terns, where they nest along the river on sand bars. I have seen the crow destroying the nests of terns, as described in a short article in *The Oologist* for February 1939, page 24."

Albert J. Kirn tells me that in Texas he has seen crows harassed by a marsh hawk and has also seen a crow attacking a marsh hawk. In southern and eastern Texas he finds them fairly common, mostly in river bottom woods, but thinks that the resident birds do not range very far west in the State.

The measurements of 40 eggs of the southern crow in the United States National Museum average 41.4 by 28.9 millimeters; the eggs showing the four extremes measure 47.3 by 30.2, 42.9 by 31.2, and 35.8 by 20.2 millimeters.

Dr. Walter P. Taylor tells me that he called up a crow that came within 150 feet of him and sat in the top of a tree. To his surprise "it began to sing. One would never suspect that such tender notes could come from the raucous throat of a crow. The notes resemble somewhat the clucking of a rooster when he is calling hens to some dainty morsel he has found. The crow's song is more varied, however; sometimes he adds a high-pitched tone, and then again continues with his clucking and gurgling noises."

CORVUS BRACHYRHYNCHOS PASCUUS Coues

FLORIDA CROW

HABITS

The Florida crow is smaller than the eastern crow, except for its bill and feet, which are relatively larger and heavier. It is somewhat larger than the southern crow *(paulus)*, which has a smaller and slenderer bill.

The Florida crow *(pascuus)* is generally distributed over peninsular Florida, except in the northwestern part, west of the Aucilla River; it apparently intergrades with *paulus* somewhere in the region of St. Marks. I have met with it in various parts of the State but found it nowhere especially abundant, much less common, in fact, than crows are in many other parts of the United States. We found it most commonly in the flat pine woods, especially about the small cypress swamps, but saw it also in the mixed oak and palmetto hammocks and on the prairies.

Nesting.—What few nests we saw were in the thick groves of tall, slender longleaf pines. Arthur H. Howell (1932) says: "The nests are frequently placed in oak trees in the hammocks, sometimes in pine trees near the border of a cypress swamp, or in a lone tree on the prairie, 7 to 40 (rarely 60) feet above the ground. They are composed of oak twigs and Spanish moss, and lined with horse hair, cabbage-palm fiber, and small pieces of bark."

Bendire (1895) says of some nests collected by Dr. Ralph: "Several nests were found by him in tall, slender pine trees in low, flat pine woods, usually bordering on swamps. The nests were located in the tops of trees, on horizontal limbs, and close to the trunk, at distances varying from 45 to 70 feet from the ground. They are usually composed of small sticks, lined first with Spanish moss and then with strips of cypress bark; occasionally a few feathers from the sitting bird, hair from cows' tails, bunches of fine grass, and grass with the rootlets attached entered into the composition of the linings, and in one instance the eggs were laid on about half a pint of fine rotten wood. The nests average in measurement about 24 by 9 inches in outer diam-eter, the inner cup being about 16 inches in width by 5 inches in depth' [the 9 inches probably refers to the height and not the diameter].

Harold H. Bailey (1925) says that they nest in "almost every kind of tree from mangrove, gumbo limbo, and cabbage palm of southern keys to pine, oak, and hardwood trees" farther north.

Eggs.—This crow lays three to six eggs, most commonly four or five, which are indistinguishable, except for a slight average difference in size, from the eggs of other crows. The measurements of 40 eggs in the United States National Museum average 41.1 by 28.7 millimeters; the eggs showing the four extremes measure **45.5** by 20.2, 43.2 by **30.9, 37.7** by 29.0, and 40.6 by **20.2** millimeters.

Food.—Mr. Bailey (1925) says: "They have little chance [in south-ern Florida] to feed on or destroy the farmers' grain, or work in the plowed areas for insect life, but resort to food such as frogs, lizards, small snakes, large grasshoppers, and snails; while during the breeding season the colonies of herons, ibis, anhinga, and other water birds are robbed of eggs or even small young. In every part of the country where I have studied them, I have found them very destructive birds as a whole."

Behavior.—The habits of the Florida crow are much like those of crows elsewhere, though it seems to be tamer and more sociable, less shy, probably because it does less damage to crops and is not persecuted so much as are the more northern subspecies. D. Mortimer (1890) writes:

It is common to see it feeding about the streets and vacant lots of Sanford, especially when the palmetto fruit is ripe enough to eat. It associates freely with the Boat-tailed and Florida Grackles, and also with the Red-winged Blackbird and the Rice-bird, and I have seen flocks including all these species enjoying themselves about the town. It always retreats before any small bird that undertakes to chase it, though it does so apparently because it is too indolent to drive off its assailant, and not on account of timidity. Omnivorous in the fullest sense, it is always on the lookout for any edible morsel. I have seen Florida Crows attach themselves to the Osprey as soon as the latter captured a fish, and tag it about as if to secure any scraps that might fall during the meal. The Osprey is disturbed by this intrusion and tries to strike the Crows with its wings if they come too close.

Voice.—In addition to the ordinary crow notes, two observers have noted some notes that seem to be peculiar to this subspecies. Mr. Mortimer (1890) says: "The Florida Crow has a peculiar note that I never heard uttered by any crow at the North. It is a loud, rattling sound something like the cry of the Cuckoo, and puzzled me much as to its source until I detected the bird in the act of producing it." And Mr. Howell (1932) refers to what is perhaps the same note: "It suggested the rattling call of the Sandhill Crane, though not so loud, and resembled, also, the 'churring' note of the Red-bellied Woodpecker."

CORVUS BRACHYRHYNCHOS HESPERIS Ridgway

WESTERN CROW

PLATES 43-45

HABITS

The western crow is decidedly smaller than the eastern crow, with a relatively smaller and slenderer bill. It is very close to the southern crow *(paulus)* in size, but it has a longer wing and a slightly smaller bill; furthermore, it is widely separated from it in its breeding range. Its range, as given in the 1931 Check-list, is "western North America, from central British Columbia, southern Saskatchewan, and Montana south to northern Lower California and central New Mexico." It apparently breeds very sparingly, if at all, in the extreme southern portions of its range, where it occurs mainly as a winter visitor. Just where it intergrades with the eastern crow on the north and east does not seem to be definitely established. We listed the birds we found in southwestern Saskatchewan as *hesperis,* and a bird taken at Walsh, in southern Alberta, was referred by Dr. Bishop to this race. Frank L. Farley tells me that the birds around Camrose, central Alberta, are of the eastern race. The western crow is very irregularly distributed throughout its range, being rare or entirely lacking in many regions and exceedingly abundant in others; in the regions where it is abundant it is much more numerous than the eastern crow is anywhere, often nesting in colonies.

Dawson (1923) says: "The crow in California is no such constant factor of bird life as he is in the East. He is, instead, very local and sharply restricted in his distribution, so that to a traveller the appearance of Crows is rather a novelty, something to be jotted down in the field-book; and Crow country can scarcely comprise more than a twentieth part of the total area of the State."

Nesting.—About Crane Lake, Saskatchewan, we found a few pairs of crows nesting in the small willows; seven nests were recorded in my notes during the latter half of June, all of which contained young. I found crows nesting at two quite different localities in California. On April 10, 1929, in San Diego County, while exploring a long row of sycamores along the banks of a dry stream, I saw a number of crows' nests and many of the birds. The nests were all well up near the tops of rather large sycamores; many of them were apparently occupied, as the birds were very solicitous; but, as the trees were hard to climb and as I did not flush any birds off any of the nests, I did not disturb them. Again, in Ventura County, on April 27, M. C. Badger and I found crows very common and noisy in a large tract of small cottonwoods and willows along the Santa Clara River; we saw a number of nests, mostly in small live cottonwoods, but some in dead cottonwoods or in willows and 15 to 20 feet from the ground; those that we examined were empty. They did not differ materially from other crows' nests.

It seems to be characteristic of the western crow to build its nest at low elevations, as well as in groups or colonies; small trees or bushes seem to be satisfactory as nesting sites, and nests have been found even on the ground. Major Bendire (1895) says that at Fort Lapwai, Idaho, he "occasionally found them breeding in what might be called small colonies, and this was not due to scarcity of timber for nesting purposes; in fact, I once saw here three occupied nests in a single small birch tree, where a number of good-sized cottonwood trees were to be found close by and equally suitable. * * * Cottonwoods, junipers, and willows are most frequently used. Nests are usually placed at heights varying from 20 to 60 feet; but I have found some barely 6 feet from the ground, and in many localities in the West they are rarely placed over 20 feet up. Here also they are said to occasionally nest on the ground, but I have never observed this personally."

Capt. L. R. Wolfe (1931), however, did find a nest on the ground in Albany County, Wyo., and published a photograph of it. "It was in the short grass, on flat, open prairie. The nest was placed in a depression which at one time might have been the entrance of a badger hole. The depression was such that the rim of the nest was just level with the surface of the ground, and it was well filled with grass, weeds and small pieces of sage and willow. The nest had an outside rim of weeds, sage and willow twigs and a few small sticks and was lined with strips from weeds and with cow's hair. The general construction and bulk of the nest was about the same as any tree nest of the species. A few larger sticks and twigs were scattered around on the ground surrounding the nest. This nest contained seven eggs."

W. E. Griffee writes to me from Oregon that nests he found near Portland were mostly in "trees along the sloughs on the Inverness Golf Course, where the crows, like other birds, are protected." On April 25 and 26, 1940, in Lake County, east of the Cascades, he collected seven sets "from scrubby willow clumps out in the Chewaucan Marsh," and thinks he could have taken 30 or 40 more sets there in those two days, if he had concentrated on them. There must have been a large concentration of breeding crows in that region. A still larger concentration is mentioned by Leon L. Gardner (1926) in Klickitat County, Wash. On Rock Creek, crows were found at their noon siesta, and many old nests were located with an abundance of evidence in feathers and droppings that for miles up and down the creek a vast rookery existed. Although this was in August, when the crows had congregated to feast in the almond and apricot orchards, many of the vast hordes referred to later probably nested in that rookery where the nests were seen.

J. A. Munro has sent me the data for 14 nests, found in the brush along the creek near Okanagan Landing, British Columbia; 10 of these were in willows, and one each in an alder, a blackhaw, and a poplar; the heights from the ground varied from 10 to 20 feet.

Eggs.—Five or six eggs form the usual set for the western crow, but four or seven are often laid, and as many as eight or even nine have been recorded. J. G. Suthard tells me that he once found a set of nine eggs, eight intact and one broken. "The ninth egg had been broken and the shell telescoped onto another egg, to which it was firmly attached by the dried yolk and albumen. All the eggs were similar in size and shape." Three other nests in the vicinity were examined, in which the "eggs were definitely different from this set."

The eggs of the western crow are similar to those of the eastern crow, except in average size. The measurements of 40 eggs in the United States National Museum average 41.1 by 28.8 millimeters; the eggs showing the four extremes measure **46.2** by 31.2, 44.7 by **31.5**, **35.8** by 26.4, and 37.7 by **24.4** millimeters.

Food.—Like other crows, the western subspecies is omnivorous; it probably does some good in the destruction of harmful insects and rodents, and as a scavenger; but in many places it has formed the habit of congregating in enormous numbers to feast on cultivated nuts and fruits, which makes it a serious menace and requires effective control measures to save any of the crops.

Mrs. Wheelock (1904) says that "in California, acorns, beechnuts, berries of various shrubs and trees, seeds and all kinds of fruit, with insects such as locusts, black beetles, crickets, grasshoppers, spiders, cutworms, angleworms, and injurious larvae form a large part of its daily menu. In addition small mammals and snakes, frogs, lizards, snails, crawfish, fish, all kinds of dead flesh, and the eggs or nestlings of other birds are his victims. * * * The fact that all feathered creatures are arrayed against him is proof to me that, from the bird-lover's standpoint, he does more harm than good."

Ralph H. Imler (1939), in his comparative study of the food of crows and white-necked ravens in Oklahoma, found that the crows were apparently more beneficial in their feeding habits than the ravens since they ate many more insects and weed seeds. His analysis of 14 crow stomachs showed the following proportions: "Beetles, 4.6 percent; grasshoppers, 9.4 percent; mammals, 1.2 percent; grain, sorghums, 24.7 percent; corn, 24.9 percent; melons and citron seeds, 18.9 percent; sunflowers, 16.3 percent."

Some of the items mentioned by Mrs. Wheelock may be placed to the credit of the crow, and probably the large percentages of grain in Mr. Imler's report may be waste grain and therefore neutral; but there is another side to the picture, which is as black as the crow's plumage. Mrs. Nice (1931) says that "in northern Oklahoma crows have become a serious pest in pecan orchards" and describes their crafty methods of work and the none too effective methods of control. "Vast numbers have been killed in Oklahoma: 10,000 in one week near Chickasha in February, 1926, 11,000 in Payne County during the winter 1927-28, 3692 in two nights by means of dynamite near Vinita in January, 1929, according to the newspapers; but vast numbers remain."

Maj. Leon L. Gardner (1926) tells an interesting and most remarkable story of an immense congregation of crows and the devastation that they wrought: "In the region of Goodnoe Hills, Klickitat County, Washington, a very promising enterprise in raising almonds and apricots was developing. It was reported, however, by the farmers of that region that in fall enormous flocks, amounting to 'millions of crows,' came into this region and destroyed practically the entire crop of fruit and nuts, together with considerable acreages of watermelons." When he arrived, about the middle of August, "the almonds were ripening fast and crows had assembled in mass from the surrounding country for the annual feast." He continues:

They were in flocks of hundreds to thousands. The usual formation was in one enormous flock which worked as a unit in some selected orchard with a few outlying and unimportant groups feeding at random from other orchards. When in the air, this large host looked at a distance like a huge cloud of gnats.

It was difficult to estimate the exact numbers but an approximation could be made with the larger group when they settled to work in an orchard. In a 20-acre almond orchard there were about 1500 trees. To each one of these trees one could count from ten to thirty Crows with an average of fifteen to the tree. The flock on our arrival numbered perhaps 15,000 which, in a short time, nearly doubled in size until we estimated fully 30,000 members in the various groups. * * * With regard to the almond damage there was no argument. The destruction of an $800 crop was complete in two days after which the Crows moved on to a new orchard. * * *

It was the practice of the Crows, after a hot afternoon's work, to spare themselves the trouble of flying any considerable distance to water by feeding on watermelons. They were never seen to attack melons in the morning but always after a dry day's work. Furthermore green melons were sought and eaten as well as ripe ones indicating it was the moisture they were seeking. In any event the damage amounted to practically 100% of the crop, no melon being spared unless it happened to be concealed in the vines.

Various methods of control or protection of the crops were tried, but with indifferent success. Shooting served only to drive the crows from one orchard to another, and they paid no attention to scarecrows or to belling or stringing the trees. Poisoned carcasses of rabbits were scattered about, but after a few crows had been poisoned the others soon learned to avoid these baits. Poisoned watermelons proved more effective in protecting this crop, for, after a few crows had been killed, no further visits were made to the melon patches. Almonds, slit open, poisoned, and scattered in conspicuous places in the orchards, finally succeeded in driving away the crows, though "the actual number of crows poisoned was extremely small not exceeding 1% of the flock."

He says in conclusion: "The use of poisoned almonds, when properly conducted, proved successful in protecting the crops but demonstrated anew the exceptional sagacity of this bird. The first reaction was one of extreme panic at some of their number being fatally affected by their chief article of diet. This was manifested by tumultuous clamoring and confusion of the flock while sudden sallys and forays were made into distant parts of the Hills only to be met by the same fatal consequences. The flock then rapidly reacted to the changed environment by abandoning attempts at feeding from the almonds and indeed, by departing from the entire region."

There is another score against the crows of western North America, the destruction of the eggs of waterfowl in the great breeding grounds of ducks in the Middle West. We noticed that the nests of crows that we saw in Saskatchewan were largely congregated around the shores

of the lakes and sloughs where ducks were breeding. On one small
island in Crane Lake we counted 61 ducks' nests in a few hours' search;
the following year this island was practically deserted by the ducks;
we charged the damage largely to a coyote and a family of minks, but
very likely the crows found here an abundant food supply.

Frank L. Farley writes to me that crows have so increased in central
Alberta as to become a serious menace to waterfowl. He (1932) writes:

It is significant that as the crows gained in numbers there was a corresponding
decrease in the number of ducks, particularly of the marsh-nesting species. In
the choice of nesting sites it was noted that the crows favored wooded areas
adjacent to lakes and marshlands where ducks nested, this no doubt for the
purpose of being close to a rich food supply during the nesting season. Mr.
Francois Adam, a former prominent farmer of the Edberg district, and on whose
farm are extensive marshes, told the writer of the discovery of twenty-two ducks'
nests on his place one Sunday in May. The following Sunday, being suspicious
all was not well with the nesting ducks, he again visited the marsh and was surprised to find every nest empty, and many crows busily engaged in every part of
the marsh, searching for nests that had been overlooked. He stated that there
were a dozen crows' nests in the willows surrounding the lake, and others nearby
in scattered clumps on the prairie. It is evident that in such places ducks could
not carry on nesting operations successfully.

Eastern crows, which are usually not too abundant anywhere, may
not do enough damage to offset the good that they do, making their
economic status at least neutral. But the above samples, of which there
are probably plenty more, show what damage they can do when concentrated in large numbers.

The western crow, also, has its good traits. S. F. Rathbun writes to
me from Seattle: "In the cultivated and more or less open sections
lying along the eastern side of the Sound, on occasions early in spring,
I have seen numbers of western crows on their northward movement.
Wherever the locality had freshly plowed fields, hundreds of crows
were on the ground, gleaning every kind of animal food exposed by the
plow. The feeding birds never were disturbed by the farmer, who
usually regarded them with favor because of the good work the crows
were doing.

"One food item, of which this crow is fond, is the fruit of the red-
berried elder, *Sambucus callicarpa,* a more or less common shrub of the
bottomlands of western Washington. When this bush hangs heavy with
its brilliantly colored berries, one often finds the crows eating them. While
doing this they are noisy, for the birds will try to alight on the tops of
the fruit-laden bushes, and, as these fail to support them, many birds
fall fluttering to the ground amid much excitement and commotion.
Once I shot a crow when it was feeding on the berries. I found its
gullet packed with the fruit and its stomach also; this organ with the

digestive tract proved to be so deeply dyed a dark red that it appeared
to show that, for some time at least, elderberries had been the chief
food of the bird."

Behavior.—There is little to be said about the behavior of the western
crow, which does not differ materially from that of its eastern relative.
It is the same clever, sagacious bird, wary when in danger and tame
where it feels secure. Ridgway (1877) saw three individuals at a stage
station in Nevada that "walked unconcernedly about the door-yard with
the familiarity of tame pigeons, merely hopping to one side when approached too closely." On the other hand, Henshaw (1875), in Arizona,
found them "quite numerous, associating freely with, and apparently
the boon companions of the ravens. Yet, even here, I found that they
had lost little of their traditional shyness, and it was some time ere I
procured a specimen. Gun in hand, I found no difficulty in approaching
the trees where sat the ravens, looking down upon me with a comical
glance of wonder, tinged with a slight suspicion that all was not just
as it should be. But the crows had long before taken the alarm, and
made themselves scarce, and from some secure perch sent back their
warning *caws,* given, as it appeared to me, with more than the usual
earnestness, as though deprecating the stupidity of their big cousins."

Enemies.—Probably western crows occasionally attack hawks or owls,
just as the eastern birds do; and sometimes the tables are turned.
Joseph Mailliard (1908) tells of a pair of Cooper's hawks attacking a
flock of crows that were quietly perched in the tops of some dead trees.
The hawks did some good team work, one attacking from above and one
from below, but the crows were too alert and no serious damage was
done before Mr. Mailliard shot both of the hawks.

Fall.—Western crows wander about more or less in fall and winter,
and there is a limited migration from some parts of the breeding range,
a gradual southward drift that extends the range of the subspecies somewhat south of its summer range. There is probably, also, a retreat
from some of the higher altitudes down into the valleys and about the
ranches in search of food, and perhaps a coastwise trend. Theed Pearse
tells me that some cross over from the mainland to Vancouver Island,
where they associate with the northwest crow *(caurinus).* The two can
be easily recognized by their voices.

Joseph Mailliard (1927) mentions a migratory movement in Modoc
County, Calif.: "In September, 1925, the crows gathered as they had
in the previous year. The number seemed to·reach the maximum about
September 23, when I estimated the size of the band to be in the
neighborhood of 1,000 individuals, all feeding in the stubble field back
of our quarters. Ten days after this, small numbers were noted mov-

ing toward the south, which movement continued daily until comparatively few remained on October 15, when our party left the field."

Winter.—Some western crows spend the winter in the northern parts of their range, for J. A. Munro tells me that sometimes large flocks are seen in the vicinity of Okanagan Landing, British Columbia, in winter. "They are extremely local in their feeding habits during winter, remaining in the vicinity of slaughterhouses, or other places where food is easily obtainable, and returning to the same roost, often several miles away, every evening."

The winter population of crows in Oklahoma, on which so much destructive bombing has been done, seems to consist largely of crows from farther north.

Kalmbach and Aldous (1940) report that "the banding of 714 Crows in south central Oklahoma during the winter of 1935-36 has yielded, during the three and one-half years following their release, 143 returns, slightly more than 20 percent of the birds banded." They say:

Analysis of these returns shows that, of the 65 Crows recovered during the breeding and rearing season (April 1 to August 31), 49 (75 per cent) were killed in the Prairie Provinces of Canada. The dates and locations of numerous other returns recorded in the states north of Oklahoma indicate that many others of this group of Crows may have been on their way to or from Canadian breeding grounds. During this same period of the year not one of the winter-banded Crows was recovered in Oklahoma, clearly indicating that winter Crow control in Oklahoma can have little or no effect on nesting upland game or insectivorous birds of that state.

Although winter Crow control in Oklahoma is destined to remove some birds that would enter the problem of Crow-waterfowl relationships in the Canadian provinces, the effect of this control is certain to be much 'diluted' if the results are to be judged in a continental perspective. This comes about because only a portion of the Crows in Canada can be classed as duck-egg predators, and because the Crow, in what might be termed destructive abundance, occupies possibly only a sixth of the duck-nesting area of Canada and Alaska.

CORVUS CAURINUS Baird
NORTHWESTERN CROW
HABITS

The crows of the Northwest coast from the Alaska Peninsula and Kodiak Island southward as far as the Puget Sound region of Washington were originally described as a distinct species, largely on account of their coastwise habitat and a somewhat different voice. Many modern writers, including the framers of the 1910 Check-list, have listed *Corvus caurinus* as a species. But it was reduced to the rank of a subspecies in the 1931 Check-list; it will now be restored to full specific rank.

It is similar in appearance to *hesperis* but is smaller, with relatively smaller feet.

Its favorite haunts are on the seashore, from which it seldom strays very far; it is a common resident bird about the wooded shores of the bays and on the beaches, where it feeds with the gull on shellfish and refuse thrown up by the waves. Theed Pearse writes to me that on Vancouver Island it is now showing signs of spreading out into many square miles of logged-over and burnt-over hillsides near the shore but that its main habitat is on the shores, especially where there are small coniferous trees.

A. M. Bailey (1927) says that in southeastern Alaska these "crows are especially numerous about the towns and villages, hanging about the camps for food. At low tide, the flocks repair to the flats, where they secure an easy living among the mussel beds."

Nesting.—J. H. Bowles (1900) writes:

On the Tacoma Flats, at the head of Commencement Bay, is a small cluster of Siwash Indian houses, which are bordered by a line of scrubby apple and cherry trees. In these trees six or seven pairs of this sociable little crow band together in a colony during the nesting season. The nest is placed in a crotch at a distance from ten to eighteen feet above the ground, the same one being made over each returning season. On one occasion I saw two occupied nests in an apple tree only twenty feet high. Its appearance differs greatly from that of *americanus*, as it closely resembles a round basket having a very slight projecting rim of sticks. The average rim of projecting sticks in a series of *americanus* I have found to be 9.78 inches, while that of *caurinus* is only a trifle over 4 inches. The inner dimensions average about 7 inches in diameter by 4 inches in depth. The composition also is nearly the same, only the material used is much less coarse, being a foundation of fine sticks and mud, lined with cedar bark.

Mr. Bailey (1927) "found a nest in Patterson's Bay, Hooniah Sound, May 17, which was about twenty feet from the ground in a small hemlock. The nest was a rather bulky affair of spruce twigs, lined with dried grass, while the interior cup was composed entirely of deer hair. There were four eggs in the nest. Crows were abundant on Forrester Island, and it was there that Willett called my attention to a peculiar habit of theirs, that of nesting under boulders on the beach. They placed their nests far back in rather inaccessible places."

S. J. Darcus (1930) says that on the Queen Charlotte Islands "many nests were found, all built on the ground beneath bushes or windfalls close to sea shore." Mr. Pearse tells me that on Vancouver Island most of these crows resort to the vicinity of the sea for nesting and nests will be found in quite low bushes and even in the side of a sandy bank. On June 16, 1940, a nest containing four eggs was found about 8 feet from the ground in a small fir in the logged-over area. Earlier reports of nests roofed over, like those of magpies, were probably based on incorrect identification. Mr. Rathbun writes to me: "For several years my home was near the crest of a high bluff along the Sound, its base

bounded by the beach. The abrupt side of the bluff was thickly covered
by a second growth of evergreen and deciduous trees, some of good size,
and in several of the former a number of pairs of northwestern crows
nested each spring."

Sidney B. Peyton writes to me that these crows are numerous on
Forrester Island, where the majority of the nests were not over 8 feet
from the ground in the thick spruce trees. One was "in a hole in a
cliff about 15 feet up," and three others were under boulders on the
beach "about 100 feet above the high tide mark."

Richard M. Bond has sent me some notes on this crow; he says that
on Bainbridge Island in Puget Sound, "where the timber had only been
gone over lightly for the best trees, the forest was almost in its virgin
state. Here I was able to locate only two occupied nests, both about
two-thirds of the way up fairly large Douglas firs—about 70 feet from
the ground. In the San Juan Islands, even in virgin stands, the trees
are in most places very small, and nests are easy to locate from the
ground. Douglas fir is here the commonest tree, and though hemlock,
western red cedar, alder, and others are also present in some numbers,
I have never found a crow nest in any tree but the fir. The crows nest
on the main islands rather like the western crow does; that is, in scattered groups, but they also nest on some of the small islets of an acre
or less, where there are only two or three scraggly firs. I do not remember finding more than one nest on such an islet."

Eggs.—This crow lays ordinarily four or five eggs. They are indistinguishable, except in size, from the eggs of other crows and probably
a large series would show most of the variations common to the species.
The measurements of 40 eggs average 40.4 by 28.2 millimeters; the
eggs showing the four extremes measure 44.2 by 28.8, 40.8 by 29.8,
36.7 by 27.9, and 40.9 by 25.9 millimeters.

Young.—In the locality mentioned above, S. F. Rathbun had a good
chance to watch the behavior of the young crows, which, early in July,
were still being fed to some extent by their parents; "now and then one
of them would sidle up to an adult and stroke the old bird's beak, evidently coaxing to be fed." He says in his notes: "It is interesting to
watch the old and young birds; there are upwards of 50 of them. The
other day, during a strong wind, many of the crows played about in it;
some of their aerial evolutions were most graceful and reminded one
of the raven's flight ability. Those I watched seemed to battle the
wind for the pure love of the sport, old and young birds alike indulg-
ing in it.

"All the crows were drifting around in the wind just before sunset.
There are now almost 70 of the birds. The young among them are still

practicing flying, and some fly gracefully for they rise and fall with a floating motion, apparently without effort. The old birds are easy to distinguish, for they sit quietly in the trees and gravely watch their young at play."

Mr. Pearse tells me that he has seen young on the wing as early as June 10 and has seen young just out of the nest as late as August 23. He seems to think that two, or possibly three, broods may be raised in a season.

Food.—The main feeding grounds of these small crows are on the beaches, where they are useful as scavengers, picking up the refuse thrown out by the fishermen, and where they show no fear of the natives, who never molest them, but they are shy of strangers. There they feed also on shellfish, crabs, and any edible refuse thrown up by the waves. In winter they find an ample food supply on the extensive beds of mussels on the tidal flats. In summer they frequent the salmon streams to feed on the dead fish, and are welcome as scavengers about the salmon canneries. Mr. Pearse tells me that late in summer and in fall berries such as wild cherry and saskatoon form a large part of their food; they eat fruit also and are especially fond of pears and apples, though they ruin more than they eat; in the fall of 1935, after an unusually early frost, they fed on the frost-rotted apples that still hung on the trees.

Mr. Bailey (1927) writes: "At low tide, the flocks repair to the flats, where they secure an easy living among the mussel beds. It is a common sight to see Crows darting in the air, as they drop mussels upon rocks, to break them. If the wind is blowing, they allow for the curve, and usually do not make many misses in their endeavor to hit a certain boulder. * * * These birds, too, are especially bad about plundering the nests of their neighbors and no species is safe from them, for they are continually hunting, possessing a boldness even greater than the Raven. They rob the sea birds nesting under boulders as well as the Murres upon the cliffs. They are not so conspicuous in their plundering however, as the Ravens, for they eat their eggs where they find them, and so probably put their time in to better advantage."

The presence of a human being in a sea-bird colony sends all the gulls, cormorants, murres, and pigeon guillemots off their nests, which is the signal for the crows to rush in, grab an egg from an unprotected nest, and fly off with it; the crows return again and again as long as the rightful owners are kept off their nests; this results in great destruction among the eggs and young of these colonial birds, for which some overzealous bird photographer may be unwillingly responsible. The eggs and young of land birds probably suffer to a less extent. Mr.

Pearse tells me that some young birds are taken, but the crows do not seem to be persistent in hunting for them, though some individuals may get the habit. He once saw a crow that was apparently watching to locate a robin's nest and was being mobbed by a lot of flycatchers, warblers, and chickadees. He next heard the agonized cries of a young robin, which the crow had captured and was carrying off; the old robins attacked the crow and made it drop the young bird. "The other birds in some way recognized the crow as dangerous and kept up their mobbing. Though I have seen the northwestern crow working through wooded areas, evidently looking for young birds or nests, there is none of the systematic beating of the ground that may be seen done by the western crow; moreover, I have seen very few cases of nests that may have been destroyed by crows."

R. M. Bond sends me the following notes on the feeding habits of the northwestern crow: "I have seen crows foraging in fields, where they were seen to capture grasshoppers. They also, in one case, were observed eating ripe wild blackberries *(Rubus vitifolius)*. I have also seen them feeding behind a plow in company with Brewer's blackbirds and gulls." He says that they had favorite times for feeding on the beaches: "One was near high tide, when the incoming water separated the house garbage from the ashes, with which it was frequently dumped, and when the innumerable amphipod 'sand fleas' were retreating before the water to the shelter of windrows of kelp and seaweed. I had a blind in a hollow log of driftwood and could watch the crows eat enormous numbers of sand fleas, as the flock worked by me. The other favorite period was near low tide, when cockles and gastropods were exposed.

"Carrion was a favorite food. This consisted mainly of dead fish that washed up on the shore. Dead dogs, cats, horses, etc., were also eagerly eaten, though they amounted to a very small percentage of the available food. Once a dead porpoise washed ashore on Blake Island, and for two or three days there was a stream of crows passing across about three miles of open water to this feast and back, apparently to feed their young."

Stomach analysis of three specimens by J. A. Munro (MS.) showed that the bulk of the food consisted of shore crabs and small mollusks; crab remains amounted to 80 percent in one case, and small mollusks to 80 and 60 percent in the other two cases. Mollusks and crab remains were found in all three stomachs, and the remainder of the food included a few insect remains, fish eggs (probably sculpins), oat husks, and miscellaneous vegetable matter.

Behavior.—As northwestern crows apparently do little damage to human interests, they are much tamer than crows elsewhere and pay but little attention to human beings. They make themselves at home about the Indian villages, where they are almost as tame as chickens and hardly move out of the way of the children playing on the beaches. Mr. Pearse's notes contain several references to the behavior of these crows. He has seen 12 crows "vigorously chasing a raven"; again he has seen the two species feeding side by side, though the crows recognized the "superiority of the raven and would not contest the feeding grounds"; crows feeding on berries hurried away when a raven came into the bush. He has seen nesting crows drive away a bald eagle that had settled on a tree nearby, making stoops at it, the eagle squealing as though at least annoyed; and he says that they will frequently attack a flying eagle, if it comes near where they are feeding; sometimes the eagle will turn at the crow, to strike it with its talons, which drives away the latter.

He tells of one of a pair of crows that had lost part of its beak, perhaps in a trap; it was being fed by its mate, "which regurgitated the food. The healthy bird was crooning to it and stroking it with its beak, a really touching sight."

One day, in July, he saw "two diving and swooping around in a stiff breeze, stooping at each other and turning over, a kind of game of tag. At times a flock will plane-dive down to the ground, and this usually presages a change of weather, usually wind."

Mr. Munro tells me that on four occasions in January and February he has seen a heavy flight, totaling about 800 birds, passing over Departure Bay about dusk and apparently settling in their winter roost in some thick woods.

Voice.—Ralph Hoffmann (1927) says: "A trained ear can usually detect the difference in their notes from those of the Western Crow; they are usually slightly hoarser and lower in pitch but vary in pitch and quality and are at times very close to the Western Crow's. In the mating season they have a 'gargling' note similar to that of the Western Crow."

Mr. Bailey (1927) writes: "They are probably the best imitators of their family in Alaska, and the variety of their notes is unusually large. Their most characteristic one is noted when the old bird is feeling especially foolish, for they duck their heads toward their feet, and then give an upward tug, at the same time emitting a sound like the pulling of a cork from a bottle."

R. H. Lawrence wrote to Major Bendire (1895) of a vocal performance that may have been part of a courtship display: "A flock of about one hundred and twenty were noticed February 7, 1892; a few were perched apart on a tree or snag, uttering strange sounds, like 'koo-wow,

kow-wow, koo-wow,' the last syllable drawled and accented or emphasized; then, with a slight spreading of the shoulders and the tail, the
head being down and the tail drooped, they produced by a curious
chattering of the bill a sound (not made in the throat, I judged) which
resembled that of horny plates struck together, and causing an odd
shuddering of the head and even of the body. This was repeated a few
times, varied with a noisy 'caw, caw.'"

Fall.—Mr. Pearse writes to me that on Vancouver Island "the locally
bred crows commence to flock as early as the middle of August, but it
would be at least a month before the outside birds would arrive. Most
falls there is a considerable immigration to the farmlands from outside
areas, probably from inlets farther up the coast or from the mainland.
At times during winter 1,000 birds will be feeding together on the
cultivated areas. Banding operations show that there is a southerly
movement of the locally breeding crows in fall and that birds banded
in winter go to the mainland the following spring. Each year the crows
disappear from here the end of August, and very few are seen until
a month later." He also has seen some evidence of a northward migration in spring.

CORVUS OSSIFRAGUS Wilson

FISH CROW

PLATE 46

HABITS

This small and well-marked species of crow is widely distributed
along the Atlantic and Gulf coasts, as well as in the lower valleys of
some of the larger rivers. It reaches its northeastern limit in southern
Massachusetts, where it is a rare and local straggler, mainly in spring.
I am quite sure that I have seen it on two occasions in Bristol, R. I.
It is a fairly common summer resident on the coast of Connecticut,
chiefly in the western part, and on certain parts of Long Island, N. Y.
From New Jersey southward it is an abundant bird and practically
resident.

Its favorite haunts are the coastal marshes and beaches, the banks
of streams, and to some extent the shores of inland bodies of water.
In Florida, the numerous streams, lakes, and marshes furnish suitable
haunts for them over a large part of the inland country, especially
where they can prey upon the breeding colonies of herons and other
water birds. Dr. Samuel S. Dickey tells me that he has seen them

along the banks of inland rivers in central Pennsylvania, as far west as Harrisburg and Columbia.

Courtship.—Dr. Dickey (MS.) writes: "During the first two weeks of April fish crows become especially animated and proceed with mating impulses. Generally two males are seen to bicker over a single female. The three of them then hurry through the high canopies of crack willows, elms, oaks, and even some evergreens. They will half unfold the wings, lean back against boughs, and open their red beaks in a seeming defensive attitude. Then away they glide, from the trees of the stream banks, across wide plantations of truck gardeners. They will, on breezy days, dally with one another, and even touch wings and heads. In all, they have a playful, captivating manner in midair at this time of year."

Nesting.—Aretas A. Saunders writes to me that in the vicinity of Fairfield, Conn., where the fish crow is a "regular, but rare summer resident," nesting takes place late in April or in May." The nests are generally in small colonies, two or three pairs with their nests not far apart in a certain locality. I have found such colonies in two types of localities—swampy woodlands where the trees are tall and the nests high up and rocky places on the edge of a salt marsh, where the rocks stand up like islands in a salt marsh sea and are clothed with red cedars and pitch pines. Nests in such places are in the pitch pines and not very far up. Such localities are used year after year if conditions are not disturbed. At present I know of but one nesting locality of the swampy woods type."

I find in Owen Durfee's notes for May 10 and 11, 1903, the records of two Connecticut nests, also near Fairfield. The first was 64 feet from the ground in an 11-inch black oak. "The nest was composed of small, dry sticks, well mixed in with old cornstalk strings. It was placed in the topmost crotch of the tree, where the diameter was only 2 inches, the tree being only about 4 feet higher. It was 14 inches in diameter and built up 14 inches high. Inside it was 7½ inches in diameter and hollowed 5½ inches. It was lined, but not felted, with strips of grapevine bark." The second nest was similar, 61 feet up in a 13-inch chestnut and about 9 feet from the top of the tree. It was 18 inches in diameter and built up 12 inches in a three-pronged crotch. "The lining was principally of strips of inner bark of the chestnut, with two large clumps of white horsehair and a little grapevine bark."

The only fish crow's nest I have ever examined was found near Little Egg Harbor, N. J., on May 27, 1927. In a large patch of baccharis bushes on a low sand dune on the edge of Little Sheepshead, I found a colony of seven or eight nests of the green heron. The crows had robbed three or four of the heron's nests. The crow's nest was located 7 feet up in one of the largest of the baccharis bushes. It was made of dead sticks and twigs and lined with strips of inner bark and a few feathers. It measured 14 by 15 inches in outside and 7 inches in inside diameter; it was hollowed to a depth of 6 inches.

T. E. McMullen has sent me his data for 138 nests of the fish crow, found in New Jersey and vicinity. Most of these, 80, were in holly trees, 12 to 30 feet from the ground; 34 were in cedars, 5½ to 25 feet up; 9 were located in oaks, at heights varying from 18 to 50 feet; 9 were placed in pines, 17 to 90 feet from the ground; and there was one each in a beech, a gum, a sassafras, and a wild cherry, and two in maples, all at intermediate heights.

Two nests have been reported at heights far above those already mentioned. The Rev. H. E. Wheeler (1922) mentions a nest, found on the bank of the Arkansas River, that was "well toward the top of a huge sycamore 110 feet from the ground." This nest "now contained no rootlets, but was lined with a mass of sycamore balls and horse hair!" (This was after the eggs hatched. Before that the nest was "lined with leaves and rootlets.") But Arthur T. Wayne (1910) reports the loftiest nest of which I can find any record: "About twenty-five years ago this species used to breed regularly in St. Paul's churchyard, in the city of Charleston, where it placed its nest in the topmost branches of a gigantic sycamore tree fully one hundred and fifty feet from the ground, and it also bred in later years in private yards along East Battery."

Major Bendire (1895) writes: "A nest taken by Dr. Ralph near San Mateo, Florida, was composed of sticks with a little Spanish moss attached to them, and was lined with pine needles, strips of cypress bark, and old Spanish moss. It was placed in the top of a slender pine tree, in low, flat pine woods, 81 feet from the ground. Some nests are lined with dry cow and horse dung, cattle or horse hair, dry leaves, eelgrass, and shreds of cedar bark, while pine needles seem to be present to some extent in most of them. They are mostly placed in evergreens, such as pines and cedars, and generally in the tops, either in natural forks or on horizontal limbs, close to the trunk, usually 20 to 50 feet from the ground. They prefer to nest near water, but occasionally a pair will be found making an exception to this rule, and nests have been found fully 2 miles away from the nearest stream or swamp."

In the nesting site photographed by Mr. Grimes (pl. 46), two or three pairs nest every spring in the tall slash pines; the highest fork that will support the nest is usually selected.

Eggs.—The fish crow lays ordinarily four or five eggs to a set, rarely more. These are exactly like the eggs of the other crows, except in size. They show all the ordinary variations in color, pattern, and markings that are to be found in the eggs of the eastern crow. The measurements of 46 eggs, in the United States National Museum, average 37.17 by 26.97 millimeters; the eggs showing the four extremes measure 42.9 by 27.4, 37.8 by 28.7, 34.5 by 27.5, and 37.7 by 25.2 millimeters.

Young.—Bendire (1895) says that "both sexes assist in incubation, which lasts from sixteen to eighteen days, while the young remain in the nest about three weeks. Only one brood is raised in a season, but if the first set of eggs is taken they will lay another, and not infrequently in the same nest."

Plumages.—The young fish crow is hatched naked and blind, but it soon acquires a scanty growth of grayish-brown natal down. This, in turn, is replaced by the juvenal plumage, which is practically completed before the young bird leaves the nest. The juvenal body plumage is dull brownish black, blacker above and browner below; the wings, except the lesser coverts, are much like those of the adult and so is the tail, but they are somewhat less lustrous black with greenish reflections; the bill and feet are grayish black.

The postjuvenal molt, which involves the contour plumage and the lesser wing coverts, but not the rest of the wings and tail, begins in July and is completed by September or earlier. This produces a first winter plumage, which is much like that of the adult, but somewhat duller. At the first postnuptial molt, which is complete, during the following summer, the young bird becomes fully adult. Adults have one complete, annual molt during summer and early fall. The sexes are alike in all plumages.

Food.—Like other crows the fish crow is largely omnivorous, with a long list of acceptable material available. As it spends most of its time along the seashore, the banks of streams, and the shores of inland bodies of water, its food consists largely of various kinds of marine or aquatic life, or other material washed up on such shores. It may often be seen hovering over the water, like a gull, looking for floating objects that it can pick up. On the beaches and salt marshes these crows feed on small crabs, especially fiddlers, shrimps, crawfish, dead fish and perhaps some live fish, and any kind of carrion or offal that they can find. They steal the eggs from the nests of terns, willets, Wilson's plovers, and clapper rails. William G. Fargo (1927) says that they have regular feeding stations where they bring their food to eat it; under a small yellow pine at Wakulla Beach, Fla., in a space about 4 by 6 feet, he found the remains of 79 or more clapper rails' eggs, one willet's egg, two Wilson's plovers' eggs, seven hens' eggs, several turtles' eggs, one fish head, and one rock crab.

Fish crows do immense damage in the heron colonies in Florida; wherever I have been in the many breeding colonies, fish crows have always been flying about, looking for a chance to steal the eggs from an unguarded nest. As the herons all leave their nests as soon as a man approaches, the crows have plenty of chances to enjoy a good feast, and they make the most of it. They rob the nests of all the herons, large and small, as well as the ibises, spoonbills, anhingas, and even cormorants. While we were photographing for parts of two days in the great Cuthbert rookery, nearly all the nests within sight of our blinds were completely emptied; and our experience was similar elsewhere in Florida. Howell (1932) says that they "perch on the bushes, watching for a sitting bird to leave its nest, whereupon they immediately swoop down and carry off an egg. In the large rookery at Orange Lake, it is estimated that two-thirds of the nests are robbed by the crows, which are there very abundant."

Fish crows are sometimes seen in the plowed fields, picking up grubs; they are also said to eat ants, and several observers have mentioned grasshoppers in their food. N. B. Moore says in his notes, made many years ago, that these crows alight on the backs of cattle, to pick up the ticks that are burrowing into the skin and sucking the life blood from, as well as annoying, these animals; this may be an ancient habit, as it does not seem to have been recently observed.

Bendire (1895) states that on the Smithsonian grounds in Washington they "have been noticed repeatedly carrying off and eating the young of the English Sparrows." Wilson (1832) writes: "There is in many of the ponds there [Georgia], a singular kind of lizard, that swims about with its head above the surface, making a loud sound, not unlike the harsh jarring of a door. These the Crow now before us would frequently seize with his claws, as he flew along the surface, and retire to the summit of a dead tree to enjoy his repast."

The vegetable food includes a variety of berries, fruits, and seeds, such as pokeberries, mulberries, hackberries, huckleberries, the fruits of red cedar, sour gum, palmetto, magnolia, holly, dogwood, papaw, red bay, catbrier, and mistletoe, and the seeds of locust, wildrice, etc. Some grain is eaten, such as corn and oats, but most of this is probably waste grain picked up in the fields after harvesting. Probably some cultivated fruits are taken, but not enough to be of great economic importance.

Audubon (1842) mentions the berries of the dahoon *(Ilex cassine)*; "they are seen feeding on them in flocks often amounting to more than a hundred individuals." They are also fond of the berries of the Chinese tallowtree *(Sapium sebiferum)*. "The seeds of this tree, which is originally from China, are of a white colour when ripe, and contain a considerable quantity of an oily substance. In the months of January and February these trees are covered by the Crows, which greedily devour the berries." He adds that they eat pears, and are very fond of ripe figs; they do considerable damage to the latter and have to be driven away from the fig trees with a gun.

According to Mr. Howell (1932), "Scott says that in October the birds congregate in enormous flocks and feed extensively on palmetto berries. Nehrling states that they eat the fruits of the cocos palms. Oranges and tomatoes are sometimes eaten, but apparently the habit is not sufficiently prevalent to result in much damage."

Harold H. Bailey (1913) says that in Virginia considerable damage is done to the peanut crop. "As the farmers turn their hogs into the peanut fields to fatten on the nuts left in the ground after taking off the vines, the Fish Crows thus rob the hogs of a great amount of food, while many pounds of nuts are taken from the stacks while the peanuts are still on the vines drying."

Behavior.—The fish crow does not differ materially in its habits from its better-known and larger relative. Its flight is similar, but it is quicker and more given to sailing, giving a few flaps of its wings and then sailing along for a short distance. It often poises in the air, hovering on rapidly beating wings, as it scans the ground or water beneath it for possible food. When a number of these crows are together, they often indulge in circling maneuvers, flying around in a confusing formation and then straightening out and proceeding on their way. Audubon (1842) writes:

While on the St. John's river in Florida, during the month of February, I saw flocks of Fish-Crows, consisting of several hundred individuals, sailing high in the air, somewhat in the manner of the Raven, when the whole appeared paired, for I could see that, although in such numbers, each pair moved distinctly apart. These aerial excursions would last for hours, during the calm of a fine morning, after which the whole would descend toward the water, to pursue their more usual avocations in all the sociability of their nature. When their fishing, which lasted about half an hour, was over, they would alight in flocks on the live oaks and other trees near the shores, and there keep up their gabbling, pluming themselves for hours. Once more they returned to their fishing-grounds, where they remained until about an hour from sunset, when they made for the interior, often proceeding thirty or forty miles, to roost together in the trees of the *loblolly pine.*

Fish crows are more sociable and more nearly gregarious in their habits at all seasons than are their northern relatives. They are seldom seen singly; they often nest in small colonies or groups; and wherever there is food to be obtained, especially in the vicinity of heron rookeries, they are always to be found in large numbers. But the biggest aggregations are to be found in the winter crow roosts. M. N. Gist, the warden at the Orange Lake rookery, estimated the winter crow population at that locality as 50,000, some of which may have been Florida crows, according to Mr. Howell (1932), who adds: "At Goose Creek, Wakulla County, in January, 1920, we observed long lines of Fish Crows every morning shortly after sunrise, flying westward along the beach from the direction of St. Marks Light. Several residents of the neighborhood told us that the birds roosted on beaten down tracts of rushes and drift in the marshes along the lower course of the St. Marks River. At Panasoffkee Lake, Crows are said to roost in large numbers in willow bushes in the marsh at the edge of the lake. At Lake Monroe, February 18, 1897, Worthington saw a flock of about 2,000 Fish Crows going to roost in rushes."

At North Island, S. C., early in December 1876, Maynard (1896) saw a great flight of fish crows that he thought were migrating. "They were evidently migrating for they came down the coast in an almost unbroken stream and continued to fly all day. I think I saw more pass the island than I ever saw before. It did not seem possible that there could have been so many of these Crows in existence for they could be counted by tens of thousands." This may have been merely a local movement, for the birds might have been seeking shelter from the hard, cold northeast wind that was blowing at the time; and fish crows are known to spend the winter much farther north.

Voice.—The note of the fish crow is quite different from that of our common crow, shorter, less prolonged, more nasal, staccato, and not so loud; it is hoarser, as if the bird had a sore throat or a cold. I wrote it in my notes as *cor,* or as an exact pronouncing of the word "car." Mr. Wheeler (1922) writes it *caa-ah,* and refers to a two-syllabled note, *ah-uk.* Bendire (1895) says: "Their call notes appear to be less harsh and are uttered in a more drawling manner than those of the Common Crow; they are also more variable. They consist of a clear 'cah' or 'cahk,' repeated at intervals of about thirty seconds, and are usually uttered while the bird is perched on the extreme top of a tree. They also utter a querulous 'maah, maah' or 'whaw, whaw,' varied occasionally to 'aack, aack,' or 'waak, waak.' It is almost impossible to reproduce such sounds accurately on paper, and no two persons would render them alike."

Field marks.—The most reliable field mark for the fish crow is its voice; and this can usually be counted upon to identify it; there is, however, a chance for confusion when young common crows are first on the wing and giving their weak calls. The appearance on the wing is slightly different; the wing of the fish crow seems to be more pointed at the tip of the primaries, and broader at the base, where the secondaries are relatively longer than in the common crow, but the difference is not easily detected. Fish crows are inclined to soar or to hover and are often more gregarious than the common species. The difference in size is an unsafe character, unless the two species can be closely compared.

Enemies.—All small birds hate crows and will drive them away from the vicinity of their nests, for the protection of their eggs and young. I have twice seen red-winged blackbirds attacking fish crows, just as kingbirds attack the larger crows. The herons are the chief sufferers from the depredations of fish crows. Perhaps some of the larger herons may destroy the young of the crows. The following incident is suggestive. Mrs. C. W. Melcher, of Homosassa Springs, Fla., tells me the following story: "One day in spring I heard the raucous cry of the Ward's heron, but with it was mingled an unusual note of distress. I ran to the porch just in time to see the heron fly into the river, where he sank to his body. Close behind him came a fish crow, and, as the heron sank into the water, the crow flew about his head and delivered several telling strokes, the heron meantime emitting loud cries of fright and distress. At last the crow ceased his chastisement and flew away. Then the heron laboriously lifted himself out of the water and flew away squawking. A day or two later I again heard the distress note and ran to look. This time they were in the air, the heron squawking as he flew, with the crow in full pursuit. At intervals for about ten days I saw the same performance."

Harold S. Peters (1936) lists two species of lice, *Myrsidea americana* and *Philopterus corvi,* that have been found on fish crows as external parasites.

DISTRIBUTION

Range.—Atlantic and Gulf coast regions of the United States; not regularly migratory.

The range of the fish crow extends **north** to northwestern Louisiana (Caddo Lake); central Arkansas (Little Rock); central Alabama (Coosada); northwestern South Carolina (Greenwood); central Virginia (Charlottesville); southeastern New York (Rhinebeck); and Rhode Island (Warren). **East** to the Atlantic coast from Rhode Island (Warren) south to southern Florida (Royal Palm Park). **South** along the Gulf coast from southern Florida (Royal Palm Park, Fort Myers, and Apalachicola) to southeastern Texas (Orange). **West** to southeastern Texas (Orange) and northwestern Louisiana (Caddo Lake).

During some winter seasons the species may withdraw from the northern parts of its range, but it is usually found at this season north to Long Island.

Casual records.—There are several records for Massachusetts, both in coastal areas and in the Connecticut Valley. Most of these are in March and April. Reported occurrences north of this State lack confirmation.

Egg dates.—Connecticut: 23 records, May 5 to June 6; 11 records May 10 to 15, indicating the height of the season.

Florida: 7 records, April 6 to May 13.

New Jersey: 106 records, April 29 to June 21; 54 records, May 12 to 22.

Virginia: 50 records, May 4 to June 10; 25 records, May 14 to June 10.

CORVUS FRUGILEGUS FRUGILEGUS Linnaeus

ROOK

CONTRIBUTED BY BERNARD WILLIAM TUCKER

HABITS

The rook is admitted to the American list on the basis of an accidental occurrence in Greenland. Schalow (1904) states that a male was shot by Petersen on March 23, 1901, at Kungarsik, near Cape Dan, on the east coast, and points out that as young birds are not rare as vagrants in Iceland this example may be supposed to have reached Greenland from there. This bird is stated to be preserved in the Museum at Copenhagen.

Few birds are more familiar in England than the rook, as might, indeed, be inferred from the fact that the term rookery, applied to its nesting colonies, is an everyday word in the English language and has been adopted as the most natural term to apply to populous breeding colonies of such different birds as penguins and seafowl and even, rather oddly, of seals. Rooks are a part of the English landscape. Their social habits and predilection for nesting close to human habitations both help to make them familiar, and the bulky nests high in the leafless tree tops of copse or hedgerow make the deserted rookery in winter as conspicuous as it is in spring by reason of the bustle and clamor of its inhabitants.

The rook is primarily a bird of agricultural country with sufficient trees to afford it nesting sites, but not too heavily wooded, for it feeds mainly on open ground, resorting to both pasture and arable land. Moorlands, heaths, marshes, and unreclaimed land are not so much favored, though rooks may be met with at times on all such types of ground and in some districts not rarely.

Rookeries being easily located and the nests large and easy to count with only a small margin of error, the rook is an excellent subject for census work, as a result of which the breeding population of the species over large areas of Great Britain has been accurately determined in recent years. The average density in typical agricultural country is found to be about 16 nests (or 32 breeding birds) to the square mile, with a variation, in cases of areas over 100 square miles, from 5 nests (North Wales) to 33.5 nests (Upper Thames Valley) a square mile.

Courtship.—A fair amount has been written about the sex behavior of the rook. It has been especially studied by Edmund Selous (1927) and G. K. Yeates (1934), and others have contributed miscellaneous observations, but the subject would still repay further attention. The ordinary courtship display is of a simple kind and may often be observed in the opening months of the year. The male bird, either in a tree or on the ground, droops his wings and bows several times to the female with outstretched neck, accompanying the movement with cawing and fanning out of the tail. The female may or may not be disposed to respond to these advances, but, if she is, her reaction usually takes the form of fluttering her wings with the body depressed in a crouching position. She may even make a slight answering bow from time to time, and sometimes a display takes place in which the two sexes behave similarly, both birds fanning their tails and bowing to one another and at least on occasions both fluttering their wings.

Wing-fluttering accompanied by elevation of the tail is the female's normal expression of readiness for coition, and she may take the initiative in soliciting without any preliminary advances by the male. The elevation of the tail is the diagnostic action in this connection, for the wing-fluttering should perhaps be regarded as primarily a food-begging action. Ceremonial feeding and coition are, however, so closely connected that it is doubtful how far actions related to one or the other can be properly dissociated. The display commonly leads up to the presentation of food by the male, and this is generally followed by coition, which in the breeding season normally takes place only on the nest. Sometimes, however (though the contrary has been stated), it may occur on a branch or on the ground. Coition and ceremonial feeding occur well into the incubation period, but the associated display is then hurried or absent. Often the male "simply flies straight down from a bough above on to the female's back, gives her food and simultaneously amidst much wing-flapping mating is accomplished" (Yeates, 1934). It should be observed that during incubation, which is normally performed by the female only, the male habitually supplies his mate with food, but the feeding has then an obvious function to perform as such and is no longer of a purely ceremonial character. Recrudescence of sexual behavior takes place long before actual breeding commences. Sporadic displays, and occasionally even coition, may be observed in the fall, and both have been recorded as early as October, though at least as regards coition this must probably be regarded as exceptional. From late in November to December, when the weather is mild, coition seems to be not uncommon, and ceremonial feeding has been observed from the end of December. A mutual fondling of bills, which is often observed in mated birds, has also been recorded in fall. These expressions of affection outside the breeding season are probably in the main not merely promiscuous. There is good reason for supposing that rooks pair for life, as is known to be the case in such solitary Corvidae as the raven, and that "married couples" maintain their association in the flocks. Nevertheless a certain amount of promiscuity does take place at the rookeries, in the form of sudden assaults on incubating females by intruding males in the absence of the regular mate. In this connection reference must be made to the violent scuffles between several or a number of birds which occur from time to time in every rookery, centering round a nest. Selous (1927) was the first to recognize that these are, at least generally, attacks by neighbors on a pair engaged in the sexual act. But Yeates (1934), who had the advantage of making his observations from a hide in the tree tops, obtained fairly strong evidence for the unexpected conclusion that the attacks are generally confined to promiscuous mating where the male is an interloper. Although he observed coition repeatedly he found that such mobbings occurred only occasionally, and in three instances observed while he was specially concentrating on this point there was a very strong presumption, amounting to virtual certainty in two of them, that the male involved was not the mate of the female. He writes:

"On these three occasions referred to the evidence in two of them was, to my mind, quite certain. At one nest a male came down, mated and was mobbed and driven off. The very next minute the rightful male came with food. He could not possibly have collected it and returned in the interval. At the second nest mating took place and a very violent mobbing scene resulted (there were four birds attacking). Within a few minutes the rightful male came and again mated—and he was left in peace. The third instance was a little more uncertain—but was of a similar nature to the first."

The subject of these mobbings deserves further study. If Yeates's conclusion is correct—and his evidence cannot be lightly dismissed—it would indicate a very singular state of affairs and one presenting an intriguing problem to students of bird behavior and psychology, since it is certainly not to be explained by attributing a sense of morality to the birds! It should not be overlooked, however, that in various other species of birds the sight of a pair engaged in the sexual act has been observed to have a very provocative effect on other individuals, which are stimulated thereby to interfere in very much the same way that has been described in rooks—and this quite irrespective of the "legitimacy" or otherwise of the nuptial behavior.

What may be regarded as a kind of courtship—or display flight, though its full significance is not altogether clear, may sometimes be noticed, several birds following one another with peculiar slow wing beats. Headlong dives from a height and other aerial evolutions may sometimes be observed at the beginning of the breeding season, but such performances have apparently no sexual significance (except indirectly as an expression of excitement) and are much more characteristic of the fall, under which heading they are further described.

Nesting.—Rooks are colonial birds, normally building their nests in tall trees, and it appears to be a matter of indifference to them whether the trees are in compact groups or scattered. Rookeries may be built on the one hand in trees dispersed over open parkland, fields, or lawns, irregularly spaced along hedgerows or in closer rows forming windbreaks or avenues, or on the other hand may occupy more compact groups of trees forming copses, spinneys, plantations, or small woods or in the shrubberies of gardens. More rarely a rookery may be situated on the borders of a large wood, but it is probably safe to say that no rookery is ever found far inside any extensive and uninterrupted tract of woodland. A great many rookeries are near farms or buildings or in the grounds of country houses. No doubt the tendency to nest near farms may be partially accounted for by the fact that very often a farm has a spinney or a windbreak planted near it, as well as by the better food supply near such settlements, and no doubt the well-timbered character of the grounds of so many country houses is sufficient to account for the occupation of many such sites. But the observer who critically notes the surroundings of a large number of rookeries will probably find it difficult to resist the impression that the birds have often deliberately selected a site near a building though others were available.

Rooks are not averse to nesting in trees in towns provided suitable feeding grounds are available fairly close at hand. On account of its parks Inner London preserved a few rooks until comparatively recently. A small rookery that existed for many years in the garden of Gray's Inn in the City lasted till 1915, its abandonment being variously attributed to disturbance by recruits drilling under the trees or to the depredations of carrion crows. Other details about London rookeries are given by Macpherson (1929).

In hilly or partly hilly districts the main concentration of rookeries will be found in the lowlands, the density of rook population beginning to fall off at a comparatively inconsiderable elevation. In southern and midland England, at any rate, the decrease above about 400 feet is quite definite, though it is evident that the determining factor is the more extensive cultivation of the lowlands, which provide better feeding grounds than the hills, and not altitude as such. In the writer's home county of Somerset quite large rookeries of 200 nests or more occur up to 1,000 feet, and the highest site (with 38 nests in 1933) is at 1,350 feet. On the Carboniferous limestone plateau of Derbyshire nearly all rookeries are between 1,000 and 1,200 feet.

Rooks nest in both broad-leaved trees and conifers, and, provided the trees are of substantial size and of a habit of growth such as will provide suitable lodgement for the nests, they seem to have no special preferences, their choice of trees in any area depending primarily on the relative abundance of the species of tree available. Occasionally rookeries are found with the nests built in saplings of only some 25 to 35 feet in a hedgerow, but such sites are not common. Quite exceptionally nests have been built on buildings such as church spires. Up until 1835 a pair occupied such a nest on the weather-vane of the steeple of Bow Church, in London, and other cases are recorded by Yarrell (1882).

The size of rookeries varies a great deal, from half-a-dozen nests, or even fewer, to hundreds. Rookeries of over a hundred nests are common, but small colonies are most numerous and in most districts the commonest size for a rookery is something under 25 nests. The largest English rookery, to the best of the writer's knowledge, is one of over 600 nests in a small wood in Oxfordshire, but in parts of Scotland there are immense rookeries of over 1,000 and even over 2,000 nests, which have no parallel south of the border. Several colonies of the same order of size (the largest with 2,400 nests) exist in Holland. In both countries it seems possible that the great size of the colonies may be correlated with a certain scarcity of suitable sites in areas not so well timbered as many in which rooks are found.

It should be observed that while some rookeries are compact others may be dispersed in irregular groups over a considerable area, and in dealing with these latter the student is soon confronted with the question, What constitutes "a rookery"? Groups situated close to one another are obviously essentially parts of a single colony, but what degree of separation justifies us in speaking of two groups as two distinct rookeries? Many factors have a bearing on the problem, which is too complex to discuss here, but it may be said that in the present state of knowledge any criteria adopted must necessarily be somewhat arbitrary, and the point is mentioned mainly in order to stress that statements as to the dimensions attained by individual rookeries will be affected in a certain proportion of cases by the criteria employed. But for the most part the large colonies mentioned would be reckoned as single rookeries on any reasonable scheme.

At the opposite extreme to these giant colonies, isolated nests are not very rare, but as a rule they have little permanency, and it has been repeatedly stated that isolated nests situated at all close to a regular rookery are liable to be raided by the occupants of the latter, such individualistic tendencies being regarded with disfavor in rook society. But more critical observation on this point seems desirable.

Rooks are early breeders, but, although the rookeries are visited from time to time in the winter and more frequently as the season advances, the serious business of nest building or repair rarely begins before late February. The nests are generally built in the topmost, slender branches of trees, often several or even a considerable number in one tree, and are frequently very difficult or almost impossible for even a good climber to reach, though an enterprising egg collector or photographer will not as a rule have great difficulty in finding a rookery where the nests are more accessible. They are built of sticks, solidified with earth and lined with grasses, dead leaves, moss, roots, straw, and the like. Wool and hair, beloved of the carrion crow, are only quite exceptionally employed and then only in small quantities. Exceptionally the use of feathers in quantity has recently been recorded, where a plentiful supply happened to be available close at hand. Both sexes build, the cock doing most of the collecting and the hen most of the arranging. The sticks are broken off from trees or pillaged from other nests and are not collected from the ground. Even a stick accidentally dropped is not ordinarily retrieved, though rarely one may be picked up again. Eggs are usually found in the latter half of March or early April. The task of incubation is performed solely by the hen, to whom the cock brings food at the nest, and sometimes, but not always, begins with the first egg laid. As an exception a case of a male taking a turn on the eggs has been recorded (Nethersole-Thompson and Musselwhite, 1940). The Rev. F. C. R. Jourdain (1938), from whom some of the above details are also quoted, states that the incubation period is 16-18 days. Not all the nests are built at once; a few may go on being added far into April, perhaps by young birds coming into breeding condition for the first time.

Eggs.—The eggs are of the usual *Corvus* type, but rather small. The following condensed description is given by the Rev. F. C. R. Jourdain in the work already quoted:

"Usually 3-5, sometimes 6, rarely 7; 8 and 9 recorded: vary much as Crow's: ground-colour from light bluish-green to green and greyish-green but never so blue, and rarely show much of ground-colour, being more uniformly marked with shades of ashy-grey and brown. Erythristic varieties have occurred abroad and also Northern Ireland (H. T. Malcomson). Average size of 100 British eggs, 40.0 x 28.3, Max.: 47.1 x 26.2 and 39.5 x 30.5, Min.: 35.1 x 27.1 and 44.2 x 25.8 mm., averaging smaller than Crow's."

Young.—The fledging period of the young is given by S. E. Brock (1910) as 29 to 30 days. Yeates (1934) found that for the first 9 or 10 days the male collects all the food, but after this the female also takes a share in the work. The food is brought in the capacious pouch under the tongue, which produces a prominent swelling under the chin, conspicuous in birds coming into the rookery after a foraging excursion. When the time comes for fledging the young birds, according to Yeates's observations, are enticed out of the nest by the female, who refuses to bring food to the nest but waits with it in the branches, calling to the chicks until they venture out. They remain for some time in the branches until their wings are strong enough to support them and finally join the old birds in the fields, where the parents continue to feed them at first. Mortality before leaving the nest is severe. Four young hatched may be taken as a fair average, but counts quoted by Yeates show that on an average at most only two chicks to a nest are fledged. Only one brood is normally reared, but cases of breeding in fall and even as late as November have been recorded.

Plumages.—The plumages and molts are fully described by H. F. Witherby in the *Handbook of British Birds* (1938).

Food.—The food of the rook is thus summarized by Jourdain (1938): "In agricultural areas corn is staple food, but potatoes, roots, fruit, acorns, walnuts, peas, berries, and seeds also recorded. Animal food includes insects: Coleoptera (many injurious species), also larvae, larvae of Lepidoptera, Dermaptera, Orthoptera, Hymenoptera, Hemiptera, Diptera, and larvae, etc.: also earthworms, Mollusca (snails and slugs) : millipedes, spiders. Carrion (dead lambs, etc.) occasional: birds killed in hard weather and young or eggs frequently taken (game-birds, duck, Stone-Curlew, Lapwing, and many species of small birds) : small mammals (mice, shrew, young rabbit) : small fish also recorded." W. E. Collinge (1924), who analyzed the contents of 1,306 stomachs, found that the food was made up of 59 percent vegetable matter and 41 percent animal matter. The vegetable matter was made up of 35.1 percent cereals and 13.4 percent potatoes and roots, and only 6.1 percent of items considered "neutral" from an agricultural standpoint. Of the animal total 28.5 percent consisted of forms considered injurious to agriculture (the great bulk being injurious insects), while 3.5 percent consisted of beneficial insects and 9 percent of "neutral" insects and earthworms. On this basis 52 percent of the rook's food consumption inflicts damage to agriculture, and only 28.5 percent is beneficial. The influence of the rook on British agriculture has been much discussed, but until recently all such discussions suffered from the vital defect that the crucial information on the actual density of the rook population was lacking. But thanks to recent accurate census work over large tracts of agricultural country in England, taken in conjunction with the requisite statistics on crop production and Collinge's data already quoted, it can now be stated with considerable confidence that in spite of widely held opinions to the contrary the numbers of rooks are nowhere sufficient to exert any important effect on the crop production of the country, or of any considerable district, as a whole, and this may be stressed as a good illustration of how census work undertaken primarily for its biological interest may have a very real economic value.

Behavior.—The ordinary gait of the rook, like that of other crows, is a sedate walk, which may be interrupted by one or two less dignified hops if the bird is bent on securing some tasty morsel ahead of a competitor or otherwise feels the need of hurry. The flight, when making for a definite objective, is direct and deliberate, with regular wing beats varied only by gliding where air conditions are specially favorable, as when crossing a valley or when about to pitch. But on more desultory flights about the feeding grounds and around or above the rookery more irregular wing action and a good deal of gliding may be observed. Eminently gregarious, rooks are usually seen in parties or flocks, which may be of large size, differing therein from the carrion crow, which is much more of an individualist, though it must not be supposed that either single rooks or flocks of carrion crows are very unusual.

Voice.—The cawing of rooks, though it cannot be called melodious, is to most lovers of nature a pleasant sound, redolent of the country. The ordinary note may be described as a hoarse kaah, and typically it

is of somewhat lower pitch than the more raucous croak of the carrion
crow, but actually the rook's voice has a much greater range of pitch
than the crow's. According to Nicholson and Koch (1936), who prepared gramophone records of the voices of many British birds, the
rook's vocabulary has a range of about 425-1,800 cycles a second, while
the crow's range is only about 600-750. The ordinary caw is subject to
considerable modulations and variations, as anyone may observe who
listens to the sounds in a rookery in spring or at a roost in winter.
There are also other more or less distinct notes, and Edmund Selous
(1901) has recorded over 30 sounds, but his list is unsatisfactory, as it
includes too many sounds that seem to be little more than variants of the
same essential note. I have shortly mentioned some of the more distinct
notes in the *Handbook of British Birds* (1938), but a systematic and
critical study of the rook's vocabulary has yet to be made. On occasions
of exuberance in spring rooks are sometimes moved to a kind of un-
couth attempt at song. As I have noted in the work referred to, one
such performance is described as resembling a bass or guttural reproduction of the varied and spluttering song of the starling, and other
more or less discordant variations have been noted.

Field marks.—The adult rook is easily told from other black-plumaged
Corvidae by its bare grayish-white face. But this characteristic is not
acquired until the first summer after hatching, and young birds with
fully feathered faces are not easily distinguished from carrion crows.
The bill of the rook is rather slenderer and the culmen usually less
curved, but this is not a very good character, as it is easy to find young
birds of the two species whose bills are so alike that they could not
possibly be distinguished by this feature in the field. A better character
is the loose baggy appearance of the feathering of the thighs, which is
noticeable at all ages.

Enemies.—The rook has no enemies serious enough to constitute in
any way a menace to the species. The chief enemy is man, who destroys
a certain number because of depredations on his fields and at many of
the larger rookeries organizes regular rook shoots in spring, at which
considerable numbers of young birds recently out of the nest are de-
troyed. These find their graves in rook pies, which are generally
agreed to be excellent eating, though the writer has not tried them.
The peregrine falcon, and on the Continent the goshawk, will sometimes
take a rook, and the golden eagle has also been recorded as doing so,
but this can happen only rarely, for the haunts of eagle and rook do
not overlap to any great extent and the eagle is nowhere common. The
common buzzard *(Buteo buteo)* and European sparrow hawk *(Accipiter
nisus)* are recorded as taking young birds occasionally, and if the

opportunity offers the carrion and hooded crows are not above raiding the nests of their relatives. As shown by Elton and Buckland (1928) a very high percentage of young rooks may be infected with gapeworms morphologically identical with *Syngamus trachea* of poultry. Ninety-four percent of 33 young birds examined were infested, mostly rather heavily, but adults appear to be only slightly parasitized, so that it is probable that infected young birds gradually rid themselves of the parasites as they grow older, as happens in chickens. Cram (1927) records *Corvus frugilegus* as host to the following nematode parasites: *Syngamus trachea, Acuaria anthuris, A. cordata, Oxyspirura sygmoidea,* and *Microtetrameres inermis.* G. Niethammer in the *Handbuch der deutschen Vogelkunde* (1937) gives a list of ecto- and endoparasites obtained from the rook.

Fall and winter.—Outside the breeding season rooks are as gregarious as when nesting, feeding together in flocks by day and roosting collectively at night, and their habits during this period of the year are of much interest. The general outlines of their behavior are tolerably constant, but details vary considerably according to local conditions and other factors. Their foraging excursions are not confined to the fields, for after breeding they will resort regularly to woods, more especially of oak, to feed upon caterpillars, as well as to the outskirts of the moors in hilly districts.

As the season advances the scattered parties tend to fuse together into larger flocks, but in most districts it is noticeable that these flocks contain remarkably few young birds. It is clear from several lines of evidence that from causes still not precisely determined there must be a very heavy mortality among the young during July and August. Careful observations by J. P. Burkitt (1936) in Ireland led him to place the number of young birds surviving in winter at as small a figure as about 10 percent of the number of adults, and this figure seems to be reached as early as August. But the proportion of young to adults in flocks seen in the fields is commonly even less, and many flocks consist of adults exclusively. Some observations of the same author suggest that the birds of the year independently of the adults (though commonly in company with jackdaws) tend to form parties that wander far away from the rookeries, but the subject of the habits of young rooks is one in need of further careful study.

At least in some districts from early in summer until fall parties of rooks are apt to roost in any convenient wood or copse near which they happen to find themselves, but in other cases the birds may continue to roost at their own rookery or may join up into larger roosting assemblies comprising the occupants of more than one breeding colony.

The really large winter roosts are not as a rule at full strength before September or early in October, though varying numbers may roost at these sites from the close of the breeding season. Indeed, the winter roost is normally also the site of an existing large rookery, and when it is not there is reason to believe that it is usually, if not always, the site of a former colony, as is known to have been the case in various recorded instances. [1] These large roosts are often of many years' standing and comprise thousands of birds drawn from a large area. They are commonly shared with jackdaws (*Corvus monedula*), and collectively they account for the bulk of the winter population of rooks, but in most districts there are also smaller subsidiary roosts, and here and there the members of a single rookery may roost there throughout the winter. The feeding territories corresponding to individual roosts are generally fairly constant in a broad way, but in the absence of any natural boundaries like the sea or a range of hills have apparently no very clear-cut frontiers as a rule, and there is considerable evidence that in some places flocks from different roosts may mingle amicably on the same feeding grounds.

The dispersal from the roost at daybreak is rapid, and the flocks proceed in a direct and purposeful manner to their feeding grounds, though often with a pause to visit their own rookery for a short time. The return journey, on the other hand, is usually of a markedly leisurely character. The birds begin to move in toward the roost from the more outlying areas at a comparatively early hour, and in Northumberland Philipson (1933) found that by about 1 o'clock the peripheral areas of the feeding territory were usually deserted. In the less remote areas flocks may be seen feeding in the fields considerably later, but there is a gradual move toward the roost, often in two or more stages with an interval of feeding between. Very commonly the adult birds assemble at their own rookery before moving off, and as the flocks and parties converge toward the roost they frequently combine into larger bodies. In the neighborhood of the roost there are often regularly used collecting grounds at which large numbers of birds gather and feed for a time before the final move, and in the fields immediately adjacent to the dormitory the earlier arrivals resume their feeding in a restless way for a time before retiring. As more and more birds stream in excitement rises, and the observer is treated to astonishing displays of acrobatics in the air before the fresh arrivals settle. The fields are now black with birds and at last about dusk the whole body rises as if at a word of command, and with much cawing the procession to bed begins. Above the wood the

---

[1] It will be understood that this applies to the British Isles and cannot be the case in southern Europe, where the rook occurs only as a migrant.

stream of birds breaks up again into groups and parties, and after one or two preliminary circlings the birds pour down into the trees with a renewed crescendo of cawings and other strange noises before finally settling down for the night.

The aerial evolutions referred to afford as impressive and exciting a spectacle as an ornithologist can wish to see and reveal an agility and a capacity for frolicsome behavior that are not a little surprising in these usually sedate birds. They plunge and dive headlong from a great height, roll, tumble, sideslip, and chase one another in swerving and switchback flights like a veritable avian circus troupe. Such displays, in which immature as well as adult birds participate, are not confined to roosting time, but may be seen also earlier in the day, especially in September. As mentioned under "Courtship" something of the same kind may also be observed in spring, but it is much more characteristic of the fall. It is an expression of a sort of general *joie de vivre* without sexual significance, and if the scientist needs to classify it somehow it must be reckoned as a form of social, not sexual, behavior.

Allusion has been made above to visits to the rookery during the period under discussion. Though occurring, especially in the morning soon after daybreak and late in the afternoon they are by no means confined to these times, for the birds often feed close to their breeding places and pay visits to the trees during the day. As the season advances these visits become more frequent and more prolonged, and early in the year signs of a renewed interest in building and nest repair may be observed, as already described, but the winter roosts are not generally abandoned till about mid-March. The mode of abandonment seems to vary; it may apparently take place all at once or be spread over some days up to ten or more, but sooner or later the birds are all roosting again at their own rookeries and the annual cycle begins once more.

DISTRIBUTION

[Acknowledgment is made of assistance derived in the compilation of this section from the sections on "Distribution Abroad" by F C. R. Jourdain and on "Migration" by N. F. Ticehurst in the *Handbook of British Birds* (1938).]

Breeding range.—Occurs throughout the British Isles wherever there are trees for it to breed in, but not in the Shetlands. Breeds in greater part of Continental Europe from latitude 63½° N. in Norway, 60° in Sweden, 62° in Finland and northern Russia, east to Perm (eastern Russia) and south to mid-France, northern Italy, Serbia, Bulgaria, and southern Russia. Allied races are found in west temperate and eastern Asia.

Winter range.—Breeding birds are sedentary or mainly so in temperate parts of range, but migrate from Scandinavia, north-central Europe, and colder parts of Russia. The winter range extends south to Spain and Portugal, central and south Italy, Sicily, Corsica, and Sardinia, the Balkan Peninsula, Cyprus, and southwestern Asia.

Spring migration.—Birds from northern and eastern Europe that have wintered in England leave the east coast between mid-February and the third week of April, the movement being at its height on the coast of Suffolk at the end of March and early in April. Banding records show that these birds come from as far away as northwestern Russia and as near as Holland, as well as from intermediate regions, including northern Germany, east Prussia, and Lithuania. Many birds, and at times very large numbers indeed, pass over Heligoland on the spring migration, the earliest date recorded by Gätke being February 4, and many pass through Germany in March and April on their way to the Baltic Provinces and Russia. Migrants in Italy and Greece leave in March and early April, the latest date recorded by C. J. Alexander for the Rome district being April 7. In central Spain rooks are stated to be (at least locally) common until March and in the north a flock has been observed as late as April 18.

Fall migration.—In fall (from mid-September) the main movement of rooks on the Continent of Europe is westward from the northeastern, eastern, and central regions toward France, Belgium, and eastern England. The birds that winter in the last-named area mostly arrive from the end of September to the third week of November. Alexander's (1927) earliest date for arrival in the Rome district was October 28. In western Greece, according to some observers, rooks arrive in October, and Lord Lilford (1860) says toward the end of the month, but about mid-November seems more usual. In central Spain rooks are described as being present from November.

Casual records.—Recorded occasionally or casually from east Greenland, Iceland, the Faeroes, Novaya Zemlya, northwestern Siberia, the Azores, Madeira, Balearic Islands, Malta, Algeria, and Egypt.

CORVUS CORNIX CORNIX Linnaeus

HOODED CROW

CONTRIBUTED BY BERNARD WILLIAM TUCKER

HABITS

The claim of the hooded or gray crow to a place on the American list rests on its casual occurrence in east Greenland, where Schalow (1904) states that several examples have been collected by Danish zoologists at Angmagsalik, having presumably wandered from the Faeroes by way of Iceland.

The hooded crow and the black carrion crow *(Corvus corone)* are exceedingly closely allied; indeed they appear to differ in no structural feature whatever, but only in coloring. Moreover, where their ranges overlap they regularly interbreed, producing fertile hybrids showing every intergradation of color. These considerations have led some ornithologists to argue that they ought to be treated as races of one species, and there is undoubtedly a great deal to be said for this view. At the same time, no competent biologist nowadays can doubt that racial differences frequently provide the material out of which specific differences evolve, and, this being so, the decision as to the precise point at which two diverging races become deserving of specific rank must necessarily be somewhat arbitrary. In the present case the two forms seem to be so near the border line that considerations of convenience may be legitimately allowed to carry some weight, and as it is distinctly more convenient for descriptive purposes to consider them as separate species, this practice, as followed by both the A.O.U. Check-list and the new *Handbook of British Birds,* may be the more readily accepted.

The distribution of the two birds is curious, for the range of the hooded crow cuts that of the carrion crow completely into two parts separated by many hundreds of miles, the carrion being the crow of southwestern Europe, and absent from the rest of that Continent and from western Asia, but reappearing in central, eastern, and northeastern Asia. The ranges only overlap along relatively narrow zones of contact, a circumstance justifiably stressed by those who would regard the two forms as races of one species, and in these areas, as mentioned above, they interbreed more or less freely. The hooded crow might be regarded as a geologically more recent form which arose in the intermediate area and has replaced the black form over a part of its range.

The hooded crow frequents both cultivated and uncultivated country, which may be fairly well timbered, but not densely wooded, or quite devoid of trees. It is often seen on the seashore or along the borders of lakes and estuaries.

Courtship.—The following account has been given by C. and D. Nethersole-Thompson (1940):

> While watching a flock of some fourteen birds on December 9th, 1938, the trait observed by Miss E. V. Baxter and Miss L. J. Rintoul was noted, viz., repeated jumps into the air and descent to the same place. Chough-like dives with wings nearly closed, fluttering with dangling legs and upturned wings of males(?) over females(?), and low skimming flights by flying over perched birds were also observed. During these performances there was much croaking from time to time. Display-flight of the male (20.3.38) is a series of short dives

with semiclosed wings, and sometimes a half-roll, bird croaking continuously. Aerial display in spring also includes "corkscrew" or figure-of-eight flight high in the air by a pair of birds. This is also accompanied by much calling. Another form of posturing several times watched by us shows the male bird, while perched on a tree bowing to the female. In this display, carried out several times in succession, wings are spread and tail expanded. In April, 1940, we watched coition of Hooded Crows take place on a bare, burned patch of moorland. Prior to the act the male for over a minute violently shook his raised wings and this he also continued after coition.

It appears from this description, as might be expected, that the courtship and sex behavior of the hooded crow differ in no respect from those of the carrion crow.

Nesting.—The hooded crow will nest either in trees or on some ledge of a coastal cliff, generally protected by an overhang of the rock. Unlike those of the rook, which likes to build in the slender topmost branches, tree nests are generally placed in a comparatively stout fork. Inland, even in localities where trees are rare or absent, it rarely builds in cliffs or rocks but quite frequently places its nest in bushes, sometimes quite low. Ussher and Warren (1900) state that in the west of Ireland, where it habitually breeds in bushes in this way, it usually selects one on an island in a lake, no doubt for greater security. Occasionally a nest may be built on the ground among heather on low islets in lakes.

The nest, which is built by both sexes, the male doing most of the collecting and the female most of the building, is described by Jourdain (1938) as "strongly constructed of sticks, heather-twigs, seaweed-stems, moss, and earth, lined wool, hair, and sometimes feathers." These crows usually employ a quantity of wool in lining their nests, in contrast to the rook. Jourdain also mentions that in the Shetland Islands and northern Ireland large bones have been found in the foundations of nests.

Eggs.—The following condensed particulars are given by Jourdain (1938): "Usually 4-6, very rarely 7; much resemble Carrion-Crow's; ground-colour varying from light blue to deep green, generally blotched and spotted over whole surface with shades of umber-brown, and underlying ashy shell-marks. Some have only few markings on blue ground or are entirely devoid of them: one light-coloured egg in clutch not uncommon. Erythristic variety recorded once or twice. Average size of 100 British eggs 43.5 x 30.3. Max.: **52.0** x 32.0 and 43.4 x **33.0.** Min. **39.2** x 29.8 and 44.3 x **28.4** mm."

Eggs may be found at the end of March and in April in the British Isles.

Young.—The incubation period is 19 days and is performed solely by the hen bird, who is fed by the cock. The feeding may take place at the nest or the female may leave the nest to meet her mate and stretch her wings a little. Quite exceptionally, it would seem, the male may take a turn on the nest; a change-over at the nest has been observed in the British Isles by J. Walpole-Bond, quoted by Jourdain (1938). Incubation normally begins with the first egg. The nestlings are fed by both parents, but chiefly by the hen and are fledged in four to five weeks.

Plumages.—A full account of plumages and molts is given by H. F. Witherby in the *Handbook of British Birds* (1938).

Food.—The hooded crow is a rapacious and destructive rascal, hated by farmer and gamekeeper alike. Hardly any kind of animal food comes amiss to it, and it is an inveterate egg stealer. Carrion and refuse of all sorts are greedily devoured. It will forage diligently on rubbish tips and among tidal refuse on the shore or feast more sumptuously on a carcass when it can find one. Wounded or sickly animals and birds fall victims to it, and occasionally some healthy bird may be pounced on and laid low by a vicious blow from the bill, or even pursued and captured in fair chase. The young of ducks and other birds form a comparatively easy prey, and it will range the moors systematically in search of nests with eggs. Occasionally small mammals such as mice and voles, and even young rabbits and hares, are captured. Shepherds accuse it of attacking lambing ewes and new-born lambs, and even larger lambs or other animals that it can take at a disadvantage may succumb to its attacks. A contributor to the journal *British Birds* some years ago described how two hoodies set upon a lamb some weeks old, which had got into difficulties in a marsh, and quickly killed it (Simpson, 1926). When the observer rushed up from a distance of about 400 yards both eyes of the unfortunate animal had been pecked out and it was dying, apparently from injuries inflicted on the brain through the eye sockets. Such tragedies are probably not rare. Frogs are also sometimes killed and even small fish are recorded, so that no class of vertebrates is immune from its attentions. Among invertebrates, Mollusca, including *Cardium, Mytilus, Tellina, Patella, Buccinum, Littorina,* and *Purpura,* among marine forms, as well as the fresh-water *Anodonta* and land snails *(Helix),* insects (chiefly Coleoptera, but also moths, Trichoptera, and larvae of Odonata, Plecoptera, and Diptera), spiders, sea-urchins, small Crustacea (sandhoppers and crabs), and earthworms have been recorded, and some vegetable matter, such as grain, potatoes, and turnips, is also taken. A number of the above details are quoted from Jourdain's summary of published data in the *Handbook of British Birds* (1938).

A special habit of the hooded and carrion crows, well known to modern ornithologists but recorded of the present species in Ireland more than 800 years ago by the twelfth-century theologian, traveler, and writer Giraldus Cambrensis, is that of carrying up mollusks and crabs and dropping them on the shore or on rocks or shingle in order to smash the shells. Critical observers have not generally considered that they exercise any intelligent selection of hard as opposed to softer surfaces for this purpose; nevertheless there is evidence that in some places they have learned to utilize masonry or walls for their operations. The subject is discussed by Oldham (1930).

Voice.—The ordinary note of the hooded crow is a raucous croak. It is the writer's considered opinion that there is no constant difference between the voices of the hooded and carrion crows, and in this he is supported by H. G. Alexander (MS.), a most careful and experienced ornithologist with an excellent ear. Various observers have professed to be able to detect a difference, but as to its nature their accounts are not consistent. The question was also discussed some years ago in German ornithological journals and the conclusion reached after critical investigation was the same as that just stated. Reference should be made to Meise (1928) and Kramer (1930).

The note of the crow is not only more raucous but typically rather less deep than the typical caw of the rook, but the range of pitch of the crow's vocabulary is very much less than the rook's, namely about 600-750 cycles a second as against 425-1,800 (Nicholson and Koch, 1936). Nicholson further stresses a greater resonance, more deliberate timing, and tendency to repeat three to four times with a long pause before the next repetition. The common note might be rendered as *kraah,* with an exaggeration of the nasal sound heard in such words as "twang," and also *kraarrr.* A higher-pitched *keerk, keerk, keerk, konk, konk* irresistibly suggesting a distant motor horn, a short, rattling note of aggression, and others may also be heard from the carrion crow, and there can be little doubt that they are common to both species. The croak and variants are sometimes repeated a great number of times from a tree top or some other elevated position, and at times a succession of croaking and bubbling notes functioning as a kind of song may be heard. The brooding female on the nest sometimes produces a very soft "crackling" sound, which may continue uninterrupted for several minutes and has been called a "nest-song" (R. Zimmermann, 1931).

Behavior.—The behavior of the hooded crow is much like that of other typical corvids. Its gait is a sedate walk, varied by perhaps two or three rather ungainly hops if hurried. The flight is direct, with rather deliberate wing beats. Where air conditions are favorable, as in crossing a valley or about coastal cliffs, gliding flight may be employed to some extent, but typically the wing beats are regular and uninterrupted. It does not soar like the raven.

Though breeding in isolated pairs and usually reckoned a solitary species, the hooded crow may be seen in parties outside the breeding season and even at times in flocks, while it shares with many other Corvidae the habit of occupying communal roosts, more fully referred to under "Winter," which may attain large dimensions where the species is numerous. Even in the more solitary Corvidae distinct social tendencies are observable, and assemblies of crows are sometimes clearly something more than merely fortuitous gatherings for feeding purposes. In the case of the carrion crow gatherings have been observed in which in addition to chasing or hopping among the branches of trees there are pursuits and maneuverings on the ground, sometimes with a distinct formality about them. Such behavior does not seem to have been expressly recorded in the case of the hooded crow, but in view of what has already been said as to the identity of the habits and behavior of the two species in other respects it can hardly be doubted that the same sort of thing occurs. It is difficult to assign any function to these gatherings beyond the quite general one of affording some outlet to the social urge that seems to be common in varying degrees to practically all corvine birds.

For the rest the general habits and behavior of this species are evidently closely similar to those of the American crow. Like that species, it is a wary, cunning, and intelligent bird.

Field marks.—The gray body contrasting with the black head, wings, and tail at once separates the hooded crow from the carrion and American crows.

Enemies.—Man is the chief enemy of the hooded crow, and it has been mentioned that it is very unpopular with gamekeepers, shepherds, and poultry farmers. It seems to be little interfered with by birds of prey, though no doubt the more powerful species like the peregrine will take one occasionally, and the golden eagle has also been recorded as doing so. Cram (1927) records the following nematodes parasitic in *Corvus cornix: Porrocaecum semiteres, Acuaria anthuris, A. cordata, A. depressa, Tetrameres unispina,* and *Physaloptera malleus.* A list of ectoparasites and endoparasites recorded from the species is given by Niethammer (1937).

Fall and winter.—It has been mentioned above that outside the breeding season hooded crows may be seen in parties and flocks as well as in pairs or singly, and where the species is plentiful it gathers at night in large communal roosts. The writer knows of no record of such gigantic roosts as have been described in the case of the American crow, but nevertheless they may attain considerable dimensions. Thus, roosts of many hundreds are recorded in the Outer Hebrides, where the birds generally sleep on the ground among heather on islands in lochs. Elsewhere they roost on trees and on the Continent roosts on high buildings are also recorded.

DISTRIBUTION

[Acknowledgment is made of assistance derived in the compilation of this section from the sections on "Distribution Abroad" by F. C. R. Jourdain and on "Migration" by N. F. Ticehurst in the *Handbook of British Birds* (1938).]

Breeding range.—Breeds in the more northerly part of Scotland and in Ireland; in England only occasionally and chiefly in the eastern counties. Outside the British Isles it breeds from the Faeroes, Scandinavia, Finland, and north Russia south to Denmark, Germany east of the Elbe, Czechoslovakia, western Yugoslavia, Italy, Sicily, Austria, Hungary, southern Russia to the Caucasus, and north Persia. Allied races breed in Corsica, Sardinia, the Balkans to Palestine and Egypt, southeastern Russia (?), Cyprus, Crete, Iraq, Iran, western Siberia, etc.

Winter range.—Birds from the colder parts of the range migrate at the approach of winter and spread southwestward into western Germany, the Netherlands, Belgium, and France and to eastern and southeastern England. These winter visitors in western Europe are commonest in the coastal districts. Birds in the more southern parts of the range are sedentary.

Spring migration.—Hooded crows that have wintered in England leave the east coast between mid-March and the third week of April, with extreme dates as early as mid-February or as late as May 24. The Atlantic coasts of France are forsaken about the same time. Great numbers pass over Helgoland and the Kurische Nehrung, referred to more fully in the next section. At the latter place the movement begins in February or March according to weather conditions and lasts well into April, while the passage of smaller numbers continues until May.

Fall migration.—The most famous locality for the passage of hooded crows is the Kurische Nehrung, the narrow strip of land about 50 miles long separating the Baltic from the Kurisches Haff in east Prussia and on which is situated the ornithological station of Rossitten. Here almost incredible numbers pass on the fall migration, and as the birds travel by day and commonly quite low down the migration is very spectacular. According to Niethammer (1937) it begins about September 22 and lasts to the end of November, with the peak from October 14 to 25. The young birds appear first and then the adults. Frequently according to weather conditions later waves may pass even until January. Large numbers also pass over Helgoland in autumn. On the east coast of England hooded crows arrive from about the second week in October to the third week in November, but occasionally as early as August 5.

Casual records.—In addition to the Greenland occurrences hooded crows are recorded casually from Iceland, Novaya Zemlya, and Spitsbergen among the northern countries and from southern Spain, northwestern Africa, and Egypt in the south.

CYANOCEPHALUS CYANOCEPHALUS (Wied)

PINYON JAY

HABITS

"Maximilian's jay," as it was called by some of the earlier writers, "was discovered and first described by that eminent naturalist Maximilian, Prince of Wied, in his book of travels in North America, published in 1841," according to Baird, Brewer, and Ridgway (1874). "Mr. Edward Kern, who was connected with Colonel Fremont's exploring expedition in 1846, was the first to bring specimens of this interesting and remarkable bird to the notice of American naturalists, transmitting them to the Philadelphia Academy." The bird is now known to have a wide range in the Rocky Mountain region and in the Sierras and Cascades, farther west, breeding chiefly in the pinyon and juniper belt, but wandering erratically over much of the intervening and adjacent regions at other seasons.

Blue crow, a common local name, seems most appropriate for this bird, as it greatly resembles these birds in many of its actions and habits. Its blue color gives it its closest resemblance to a jay, but its short tail and its highly gregarious habits, together with its nomadic tendencies, are hardly jaylike. Its systematic position seems to ally it more closely with the crows than with the jays.

The foothills and lower mountain ranges, where the slopes are covered with a scattered growth of nut pines or pinyons *(Pinus edulis)* and junipers *(Juniperus occidentalis)*, with perhaps an undergrowth of sagebrush, are the favorite haunts of the pinyon jay, especially during the breeding season. Here large straggling flocks of these short-tailed blue crows may be seen trailing over these stunted open forests, looking for their favorite food in the nut pines, or building their nests in the low trees. But they may be here today and gone tomorrow in their restless wanderings.

Migration.—The pinyon jay throughout most of its range is not really a migratory species, though it has been reported in flights that looked like migrations. These flights, which occur in both spring and fall, seem to have no definite north or south direction at either season but are quite as often seen moving either east or west, or in other directions. These are probably not migrations in the strict sense of the word but rather mass movements to or from breeding grounds or from one feeding ground to another. The fact that the birds fly in large flocks, and often for a long time in one direction, leads to the impression that they are migrating. There is, however, a limited migration in the northern portion of its range, where Bendire (1895) says that it is "only a summer visitor, migrating regularly."

Nesting.—Pinyon jays prefer to breed in large or small colonies on the foothills or mountain slopes below 9,000 feet, placing their nests in the pinyons, where they straggle down the slopes toward the desert scrub areas, or in junipers, which grow in such places, or in scrub oaks; the nests are usually not more than 10 or 12 feet from the ground and often lower, though James B. Dixon tells me that "one colony had nests high in the pines, 25 to 50 feet off the ground." J. C. Braly (1931) found a large colony nesting near Grandview, Oreg., of which he says: "These nests were all in small junipers from three to seven feet above the ground. During our investigations [elsewhere?] we found over fifty nests of these birds, the great majority in juniper trees from three to eighteen feet up, while a few nests were found in yellow pine trees up to eighty-five feet." Sometimes three occupied nests were found in one tree.

In Dawson County, Mont., E. S. Cameron (1907) saw no evidence of these birds breeding in colonies and found only two nests, one of which he describes as follows:

The pair were first noted to be carrying twigs on May 19, at which date the nest was about half-finished, both birds assisting in its construction. Without the guidance of the birds it is unlikely that I should have found the nest at all, placed, as it was, near the extremity of a thick pine bough and completely screened from observation except from above within the tree. The nest was of large size with a smaller interior cup, the whole of the exterior, together with a platform on which the cup rested, being composed entirely of dead greasewood sticks and a few rootlets. The width across the sticks was 14 inches, and the height of the nest 8 inches. The cup was very strongly made of dead grass, pulled by the birds into a material like tow, and so thickly matted together, that it remained intact when nearly all the surrounding sticks had been blown away. Some dead thistle leaves were woven into the rim. The inner cup was 5½ inches in diameter and 2½ inches deep.

Mrs. Bailey (1928) says that the nests are "deep, bulky, and compactly built, with a framework of twigs and shreds of bark supporting the deep, well felted cup; made variously of finer shreds of bark, plant fibers, fine rootlets, weeds, wool, hair, dry grass, and a few feathers."

She mentions a few nests found by J. Stokley Ligon in New Mexico: "He says they nest generally from March 1-31, in gray live oaks among the pinyons, though occasionally in pinyons, even where the oaks can be had. * * * On February 17, while the ground was still half covered with snow, on the southwest side of Black Mountain in the Datil Forest, at about 7,500 feet he found one nest about complete and others under construction, in scattered scrub oaks on a steep grassy canyon side. There were more than fifty birds in pairs and flocks mingling and scattering and flying about noisily. On March 3, he returned to the colony and found nests in almost all the scrub oaks of sufficient size, but never more than one in a tree. One, half completed, was in a juniper. The birds, slow to leave their nests, finally did so noisily. As it had snowed many times since his first visit, the nests were damp from melted snow. Nearly all contained four eggs, but one had five." In the same general region, and at about the same elevation, he discovered a second, smaller nesting colony on March 4; and a third colony of perhaps 150 birds was found on March 28; many of these nests held eggs.

Major Bendire (1895) tells us that "the first nests and eggs of this species were found by Mr. Charles E. Aiken, near Colorado Springs, Colorado, on May 13, 1874. * * * The first naturalist, however, who observed the nests and young of this species was Mr. Robert Ridgway, who found a colony nesting in a low range of piñon-covered hills in the vicinity of Carson City, Nevada, on April 21, 1868."

Col. N. S. Goss (1891) reports that his brother, Capt. B. F. Goss, took nine sets of eggs of the pinyon jay in May 1879 near Fort Garland, Colo. "The nests were all in high, open situations, two of them well up the steep mountain sides, and none in valleys or thick timber. All were in small piñon pines, from five to ten feet up, out some distance from the body of the tree, and not particularly well concealed."

J. K. Jensen (1923) says that "the nesting season extends from February to June, during which time fresh eggs may be found," in New Mexico. He found a set of four fresh eggs on May 18, and on March 19, "a colony of thirteen nests each containing four young, some full grown." On March 15 he located a colony of 17 nests, all with fresh sets, two of three, eleven of four, and four of five. "All the nests found were placed from two to eight feet from the ground—average height five feet, and all but one were built in piñon pines, this one being placed four feet up in a juniper."

Eggs.—Four or five eggs, oftener the former, constitute the ordinary set for the pinyon jay; as few as three incubated eggs have been found and rarely as many as six eggs or young have been recorded. The eggs vary in shape from short-ovate to elliptical-ovate, but ovate is the prevailing shape. They are only slightly glossy. The ground color is bluish white, greenish white or grayish white. This is usually evenly covered all over with minute dots or small spots in various shades of brown, from reddish brown to purplish brown; sometimes there are larger spots or even small blotches, which are apt to be concentrated about the larger end. Bendire (1895) says that "an occasional set is blotched heavily enough to nearly hide the ground color, but this appears to be rarely the case." The measurements of 50 eggs in the United States National Museum average 29.2 by 21.7 millimeters; the eggs showing the four extremes measure **32.0** by **22.6**, 31.7 by **23.4, 26.3** by 20.7, and 28.0 by **20.0** millimeters.

Young.—Major Bendire (1895) writes: "Incubation lasts about sixteen days. The Piñon Jays are close sitters and, like Clarke's Nutcracker, are devoted parents. The young are able to leave the nest in about three weeks, and may easily be distinguished by their somewhat duller plumbeous blue color. They at once form in flocks and rove about from place to place in search of food."

Mr. Cameron (1907) says: "To the best of my belief, both birds share the duties of incubation. * * * It is an interesting sight in June, to watch a flock of some hundred or more Piñon Jays which contains a large proportion of the newly fledged young. After the latter can fly well they still expect the parents to feed them, and clamor incessantly to be fed, repeating their shrill monotonous cry of *wauck* on a single note, whether on the ground or in the pine branches, voracious, openmouthed fledglings walk towards the parents, flapping their newly acquired wings to attract attention. The old birds may then be seen supplying them with grubs and insects. I observed one female feed a single offspring on the ground several times in a few minutes."

Mrs. Wheelock (1904) says that the young "learn to extract the sweet kernels of the piñon nuts before they leave" the nest. "They are also fed quite as fully on grasshoppers from which legs and wings have been carefully removed."

Plumages.—Mr. Cameron (1907) writes: "The naked slate-colored young were hatched on June 15, so that the time of incubation was about 18 days. They are fully feathered at two weeks old, being then a uniform lavender of exactly the same color as the flower of that name, with bill, legs, and feet to match. The hue is darkest on the quills and lightest on the crissum. After leaving the nest they become more ash gray, lighter below; the tail is then dark slate with a light tip, and the ends of the primaries almost black. Until after the fall moult the birds show no real blue."

The postjuvenal molt seems to be very variable as to date, on account
of the variation in the date of hatching, but it occurs before fall and
apparently involves everything but the wings. I have seen two in this
molt on August 15.

.The first winter plumage, which is worn until the following summer,
is much like that of the adult female, but much duller throughout, the
general color being bluish gray rather than grayish blue, with brownish
rather than blackish primaries and with pale-gray under parts, more
whitish in the anal region. Adults apparently have their postnuptial
molt before the middle of September, as after that date they all seem
to be in fresh plumage.

Food.—The chief food of the pinyon jay, or rather its favorite food,
is the sweet nut of the pinyon pine *(Pinus edulis)*, but it also eats
to some extent the nuts, seeds, or young tender cones of other pines,
particularly the yellow pine *(Pinus scopulorum)*. Other vegetable food
includes various wild fruits, such as the fruits of the red cedar and
the boxelder, various seeds, and some grain; these jays are said to do
considerable damage to grain crops, but probably most of the grain is
picked up as waste grain.

The animal food consists of grasshoppers, beetles, and other insects
and, to some extent, the eggs and young of small birds. J. B. Dixon
tells me that "these birds are relentless in their search through the
desert scrub for other birds' nests and destroy their eggs and young
when found." Other observers do not seem to emphasize this habit.

H. W. Henshaw (1875) says: "A large flock of these birds were
seen near Silver City, N. Mex., October, busily engaged on the ground
feeding upon grass seeds. Those in the rear kept flying up and
alighting in the front rank, the whole flock thus keeping in continual
motion." Near Tularosa, late in November, he saw "a large flock
engaged in catching insects on the wing, and in this novel occupation
they displayed no little dexterity. From the tops of the pine trees, they
ascended to a considerable height, when, hovering for an instant, they
would snap up an insect and return to near the former position, remain for a moment, and again make an essay."

Mr. Cameron (1907) adds: "Like Magpies, however, they are practically omnivorous, and a Piñon Jay has been known to meet its fate in
a wolf trap by which destructive instrument so many of the former
have perished. Like Magpies, too, Piñon Jays come about the ranch
house in the hope of receiving scraps from the table, alighting but two
or three yards from the door, or on the hitching post where the horses
are tied. They are also very fond of insect food, and may be seen
walking about as they turn over dried cattle manure in search of

coleoptera. Mr. Dan Bowman informs me that in his locality (Knowlton) soft corn on the cob has a great attraction for them."

Mr. Braly (1931) saw one of these birds feed its mate while the latter was engaged in incubation: "On coming in with food, a male usually perched on the top of a tree forty or fifty feet distant from the nest and called the female off to be fed. While being fed, she made a screeching series of calls similar to those of a young bird and continually fluttered her wings, and if the male flew to another tree, she followed, begging for more food. Having finished feeding, the male flew back to the feeding ground and the female flew directly to the nest, making it very easy to find. The feeding was closely observed and was solely by regurgitation, an unusual procedure for any of the crow or jay family."

Behavior.—Pinyon jays are among our most highly gregarious birds at all seasons, and, except in their nesting colonies, they are always restless and erratic nomads and almost always noisy, making their presence known as they sweep over the foothills in flocks of hundreds. In many of its movements this bird is more like a crow than a jay; its flight is crowlike, though considerably swifter, and has been likened to that of the robin or Clark's nutcracker; on long flights from one feeding ground to another, it often travels in compact flocks. It spends much time on the ground, where it often feeds in rolling flocks; its gait is a dignified walk or easy run, with its body more or less erect and its head held high, more like that of the starling than like the bouncing hops of the jays. If a flock is disturbed while feeding in the pines, the first one to leave gives a warning cry and the others follow in a leisurely manner, one at a time, until all are on the wing.

John T. Zimmer (1911) writes: "The birds are not particularly wary but are somewhat difficult to approach at times owing to their restless nature which keeps them constantly moving. I have been standing in the line of approach of a flock of Pinion Jays and had them settle all around and within a foot or two of me and not show the least sign of fear when I moved around among them. They would turn and peer at me and were full of curiosity. Even when I shot they would merely rise, wheel around with loud outcries for a moment or so and then settle down and continue their activities as if nothing had happened to disturb them."

Voice.—Mr. Braly (1931) says that "the female has a call given when near her nest, that closely resembles *krook, krook.* The male has a peculiar whistle-like note when one is near a completed nest and a very jay-like note when the female is disturbed from her nest." According to Mr. Cameron (1907), "their presence is always proclaimed by their shrill cry of *wī-ār whăck, wī-ār whăck;* the last note short, but the first two notes long and high pitched like the caterwaul of a cat." Ralph Hoffmann (1927) writes it differently: "Besides the mewing call *queh-a-eh,* given in flight, they utter, when perched, a continual *queh, queh, queh.*" Mr. Zimmer (1911) describes their note as a "high, nasal 'kree-kree-' or 'karee-karee-', repeated rapidly many times in succession or long drawn out." Bendire (1895) says that some of the notes "are almost as harsh as the 'chaar' of the Clarke's Nutcracker, others partake much of the gabble of the Magpie, and still others resemble more those of the jays."

Field marks.—A dull-blue, crowlike bird, with a short tail and a long, slender bill, could hardly be anything else but a pinyon jay, especially if seen flying about, or feeding on the ground, in flocks. The voice is also distinctive, if one is familiar with it; and it is very noisy.

Enemies.—The pinyon jay may be something of a nest robber, but it also has been preyed upon itself occasionally. Mr. Cameron (1907) saw the young disappear at intervals, one after the other, soon after hatching, from a nest that he was watching. They were hatched on June 16, and by July 2 only one fully fledged bird remained in the nest. Being at a loss to account for the disappearance of the young, he sat down to watch, and after a long wait he saw a pair of northern shrikes fly straight to the nest tree. Fortunately for the surviving youngster, the parent jays were at home; they attacked the shrikes and drove them away.

Fall.—As soon as the young are strong on the wing they begin to gather into larger flocks than ever and start on their erratic fall and winter wanderings. These huge flocks, numbering hundreds and sometimes a thousand or more, swoop over the foothills and open country in a rolling mass, the birds in the rear overtaking the leaders and all screaming their loudest. Their movements are not governed by climatic conditions but by the scarcity or abundance of the food supply. Even where pine nuts and cones and cedar berries are abundant, the supply is soon exhausted by the many mouths to be fed, and the flocks move on to seek new fields, with hundreds of eyes on the alert to detect the presence of any available food supply. When there is a scarcity of pinyon nuts, or other normal food, or when they have exhausted the supply, the flocks sweep down on the grainfields and may do considerable damage to late crops of beans, corn, or other cereals. All through the fall and winter, flocks may be seen coming and going, but they may be very abundant during one season and entirely absent from the same region the next season; or they may be there in hundreds one day and all gone the next.

These fall flocks sometimes indulge in interesting flight maneuvers; Henshaw (1875) quotes C. E. Aiken as follows: "At Fort Garland, Colo., in October, 1874, I saw probably a hundred of these birds in a dense, rounded mass, performing evolutions high in the air, which I have never before known them to do; sweeping in wide circles, shooting straight ahead, and wildly diving and whirling about, in precisely the same manner that our common wild pigeons do when pursued by a hawk. This singular performance, with intervals of rest in the piñons behind the fort, was kept up for about two hours, apparently for no other purpose than exercise."

Laurence B. Potter tells me that he had an excellent sight record of a pinyon jay, at short range, at Eastend, Saskatchewan, on September 16, 1910.

Winter.—At least some pinyon jays spend the winter as far north as Montana, where, according to Mr. Cameron (1907), "in midwinter, Piñon Jays seek deep ravines and love to sun themselves either on a bank or in the branches of low cedars which grow there. When thus sheltered these noisy, restless birds will sit motionless for some time without calling to each other. At this season their food seems to consist entirely of cedar berries."

At the other end of the line, in Brewster County, Tex., Van Tyne and Sutton (1937) say that "they are a characteristic species of the region in winter, but are practically never seen in summer." In intermediate regions throughout their range they are locally abundant or scarce according to where they can find their necessary food supply, traveling about in flocks, often considerably beyond the limits of their summer range.

DISTRIBUTION

Range.—Mountainous regions of the Western United States; not regularly migratory.

The range of the pinyon jay extends **north** to central Oregon (Grandview); Montana (probably Missoula, Pompeys Pillars, and Terry); and South Dakota (Rapid City). **East** to western South Dakota (Rapid City and Elk Mountains); Colorado (near Fort Lyon); western Oklahoma (Kenton); eastern New Mexico (Mesa Pajarito and Santa Rosa); and western Texas (Guadalupe Mountains). **South** to southwestern Texas (Guadalupe Mountains); southern New Mexico (San Luis Pass); and northern Baja California (San Pedro Mártir Mountains). **West** to Baja California (San Pedro Mártir Mountains, Vallecitos, and Campo); eastern California (San Bernardino Mountains, Argus Mountains, Inyo Mountains, and White Mountains); western Nevada (Carson); and central Oregon (Bend and Grandview).

Although not a regular migrant, the pinyon jay does considerable wandering, particularly in fall and winter. At such times it has been recorded north to northwestern Montana (Eureka, Fortine, and Columbia Falls); east to eastern Nebraska (Neligh, Norfolk, Lincoln, Harvard, and Red Cloud), eastern Kansas (Lawrence, Baldwin, and Wichita), central Oklahoma (Oklahoma City); and west nearly or quite to the Pacific coast, as California (Los Angeles, Pacific Grove, and Berkeley) and Oregon (Salem and Gaston). It has been recorded in summer without evidence of breeding in south-central Washington (Fort Simcoe); northwestern South Dakota (Short Pine Hills); and northern Nebraska (Holly and Valentine).

Casual records.—A specimen was reported at Eastend, Saskatchewan, on September 16, 1910.

Egg dates.—California: 9 records, April 9 to 21.

Colorado: 13 records, March 23 to May 19.

New Mexico: 34 records, February 16 to June 10; 18 records, March 15 to 28, indicating the height of the season.

Oregon: 4 records, April 10 to 15.

NUCIFRAGA COLUMBIANA (Wilson)

CLARK'S NUTCRACKER

PLATES 47-49

HABITS

Lewis's woodpecker and Clark's nutcracker were named for the two famous explorers who made that historic trip to the sources of the Missouri River, across the Rocky Mountains and down the Columbia River to the Pacific coast, as they were responsible for the discovery of these two unique and interesting birds. Capt. William Clark, who was the first one to mention the nutcracker, referred to it as "a new species of woodpecker"; and Wilson described it as a crow, Clark's crow, *Corvus columbianus*. These impressions are not to be wondered at, for its flight and some of its actions are much like those of woodpeckers, and it resembles the crows in much of its behavior. John T. Zimmer (1911) remarks: "It reminded me of nothing so much as a young Red-headed Woodpecker in that its flight was markedly woodpeckerlike and its grayish body and head and its black wings and tail with white on secondaries gave it, at least superficially, a very close resemblance to the bird mentioned." The first one I saw, while I was crossing the Rocky Mountains in a train, reminded me very much of some large woodpecker bounding across a valley. Its names, both scientific and common, are all well chosen, indicating its feeding habits, its discoverer, and the place of its discovery.

The nutcracker is a mountain bird, ranging from 3,000 feet up to 12,000 or even 13,000 feet, according to latitude and season; its breeding range seems to be mainly between 6,000 and 8,000 feet, or from the lower limit of the coniferous forest up to timber line. It is quite widely distributed in the mountainous regions from southern Alaska and southwestern Alberta to northern Lower California, Arizona, and New Mexico.

Nesting.—Many years elapsed after the discovery of the bird before a nest of Clark's nutcracker was found. This was largely due to the fact that the bird breeds at rather high elevations in the mountains and so early in the season that the ground is covered with deep snow, making traveling very difficult, slow, and limited to small areas. At the time that Major Bendire (1895) wrote his life history of the species he was not aware of the taking of any nests and eggs, except the two taken by Denis Gale in Colorado and those that he took himself near Camp Harney, Oreg., in 1876 and 1878. His account of the finding of his nests is rather interesting:

In March, 1876, I recommenced what looked like an almost fruitless search, in which I had most of the time to tramp through snow from 2 to 4 feet deep; after having examined a great many cavities, mostly in junipers, I was almost ready to give up the task, when I finally examined the pines more closely, and noticed now and then an apparently round ball on the horizontal limbs of some of these trees, which I took to be nests of Fremont's Chickaree, *Sciurus hudsonicus fremonti*, which is very common in this locality. The majority of these supposed squirrels' nests were by no means easily reached, and after trying to dislodge their occupants with sticks, stones, or occasionally with a load of shot, and invariably failing to bring anything to light, I ceased to trouble myself further about them. Being more puzzled than ever, I was about to give up the search for their nests, when, on April 22, after having made more than a dozen fruitless trips, I saw a Clarke's Nutcracker flying quietly and silently out of a large pine about 50 yards ahead of me. This tree had a rather bushy top and was full of limbs almost from the base and was easy to climb. As I could not see readily into the top from below, I climbed the tree. Failing to see any sign of a nest therein, and being completely disgusted, I was preparing to descend when, on looking around, I noticed one of these supposed squirrels' nests placed near the extremity of one of the larger limbs, near the middle of the tree, and 25 feet from the ground; it was well hidden from below, and sitting therein, in plain view from above, I saw not a squirrel, but a veritable Clarke's Nutcracker.

Between April 24 and 30 he found a dozen more nests, all containing young. "In the spring of 1877 I commenced my search for nests on March 15, but failed to see a single bird where I had found them comparatively common during the previous season. Their absence was due in this case to the lack of suitable food. No ripe pine cones were to be found, on the hulled seeds of which the young are at first exclusively fed." The following year, 1878, the birds were back again in their old haunts, and he found his first nest on April 4; it was near the extremity of a small limb of a pine about 40 feet from the ground. "All of the nests found were placed in nearly similar situations, on horizontal limbs of pines, *Pinus ponderosa*, from 15 to 45 feet from the ground, in rather open situations at the outskirts of the heavier forests, and usually on side hills with a southeasterly exposure, at an altitude (estimated) of from 5,000 to 5,500 feet."

He describes an average nest as follows:

The nest proper is placed on a platform of dry twigs, mostly those of the western juniper, *Juniperus occidentalis*, and of the white sage, averaging about three-sixteenth of an inch in thickness, and varying from 8 inches to a foot in length. These twigs, which also help to form the sides of the nest, are deftly matted together and to the smaller twigs of the limb on which the nest is saddled; they are further held together and bound by coarse strips of the inner bark of the juniper tree; these strips are mixed among the twigs and are very suitable for this purpose. The inner nest is a mass of these same bark strips, only much finer, having been well picked into fine fiber; it is quilted together with decayed grasses and pine straw, forming a snug and comfortable structure. No hair or feathers entered into the composition of any of these nests. The outer diameter measures from 11 to 12 inches by about 7 inches in depth; the cup is from 4 to 5 inches wide and 3 inches deep. The quilted inner walls are fully 1½ inches thick; it is quite deep for its size, and the female while incubating is well hidden. Nest building must occasionally begin in the latter part of February, but more frequently in March, and it appears to take these birds some time to complete one of these structures. Both parents assist in this, as well as in incubation, and the male is apparently equally as attentive and helpful as the female. While they are noisy, rollicking birds at all other times, during the season of reproduction they are remarkably silent and secretive, and are rarely seen.

Both of Mr. Gale's Colorado nests were placed in low, scrubby pines, *Pinus ponderosa;* one was only 8 feet from the ground in a tree 20 feet high; and the other was 9 feet up in a 12-foot tree. Several other Colorado nests have been reported by W. C. Bradbury (1917b), who sent H. H. Sheldon to the foothills of the Sangre de Cristo Range, in Saguache County, for two seasons in succession to collect nests and eggs of this species. A number of nests were found, mostly containing young even in March and April. Most of the nests were in pinyon pines at heights ranging from 8 to 16 feet; one was in a juniper at 8 feet and another in a large fir at only 7 feet above ground.

In Mono County, Calif., James B. Dixon (1934) found five occupied nests of Clark's nutcracker on April 9 and 10, 1934; three of these held young and two held eggs. "All of the nests were in juniper trees on steep slopes at the 8000-foot level and contrary to our expectations were located in the coldest spots, where the snow stayed on the ground the longest. It is quite likely that these locations are the freest from the wind which blows so hard at these elevations, and I feel certain the juniper trees are used because of their sturdy build and ability to withstand the wind action. All nest locations seemed to have been selected with protection from the wind in mind, as the nests were either on top of a large limb, or, if supported by a small branch, were surrounded by heavy limbs that gave protection."

J. H. Bowles (1908) found these birds rather plentiful near the west end of Lake Chelan, Wash., "where they seemed to prefer an altitude of a little over 1500 feet. Here on June 13 I located the only nest of the trip, which was disclosed to me by the parent birds carrying food to the young. It was about 150 feet up in a large bull pine, near the top where some disease of the foliage had caused an almost solid cluster four feet in diameter."

J. A. Munro (1919) reports three nests found by him and Maj. Allan Brooks in the Okanagan Valley, British Columbia, on March 9, 1912. "This was in Yellow Pine country; a series of wooded benches overlooking Okanagan Lake." The first two nests were in yellow pines, *Pinus ponderosa,* one 50 feet up and 8 feet out from the trunk, and the other 40 feet above ground; each of these nests held two fresh eggs. The third nest was 25 feet from the ground and 12 feet out from the trunk of a Douglas fir; it contained three partly incubated eggs; one of the birds was seen carrying sheep's wool to the nest.

M. P. Skinner (1916) writes thus of the nesting of the nutcrackers in Wyoming:

About February 1, at Fort Yellowstone, elevation 6300 feet above sea level, the birds are mated and the building of the nest begins, each bird of the pair doing its share. The thick top of a cedar, or other evergreen is selected, with a convenient crotch about twelve feet from the ground. First a rough platform of twigs is built. These twigs are broken from a cedar (western juniper) by a quick, wrenching jerk assisted by the cutting edges of the bill, and carried to the site. Here the material is piled in the crotch till the mass reaches a ball about nine inches in diameter and six inches high. The nest proper is deep and cup shaped, about six inches in diameter, and has walls an inch thick; it is built of cedar or pine needles and the inner lining of grass stems and shredded juniper bark, each strand turned into place by the bird squatting down on it and twisting in it. A few horse hairs and bits of strings are usually included in the lining.

Eggs.—Clark's nutcracker lays, apparently usually, two or three eggs, but often four and occasionally as many as five or even six. They vary in shape from ovate to elliptical-ovate and are only slightly glossy. The ground color is a pale shade of "lichen green," pale grayish green, or very pale, clear green, almost greenish white. They are usually thinly, evenly, and rather sparingly spotted with minute dots, small spots or flecks of pale browns, or shades of olive, gray, or drab. Sometimes the spots are more concentrated about the larger end, and sometimes the smaller end is almost unmarked.

The measurements of 50 eggs average 32.4 by 23.4 millimeters; the eggs showing the four extremes measure **35.0** by 23.4, 34.5 by **25.2, 29.2** by 23.2, and 33.5 by **21.6** millimeters.

Young.—Both sexes assist in the duties of incubation and care of the young. Bendire (1895) gives the period of incubation, "as nearly as I can judge, about sixteen or seventeen days." This agrees closely with the reported period for the European bird, 17 to 18 days. But M. P. Skinner (1916) says that in Yellowstone Park the eggs "are laid between February 28 and March 3, and the brooding commences immediately. At such a time the brooding bird is subjected to all the vagaries of truly wintry weather." "Often," he says, "she sits through raging snowstorms protected only by the tuft of cedar needles over the nest, and many times has the writer seen the bird actually on the nest with the thermometer below zero. Under such conditions she draws herself down with only her tail feathers and perhaps her bill showing above the rim of the nest. She is very fearless, even submitting to capture rather than leave the nest; when she leaves, she does so quietly, and returns immediately after the intruder is gone. After brooding twenty-two days the young are hatched, naked of course, and with their eyes closed. Four weeks later the young leave the nest and by May 5 are fully feathered and shifting for themselves. Notwithstanding this early start there is no evidence to show that a second brood is raised."

The longer period of incubation and the longer altricial period, as given by Mr. Skinner above, was probably exceptional or due to too much exposure to wintry weather. For Major Bendire (1895) says that the young remain in the nest only about eighteen days; and Mr. Bradbury (1917b) showed the altricial period to be about three weeks.

Mrs. Wheelock (1904) says that the young "were fed on piñon nuts, which were carried to the nest and hulled by the adult while perched just outside on the branch. I could not discover that any other food was brought them. At first this was given by regurgitation, but when the young were a few days old the food was supplied to them direct. As soon as they were ready to leave the nest they were coaxed by short flights to the nut pines, and readily learned to shell the nuts and provide for themselves. Then it would seem a complete change of diet was necessary; for they disappeared from these regions entirely, flocking to a locality where berries, fish, and insects abound. By the middle of June not one was left in the old breeding grounds."

Apparently the young are also fed by regurgitation *after* they have left the nest, for Taylor and Shaw (1927) write: "The nutcracker population becomes most conspicuous when the young have left the nest. The husky youngsters appear quite as large as their parents, and their squawking calls fill the air. They follow the adults with a persistence truly wonderful, awakening the echoes with their stentorian teasing. Presently the parent plunges its bill into the open mouth of the young one, and there ensues what appears to be a struggle for life or death. There is of course no occasion for concern, for this, in nutcracker society, is the orthodox method of feeding the young. The process of regurgitation complete, the participants seem to feel better all around. The respite must seem all too brief to the parent, however, for in a short time the young bird is apparently as hungry and as noisy as ever."

Mr. Dixon (1934) says that "in the event one of the parents left the nest from any cause, the other bird of the pair would immediately assume brooding duties. * * * Actual time records taken on the afternoon of the 9th of April, which was a warm sunshiny afternoon, revealed a change of brooding and feeding duties every thirty minutes on the average."

Plumages.—The young are hatched naked and with eyes closed, but, when perhaps a week or so old, they are partly covered with down (Bradbury, 1917b), the color not mentioned. The juvenal plumage is acquired before the young bird leaves the nest. Charles F. Batchelder (1884) gives the first full description of the juvenal plumage of Clark's nutcracker in more minute detail than seems necessary here. In a general way, the color pattern is much like that of the adult, but the gray portions are browner and the blacks duller. The upper parts are dull brownish gray, darkest on the rump and scapulars. The white eye ring, superciliary stripe, and the other white about the face of the adult are lacking. The general coloring of the under parts is brownish ash, darkest on the breast, most of the feathers tipped with whitish, giving an indistinct barred effect. The wings are much like those of the adult, but the white in the secondaries is more extensive, some of the primaries have a small ashy spot at the tip, the lesser wing coverts are dusky grayish brown, and the other coverts are indistinctly tipped with the same. The tail is like that of the adult, but the black in the white rectrices is more extensive. The black in both wings and tail is duller than in the adult, and the bill and feet are grayer. I have not seen the postjuvenal molt, but I have seen adults molting in July, August, and September.

Food.—Like other members of the crow family, the nutcracker is largely omnivorous, though it seems to show a decided preference for the sweet nuts of the pinyon pine *(Pinus edulis)*, eating the shells as well as the kernels. Grinnell and Storer (1924) report that a female shot on September 22 "held in its throat 72 ripe seeds of the piñon, comprising a volume of about one cubic inch." Another female taken September 25 "held in her distended throat 65 mature seeds of the white-bark pine, and some fragments, all together weighing 10 grams or close to 7 per cent of the weight of the bird, which was 146 grams." It eats the seeds of several other species of pines and even firs, extracting the seeds from the cones with its crowbarlike beak. Acorns and the berries of the cedar or juniper are included in the diet. Mr. Skinner (1916) says: "Sometimes they will tear the cone to pieces even while the cone is still fast to the branch, often perched at the very tip of a bending branch, or even underneath, clinging in a manner creditable to a chickadee or a nuthatch. More often the cone is detached and carried away to a strong limb where it is held by one foot while the bird strikes strong, downward blows at it with its pickaxlike bill. At times the bird will secure a seed at every second stroke and at the same time tear the cone to shreds."

J. A. Munro tells me that Clark's nutcrackers were noted commonly in a valley in British Columbia on May 17 and 19, 1940. "In one place a flock of twenty-five (plus) rose from a field in which spring wheat was just appearing. It seemed likely they were feeding on the sprouted grain."

Mr. Bradbury (1917b) reports that "the stomachs of the old birds examined always contained masses of pinyon shells, this far exceeding in bulk the mixture of insects and meat of pinyon nuts, about 75 per cent nut food and 25 per cent insects and other matter." One nutcracker was seen feeding on the remains of a deer.

Claude T. Barnes (MS.) thus describes the feeding habits of Clark's nutcracker, as observed at an altitude of 7,050 feet in the Wasatch Mountains of Utah: "Near me an ancient, gnarled limber pine (*Pinus flexilis*) stood on a wind-exposed knoll, raising a broad, open crown on a brown-plated trunk 2 feet in thickness. The ground beneath it was strewn with subcylindrical cones, 5 inches long and 3 inches in diameter at the base. One of the nutcrackers flew to the tree above me, alighting on the outer tip of an upper branch, where a cone was suspended. Standing above the cone and working almost upside down, it pecked with its strong, cylindrical bill at the base of the cone, clinging the while to the branch with its large toes and sharp, much curved claws. Pecking eagerly every two or three seconds, it at times almost tilted over head first, but without releasing the toe holds, fluttered back to balance. Finally, after about 40 pecks and probes at the pencil-thick stalk of the cone, the cone began to fall; whereupon it clasped the cone with its bill and flew to a thick horizontal limb below.

There it took its time in prying out the quarter-inch seeds, two beneath each scale, and swallowed them with apparent satisfaction. * * * Another bird alighted on a small tree and, as I stood only ten feet away, probed out all the seeds of a cone without severing its stalk and without minding my presence."

The nutcracker shares with the jays of the *Perisoreus* group the name of "meat bird" or "camp robber," for, especially in winter when other food is scarce, it comes freely to the camps to pick up whatever scraps of food it can find, and almost anything edible is welcome; at such times it becomes quite bold, frequenting the open-air kitchen and even occasionally entering the tent or cabin. It invades the vicinity of farms and houses, looking for kitchen hand-outs or picking up crumbs of bread or waste grain in the streets. Larger scraps of food are often carried away to be eaten at leisure or hidden for future use.

It sometimes indulges in the bad habit, common to most of the Corvidae, of robbing the nests of the smaller birds and devouring their eggs or small nestlings. J. A. Munro (1919) says that "several nests of Hermit Thrushes, Horned Larks and Pipits, that were under observation, above timber line on Apex Mountain, were destroyed by a pair of Clark's Nutcrackers." And several others have referred to this same habit.

Insects enter largely into the food of this bird during summer and before the pinyon nuts are ripe. Some time is spent on the ground hunting for beetles, ants, grasshoppers, and the destructive black crickets. Some insects are caught on the wing in true flycatcher fashion; from a perch in the dead top of a tree the nutcracker watches for passing insects, darts out and chases them in an erratic course, and returns to its perch. Mrs. Bailey (1928) says that "two were seen near camp on a log, running back and forth chasing sphynx moths that were feeding from the larkspurs bordering the log."

Mrs. Wheelock (1904) writes: "Grasshoppers and the big wingless black crickets he devours in untold numbers, and grows fat on the diet. Butterflies he catches on the wing in flycatcher fashion; grubs he picks from the bark, clinging to the side of the tree trunks and hammering like a woodpecker."

Decker and Bowles (1931) observed the feeding habits of a large flock of over a hundred nutcrackers in the Blue Mountains of Washington:

A good deal of feeding was evidently done high up in the trees, where they spent most of their time, but on frequent occasions the whole flock would come down and feed on the ground. * * * Their food when on the ground consisted principally of the large black ants, beetles and snails. The ants being in enormous numbers were eaten by the thousand, and it was very noticeable to see how careful the birds were to make sure of thoroughly killing them before eating. Every ant was beaten to a pulp before it was swallowed, so there was no chance that the powerful forceps of the insect might injure the throat or stomach of the bird. The beetles received considerably less punishment, but the body of the snails were carefully picked out of the shell before swallowing. We threw them some of our own food, but they did not seem to care especially for it, presumably because they had such an abundance of natural food. The number of black ants these birds eat must be far beyond calculation, as not one of these insects could be found for some time after the birds flew up into the timber.

Victor H. Cahalane (1944) tells an interesting story of a nutcracker's ability to locate food under 8 inches of snow; he flushed one from the ground under a Douglas fir, and found that the bird "had dug a hole three or four inches in diameter at the top, at an angle of perhaps 30 degrees, through the hard-packed snow to the sloping ground. At the bottom of the excavation, frozen to the ground litter, was a Douglas fir cone." The snow was so deep that there was no indication on the surface of the presence of the cone; the bird had done no exploratory digging, but had dug the hole with remarkable accuracy in exactly the right spot.

Behavior.—I always liked the old generic name *Picicorvus,* as it seemed particularly appropriate for a bird that so much resembles the woodpeckers and the crows in behavior and appearance. My first impression of it was that of a large woodpecker, and others, including its discoverer, got the same impression. Its flight, as I remember it, is undulating like that of a woodpecker; and most observers seem to have seen it that way. Dr. Coues (1874), however, says that "the ordinary flight is rapid, straight, and steady, accomplished by regular and vigorous wing-beats; but when flying only from tree to tree, the birds swing themselves in an undulatory course, with the wings alternately spread and nearly closed, much in the manner of the Woodpeckers."

They sometimes soar high in the air like hawks, with wings and tails widely spread, or from some dizzy height make a spectacular dive earthward. Mrs. Wheelock (1904) writes:

It is on the crests of the Sierra Nevada that these birds are found most abundantly. Here they sun themselves on the highest peaks, frolicking noisily in the clear, bracing air. When hungry or thirsty, they dart from their lofty perches and, with wings folded, hurl themselves down the cañon with the speed of a bullet. Just as you are sure they will be dashed to pieces, their wings open with an explosive noise and the headlong fall is checked in a moment. Sometimes the descent is finished as lightly as the fall of a bit of thistle down; sometimes by another series of swift flights; often by one rocket-like plunge. At the foot a mountain brook furnishes food and drink. As the shadows creep up the sides of the cañon, the Nutcrackers follow the receding sunlight to the summit again, mounting by very short flights from tree to tree, in the same way that a jay climbs to the top of a tree by hopping from one branch to another.

Nutcrackers also show their relationship to the jays by their noisy, boisterous habits, their inquisitive curiosity, and their behavior on the ground, where they hop rather awkwardly about foraging for fallen nuts and insects. Their straight forward flight, at times, is also much like that of our blue jay; and their thieving propensities are in keeping with those of the whole corvine tribe. Mr. Munro (1919) says: "Like all corvine birds, they are exceedingly curious and a passing deer or coyote will attract their attention so that the position of game can often be located by their excited cries. They come readily to an imitation of the call of the Pygmy Owl or the Horned Owl and will investigate the caller at close range."

Referring to their methods of securing pine cones, Mr. Skinner (1916) writes: "Being bold, independent free-lances these birds will vary their methods by robbing a pine squirrel of his cone; even going so far as to knock the squirrel from his limb with one blow from their bills at the end of a long, swift swoop. The pine squirrel knows this, too; and it is delicious to see the squirrel, whose own abilities as a robber are not small, glide into some protection and hurl vituperation at his enemies. Nor are the nutcrackers at all backward at 'sassing' back. Many a time the somber, evergreen forests are enlivened by such a squawking match, joined in by all the squirrels and nutcrackers in hearing."

J. Stuart Rowley (1939) says: "Near Virginia Creek on July 4, 1939, I tapped a dead pine stub and was surprised to see several nearly fledged young chickadees 'explode' in my face and fly uncertainly down a ravine. Immediately, two nutcrackers swooped down, concentrating their attack on one individual. One nutcracker seized the fledgling, whereupon it flew to a pine and proceeded to pick off feathers from the tail and wings of the chickadee before tearing it to bits and devouring it."

Voice.—Not much can be said in favor of the voice of Clark's nutcracker. It is generally conceded to be harsh, grating, and unpleasant, especially when heard in volume, as it often is, and when not softened by distance. It is a noisy bird, except when near its nest. Its ordinary guttural, squawking call is variously written as *chaar, char-r-r, chur-r-r, kra-a-a,* or *kar-r-r-r-ack,* each note repeated two or three times.

Mr. Dawson (1923) adds the following variations: "But the Nutcracker's repertory is not exhausted by a single cry. For years I was puzzled by sporadic eruptions of a strange, feline cry, *meack,* or *mearrk,* a piercing and rather frightful sound. The Clark Nutcracker proved at last to be responsible, and he was only at play! The very next morning after the mountain lion scare, we had the versatile birds as musicians. Two of them got out their little toy trumpets, pitched about a fifth apart, and proceeded to give us the Sierran reveille,

      hee hee   hee,   hee hee,
hoo   hoo   hoo hoo   [etc.]. The notes were really quite musical, and the comparison established of children's tin trumpets was irresistible. The effect produced by the two birds sounding in different keys was both pleasant and amusing. * * * The concert lasted for two or three minutes."

Decker and Bowles (1931) say that their incessant cries were heard "during the entire time that they were up in the trees. They would commence a little after daylight and we have never heard such a racket from any other members of the animal kingdom. Besides innumerable calls that must have belonged peculiarly to themselves they also included every known call of the Magpie and the Crow that is uttered by either the young or the old birds of those species. This last may be because both adult and young of the year were present and all screaming at the top of their lungs, making a din that at times grew extremely tiresome and, indeed, almost unbearable. Oddly enough, when on or near the ground they are absolutely silent."

Field marks.—The nutcracker is a fairly large bird, between a small crow and a large woodpecker in size. It has a long, sharp, black bill; its head and body are pale gray; its wings are black, with a large white patch on the secondaries; and its tail is centrally black but largely white laterally. Its behavior and its voice are distinctive, as explained above.

Winter.—"Although the Clark Nutcracker is a characteristic resident of the Hudsonian Zone, it strays both above and below this belt. In summer, after the broods of the year are fledged, some of the birds move down the mountains. * * * And at the same season they sometimes wander up over the rock-strewn ridge crests well above timber line. Some of the nutcrackers which stray to the lower altitudes remain there at least until early winter. * * * But most of the birds remain at the normal high altitudes through the winter months" (Grinnell and Storer, 1924).

In addition to these altitudinal movements the nutcrackers do considerable erratic wandering in winter, appearing unexpectedly at irregular intervals in various small cities and towns, even near the coast, notably in Monterey and Alameda Counties, Calif., where they become familiar dooryard visitors.

Joseph Mailliard (1920) writes of their winter behavior at Carmel, Calif: "The Nutcrackers had discovered that kitchen doors and back yards were good for some free 'hand-outs', and they systematically visited many such. While they fed to some extent on the Monterey pines, apparently more intent upon the tips of young buds than upon the contents of the cones, they picked also a good many scraps and bits of grain or crumbs in the streets, paying no attention to people twenty or thirty feet away, but becoming wary of closer approach. They seemed to have certain hours for being in certain places, and for the first few days of my stay appeared in the street opposite the dining room window while we were at breakfast."

DISTRIBUTION

Range.—Western United States and Canada, and Alaska; casual east to Lake Michigan and the Mississippi Valley; not regularly migratory.

The normal range of Clark's nutcracker extends **north** to central British Columbia (Fort St. James and Moose Pass); Alberta (Jasper House, Banff, and Porcupine Hills); Montana (Glacier National Park, Statesville, and Billings); and northwestern South Dakota (Short Pine Hills). **East** to western South Dakota (Short Pine Hills and Elk Mountains); southeastern Wyoming (Laramie Peak); Colorado (Estes Park, Cheyenne Mountain, and Blanco Peak); and New Mexico (Santa Fe Canyon, Diamond Peak, and San Luis Pass). **South** to southern New Mexico (San Luis Pass); Arizona (Mount Graham and Santa Catalina Mountains); and northern Baja California (San Pedro Mártir Mountains). **West** to Baja California (San Pedro Mártir Mountains and La Grulla); eastern California (Bear Valley, Florence Lake, Yosemite Valley, and Butte Lake); Oregon (Pinehurst and Crater Lake); Washington (Bumping Lake and Lake Chelan); and British Columbia (Alta Lake, Lillooet, and Fort St. James).

Casual records.—Although not a regular migrant, the nutcracker is given to erratic wanderings that sometimes take it considerable distance from its normal range. In Alaska it has been recorded on the southeast coast at Sitka and north to the Kowak River. Other Alaskan records are: Nushagak, November 5, 1885; Takotna, October 1, 1919; Farewell Mountain, September, 1921; Chatanika River, September 1922; and McCarthy, November, 1922. According to Taverner, it also has been collected at Robinson, Yukon. On the coast of British Columbia it has been recorded from Comox, February 18, 1904, and wintering on Graham Island in 1919-20. During the period from October 1919 to April 1920 it appeared in considerable numbers on the coast of southern California as at Pacific Grove, Carmel, and Santa Cruz Island, while one was killed near Hayward on February 16, 1923. One was taken at Coachella, Calif., 44 feet below sea level on September 24, 1935.

There are several records for the Great Plains region east to Manitoba, Margaret, October 1910; Iowa, Boone, September 23, 1894; Wisconsin, Milwaukee, fall of 1875; Illinois, Gross Point, October 9, 1894; Missouri, near Kansas City, about October 28, 1894, and Louisiana, October 12, 1907; and Arkansas, Earl, April 1, 1891.

Egg dates.—British Columbia: 11 records, March 9 to May 25.

California: 32 records, March 7 to April 21; 16 records, March 24 to April 13.

Colorado: 8 records, March 5 to April 16.

Utah: 6 records, March 23 to April 25.

Family PARIDAE: Titmice, Verdins, and Bushtits

PARUS ATRICAPILLUS ATRICAPILLUS Linnaeus

BLACK-CAPPED CHICKADEE

PLATES 50, 51

CONTRIBUTED BY WINSOR MARRETT TYLER

HABITS

The titmice, the family of birds to which the black-capped chickadee belongs, are widely distributed in the two hemispheres and in North America are represented by numerous genera, species, and races from the Atlantic Ocean to the Pacific. Over this vast area, in England, on the continent of Europe, and with us they are well known and very popular birds.

For our black-capped chickadee of the Northeastern United States our regard goes far beyond popularity. The chickadee is perhaps the best-known bird in its range and appears so trustful of man that we look on it with real affection. And no wonder—for chickadees are such cheerful little birds. When we watch a flock of them in winter they remind us of a group of happy, innocent little children playing in the snow. Thinking back to the early days of New England's history, we can imagine that the Pilgrim Fathers, when the chickadees came about the settlement at Plymouth in 1620, watched them as we do now. They were, perhaps, the first friends to welcome the travelers to the New World.

Many writers praise the chickadee. Bradford Torrey (1889) says enthusiastically: "It would be a breach of good manners, an inexcusable ingratitude, to write ever so briefly of the New England winter without noting this [the chickadee], the most engaging and characteristic enlivener of our winter woods; who revels in snow and ice, and is never lacking in abundant measures of faith and cheerfulness, enough not only for himself, but for any chance wayfarer of our own kind." Elsewhere, Torrey (1885) calls the chickadee "the bird of the merry heart."

Spring.—The black-capped chickadee is migratory to some extent, but, as in the case of some other permanent residents, it is often difficult, except at favorable observation points, to determine the time and extent of its northward and southward movements. Taverner and Swales (1908) state: "Our experience with the species at Detroit leads us to believe that it is more migrational than is generally supposed. They are common through the winter, but about the first of April the great bulk of them depart, leaving but a few scattered summer residents behind."

J. Van Tyne (1928) gives a vivid description of a definite migration. He says:

On May 20, 1928, while collecting at the tip of Sand Point (seven miles southwest of Caseville, Michigan), I witnessed a most interesting migration flight of Chickadees *(Penthestes atricapillus)*. Sand Point juts out nearly four miles into Saginaw Bay from the southeast, and apparently forms an important point of departure for many species of birds migrating northward across the bay. The day was clear with but little wind. At 9:30 in the morning I noticed a compact flock of over fifty chickadees flitting rapidly through the brushy growth toward the end of the point. Their strange appearance immediately attracted my attention. They seemed very nervous and tense, with necks outstretched and feathers closely compressed against the body. They made no attempt to feed, but kept moving steadily toward the end of the point. Reaching the last tree, a twelve-foot sapling, the first birds flitted upward to the topmost twigs and there hesitated, lacking the courage to launch forth. But the rest of the flock, following close behind, in a few moments began to crowd upon them. Fairly pushed off the tree-top, the leaders finally launched forth, the rest following in rapid succession. They started upward at an angle of fully forty-five degrees. After climbing perhaps a hundred feet the leaders lost their courage, and, hesitating a moment, they all dropped precipitately back to the shelter of the bushes. But once there they immediately headed for the sapling again and repeated the performance. Finally, after several false starts, they continued out over the lake toward the Charity Islands in the distance.

It was a new experience to me to see chickadees fly by day out across miles of open water.

Courtship.—The chickadee has apparently developed no ritual of courtship other than the pursuit of the female by the male—a common performance of many of the smaller birds. Chickadees are so common and so continually under our observation at close range that if they practiced any marked trait when pairing off, it would certainly have been noticed and described.

Dr. Samuel S. Dickey (MS.) says of the mating of the chickadee: "From what I am able to learn of this process, the birds grow agitated late in March and increase their vivacity during April and early in May. They hurry between aisles of trees and swerve over bypaths, and males dart at and even clasp one another. Then they part, and the more dominant male pursues and chases a female over brush piles and even to the ground. Then up they arise and hurry onward. A few such days of immoderate activity, and their nuptial rites seem completed."

Nesting.—The commonest nesting site of the chickadee is a hole, made by the birds themselves, in a dead stub or branch of a gray birch. From such a tree the decayed wood can easily be removed in dry chips to form a cavity, and the ring of strong bark holds the branch firmly together.

Arthur C. Bent (MS.) says that in Bristol County, Mass., three-quarters of the nests he has found have been in such a location, 4 to 8 feet from the ground. He continues: "Other nests have been in natural cavities in apple trees in orchards, or in other deciduous trees. I believe that chickadees almost always, at least partially, excavate their own nest cavities; I have seen them doing it; they cut through the outer bark of birch stubs with their strong little bills and easily remove the rotten wood from the interior."

Edward H. Forbush (1912) states:

A hole in a decayed birch stump, two or three feet from the ground, a knot-hole in an old apple tree, in a fence-post, or in an elm, forty or fifty feet from the ground, the old deserted home of some Woodpecker, a small milk-can nailed up in a tree, or a nesting-box at some farmhouse window, may be selected by the Chickadee for its home. Commonly it digs out a nest-hole in the decaying stump of a birch or pine. It is unable to penetrate sound wood, as I have seen it repeatedly try to enlarge a small hole in a white pine nesting-box, but it could not start a chip. Often the Chickadee gains an entrance through the hard outer coating of a post or stump into the decaying interior by choosing, as a vantage point, a hole made by some woodpecker in search of a grub. The Chickadee works industriously to deepen and enlarge this cavity, sometimes making a hole nine or more inches deep; and the little bird is wise enough to carry the tell-tale chips away and scatter them far and wide—something the Woodpeckers are less careful about

Sometimes the hole is excavated in the broken top of a leaning stump or tree, and once I found one in the top of an erect white pine stump with no shelter from the storm.

If we come upon a pair of chickadees at work excavating a cavity, we can step up very close to them and watch without interrupting them at all. Both members of the pair work at the same time but visit the nest alternately. Each one digs out a beakful of chips and flies away with it, and no sooner is one gone than the other is back at the nest, excavating. Back and forth they go, working quickly and, except for their faint lisping notes, silently. Mr. Bent (MS.) describes a pair at work. He says: "Both birds took turns at the work, digging out the rotten wood, bringing out a billful each time and scattering it from the nearby trees. Sometimes both birds would be *at* the hole together; one would watch while the other worked, but would not enter until its mate had come out; they were never both *in* the hole at the same time."

Bradford Torrey (1885) comments on such a scene, "the pretty labors of my little architect," thus: "Their demeanor toward each other all this time was beautiful to see; no effusive display of affection, but every appearance of a perfect mutual understanding and contentment. And their treatment of me was no less appropriate and delightful,—a happy combination of freedom and dignified reserve."

The nest proper is placed in the bottom of the cavity and, according to the testimony of Craig S. Thoms (1927) and Dr. Samuel S. Dickey (MS.), is made entirely by the female. The materials of the nest, as listed by Edward H. Forbush (1912) consist "of such warm materials as cottony vegetable fibers, hairs, wool, mosses, feathers and insect cocoons. Every furry denizen of the woods, and some domestic animals, may sometimes contribute hair or fur to the Chickadee's nest."

Aretas A. Saunders (MS.) states that chickadees sometimes add the wool of cinnamon fern to their nest, "the same material commonly used by the ruby-throated hummingbird."

Ora W. Knight (1908) says: "From a week to ten days is required to excavate the hole and three or four additional days to gather together [the materials] * * * which make up the nest proper." He describes a typical nest found at Orono, Maine: "This nest was placed in a cavity eight and a half inches deep near the top of a rotten white birch stub, six and two-thirds feet from the ground. The diameter of the entrance was two and a quarter inches. The nest proper measured two inches in diameter by one inch deep inside."

Eggs.—[AUTHOR'S NOTE: Anywhere from 5 to 10 eggs may be found in the chickadee's nest, but 6 to 8 are the commonest numbers, and as many as 13 have been recorded. These vary from ovate to rounded-ovate, with a tendency toward the latter shape. They have little or no gloss. The ground color is white, and they are more or less evenly marked with small spots or fine dots of light or dark reddish brown; usually these markings are well distributed, but sometimes the larger spots are concentrated about the larger end. The measurements of 50 eggs average 15.2 by 12.2 millimeters; the eggs showing the four extremes measure **16.3** by 12.2, 15.2 by **12.8**, **14.0** by 12.2, and 15.2 by **11.2** millimeters.]

Young.—Dr. Samuel S. Dickey (MS.) writes: "Before the set of eggs is complete, or when they are fresh, the parent, as is the habit of our wild ducks, covers the eggs with the lining of the nest, thus rendering them comparatively safe. I have found that it requires on an average 12 days for the eggs to hatch. When the nestlings are about three days old they agitate their heads, wing stumps, and legs and open their beaks and squeak feebly in anticipation of food. They remain in the nest for approximately 16 days. At this age the nestlings, about to be fledglings, look almost like their parents, but a shagginess or somewhat ill-kempt aspect serves to distinguish them. They are without doubt among the handsomest young birds of our mountain forests." He adds that the male feeds the female during incubation and that both parents feed the young.

Dr. Wilbur K. Butts (1931), in a study made in the State of New York of the dispersal of young banded chickadees, found that as a rule the birds wandered only a short distance, a mile or two, from the nest during the first few months of their lives.

George J. Wallace (1941) concluded, from his study of color-banded chickadees at Lenox, Mass., "that young chickadees, though obviously in company with their parents in late summer, tend to wander away from the more sedentary adults in the fall," and that "the Sanctuary flocks were not made up of family groups in winter."

Plumages.—[AUTHOR'S NOTE: The "pale mouse gray" natal down of the young chickadee is soon replaced by the juvenal plumage, or rather pushed out on the tips of these feathers, and wears away. The juvenal contour plumage closely resembles the spring plumage of the adult, but it is softer, looser, and fluffier; the black of the crown, chin, and throat is much duller; the sides of the head below the eyes are pure white; and the under parts are dull white, washed on the sides and crissum with pale pinkish buff.

About midsummer a partial postjuvenal molt takes place, involving the contour plumage and the wing coverts, but not the rest of the wings or the tail. This produces a first winter plumage, which is practically indistinguishable from the fall plumage of the adult.

Adults have one complete postnuptial molt in July and August, which produces a winter plumage that is more richly colored than the worn and faded plumage seen during spring and summer; the gray of the back and rump is more decidedly buffy; the sides and flanks are deep brownish buff in strong contrast with the white of the abdomen; and the whitish edgings of the larger wing coverts, secondaries, and outer tail feathers are broader.

Wear and fading produces a paler plumage in spring, the buffy tints becoming paler or largely disappearing and some of the white edgings in the wings and tail wearing away.]

Food.—Clarence M. Weed (1898), after a careful investigation of the winter food of the chickadee, states: "The results as a whole show that more than half of the food of the chickadee during the winter months consists of insects, a very large proportion of these being taken in the form of eggs. About five per cent. of the stomach contents consisted of spiders or their eggs. Vegetation of various sorts made up a little less than a quarter of the food, two-thirds of which, however, consisted of buds and bud scales that were believed to have been accidentally introduced along with plant-lice eggs." In his conclusion he says: "The investigations * * * show that the chickadee is one of the best of the farmer's friends, working throughout the winter to subdue the insect enemies of the farm, orchard, and garden."

W. L. McAtee (1926), writing of the chickadee's food throughout the year, says:

About three-tenths of the food of the Chickadee is vegetable, and seven-tenths animal. Mast and wild fruits supply the bulk of the vegetable food. The mast is derived chiefly from coniferous trees, and the favorite wild fruits are the wax-covered berries of bayberry and poison ivy. A good many blueberries also are eaten, but only limited numbers of other wild fruits and seeds.

The important things in the animal food of the Chickadees, in order, are caterpillars and eggs of lepidoptera, spiders, beetles, true bugs of various kinds, and ants, sawflies, and other hymenoptera. The Chickadee certainly consumes a great many spiders (which are moderately useful), but the occurrence seems inseparably connected with the bird's mode of feeding, ever prying as it does, under bark scales and into all sorts of crannies which are the favorite hiding places of spiders. It is just these methods, however, that enables the Chickadee to find so many of the eggs of injurious lepidoptera and plant lice, and scale insects and other minute pests, the consumption of which is so praiseworthy. The good the bird does in consuming these tiny terrors is so great that we must regard as far outweighed, the harm done in feeding upon spiders and parasitic hymenoptera. * * *

Codling moths and their larvae and pupae, the larvae, chrysalids, and adults of the gypsy and browntail moths, birch, willow, and apple plant lice, and pear psylla, and various scale insects are eaten by the Chickadee. Among these scales are one affecting dogwood *(Lecanium corni),* the black-banded scale *(Eulecanium nigrofasciatum)* which is quite injurious to maples, the scurfy elm scale *(Chionaspis americana),* and the oyster scale *(Lepidosaphes ulmi),* which attacks many trees and has been known to kill ashes and poplars in New York.

Among other forest pests attacked by our friend the Chickadee are the flat-headed and round-headed wood borers, leaf beetles, the white pine weevil, nut weevils, bark beetles, tree hoppers, spittle insects, cicadas, leaf hoppers, and sawflies. Other food items of the bird include a variety of beetles, bugs, flies, and grasshoppers, and a few stone flies, dragon flies, daddy-long-legs, millipeds, snails, and small amphibians.

Dr. Dickey (MS.) writes to Mr. Bent: "I have noticed that chickadees like to draw near hunters' cabins at all times of the year, but particularly during the hunting seasons. They arrive within a stone's throw of the shelters, and will inspect and peck at animal hides, fatty substances thrown out from the table, or even entrails of animal carcasses."

Lewis O. Shelley (1926) writes of a curious and evidently unusual habit that he noticed on a warm day in February. He says: "Flying from the piazza, a Chickadee lit in front of a hive. When a bee came out it snapped it up, flew into an elm, and, holding the bee in its foot, picked it to pieces and ate it. I was alarmed for fear the Chickadee would be stung, but it seemed not, for the act was performed again. Neither was it always the same bird that flew down and got a bee, but many different ones."

J. Kenneth Terres (1940) reports seeing a chickadee eating tiny tent caterpillars, too small to be detected in a stomach contents. He says: "On the morning of April 23, 1938, I again observed at close range the destruction of these caterpillars, this time by a Black-capped Chickadee, *Penthestes atricapillus atricapillus,* in a brush-grown field in Broome County, near Nanticoke, New York. When first seen, the chickadee was busily engaged in visiting a number of the newly started nests of the American tent caterpillar located in a nearby wild-apple tree, *Malus pumila.* Using an eight-power binocular at twenty feet, I observed the chickadee closely while it visited three caterpillar nests in succession. It would first tear open the web, then pick up the small worms (on this date about three-eighths of an inch long and a sixteenth of an inch in diameter) and devour them rapidly."

Behavior.—When chickadees visit our feeding shelves what impresses us most is their quickness. They flit in rather slowly to be sure, for so small a bird, and land on the shelf with a thud, often upright, grasping the edge with their strong little claws and then jerking about with such rapidity that the eye can scarcely take in their flashlike movements. When alarmed they disappear as if by magic—we see only the place where they were—an ability that must save them many times from the strike of a bird of prey.

Another chickadee propensity is the assumption of odd attitudes; they often alight up-side-down on the under side of a branch, making, it seems, almost a back somersault as they reach upward to grasp it; and they can hang, back to the ground, steady and secure, from the tip of a swaying branch. Edward H. Forbush (1907) describes thus some of the chickadee's acrobatic tricks:

I once saw a Chickadee attempting to hold a monster caterpillar, which proved too strong for it. The great worm writhed out of the confining grasp and fell to the ground, but the little bird followed, caught it, whipped it over a twig, and swinging underneath, caught each end of the caterpillar with a foot, and so held it fast over the twig by superior weight, and proceeded, while hanging back downward, to dissect its prey. This is one of the most skillful acrobatic feats that a bird can perform—although I have seen a Chickadee drop over backward from a branch, in pursuit of an insect, catch it, and, turning an almost complete somersault in the air, strike right side up again on the leaning trunk of the tree. Indeed, the complete somersault is an every-day accomplishment of this gifted little fowl, and it often swings completely round a branch, like a human acrobat taking the "giant swing." Although the Chickadee ordinarily is no flycatcher, it can easily follow and catch in the air any insect that drops from its clutch.

William Leon Dawson (Dawson and Bowles, 1909), writing of the Oregon chickadee, a subspecies of the black-capped, gives this lively account of its activities: "Chickadee refuses to look down for long upon the world; or, indeed, to look at any one thing from any direction for more than two consecutive twelfths of a second. 'Any old side up without care,' is the label he bears; and so with anything he meets, be it a pine-cone, an alder catkin, or a bug-bearing branchlet, topside, bottomside, inside, outside, all is right side to the nimble Chickadee. * * * Blind-man's buff, hide-and-seek, and tag are merry games enough when played out on one plane, but when staged in three dimensions, with a labyrinth of interlacing branches for hazard, only the blithe bird whose praises we sing could possibly master their intricacies."

There are many instances recorded of the tameness of individual chickadees. The following, by John Woodcock (1913), is a good example:

Although I had fed the Chickadees in winter for several years, none of them were tame enough to feed from the hand until the spring of 1906. A pair were nesting in one of my bird-boxes, and, as I was standing near the nest, one of the birds came toward me. I threw a piece of nut to it, which it picked up and ate. Then I held a piece on my finger-tips, and it came almost without hesitation and carried it off; this was repeated several times. Two days later he would perch on my finger and take a nut from between my teeth, or would sit on a branch and let me touch him while he was eating a nut. * * *
He grew very tame that winter, and would often swing head downward from the peak of my cap, or cling to my lips and peck at my teeth. If I held my hand out with nothing in it, he would always hop to my thumb, and peck the nail two or three times, then hold his head on one side, and look into my eyes, as if to ask me what I meant. * * *
I tamed several more Chickadees that winter; eight out of twelve, as nearly as we could count, were quite tame.
It was rather amusing when I took the 22 rifle to shoot rabbits! After the first shot was fired, I was attended by several Chickadees. They made aiming almost impossible, for every time I raised the rifle, one or two birds would perch on the barrel completely hiding the sights.

Many of us have had somewhat similar experiences.

Harrison F. Lewis (1931) describes an extraordinary experience with a chickadee that he believes was not previously tamed. He writes:

On a chilly day, with drizzling rain, about the year 1915, as I was walking on the outskirts of Wolfville, Nova Scotia, I saw a Black-capped Chickadee *(Penthestes atricapillus atricapillus)* feeding in a leafless alder bush. There was nothing unusual in its appearance, but the fact that it did not seem to heed me in the least when my path led me within a few feet of it attracted my attention. Wondering a little how near the bird I would have to go before it actively evaded me, I paused a moment, then stepped slowly in its direction. When I had advanced to the outer twigs of the bush in which it was busily feeding, it still appeared unaware of my presence, so, while expecting to see it fly away at any moment, I slowly extended my hand toward it. When my fingers were close to it I suddenly closed them upon it and had it securely in my grasp. The Chickadee seemed greatly surprised at this occurrence and struggled violently for a moment in a futile attempt to free itself, but I believe that my own surprise was equal to that of the bird, for I had confidently anticipated its escape rather than its capture. When I had recovered a little from the first shock of unexpected success, I began to doubt whether the Chickadee could be in good health. "Perhaps," I thought, "it has from some cause lost the ability to fly." I took it into a neighboring house and showed it to one or two other persons, holding it in my hand all the while, then I carried it to the open door and released it. It flew away at once with strong, sustained flight as though in the best of condition.

On the other hand, William H. Longley (MS.) speaks of "a chickadee incubating seven eggs which would bite and buffet our fingers if we put them too close, while the mate fed near by, only occasionally raising its voice expressing what may have been an objection to our presence."

The following quotations refer to the roosting habits of the chickadee. Lynds Jones (1910) says: "On numerous occasions I have started them from their night roost in the thick of a leafy grape vine in midwinter." And Henry D. Minot (1895) recounts the following observation: "February 10th. This afternoon, just before sunset, I noticed two Chickadees, feeding on the ground, and pecking at a bone, to which a remnant of meat was attached. * * * They scarcely left the ground * * * until half-past five, when one flew away over the housetop and disappeared. The other continued to hop about on the ground; and then, without any intimation of his purpose, abruptly flew to the piazza, whether I followed him. He took possession of a Peewee's nest, which stood upon the top of a corner-pillar, adjoining the house, and, having stared at me for a moment, *tucked his head under his wing,* and apparently leaned against the wall. * * * Another retires as regularly at sunset, and sleeps in a hole of a white birch, evidently once a Chickadee's nest, perhaps his own." Eugene P. Odum (MS.) says:

In fall and winter most individuals roosted in dense conifer branches rather than in cavities. However, during the winter, two cavities were discovered where single birds were known to spend the night.

There was a definite tendency for chickadee groups to roost in the same area each night, so that it was possible to station oneself at a known roosting place and observe the birds coming to roost. The flock was usually scattered, individuals seeking places in the dense foliage of different trees. In contrast with the noisy behavior of many species roosting in flocks, chickadees retire with very little calling or ceremony.

As the flocks break up and pairs form in the spring, the winter roosts were abandoned. During early spring movements the pair seems to roost wherever convenient. After the nesting cavity is excavated and the nest material carried in, the female apparently may spend the night in the cavity even before incubation begins. The male roosts outside in some tree nearby. Likewise, during incubation and the feeding of the young the female sleeps in the cavity and the male somewhere outside. After the young are twelve days old, or older, the female may remain outside at night. When the young have left the nest, neither they nor the adult birds were observed to return to the cavity. The first night out the young and adults roosted wherever they happened to be.

If we are near a chickadee when it it flitting about in a tree, making short flights from twig to twig, we hear each time it flies a faint, rustling whir of wings, or sometimes two or more whirs, if the distance be longer. This is the chickadee's method of flight—a delicate, quick flutter, and a pause, then a flutter again. When crossing a wide, open space, the bird flies slowly, undulating in the air a little—each flutter of its wings carries him upward a little way, and during the pause between the flutters he sinks again.

Katharine C. Harding (1932) reports a banded chickadee at least 7½ years old, and Dorothy A. Baldwin (1935) another of the same age. Mr. Wallace (1941) reports one that was 9 years old.

Lester W. Smith (MS.), writing to Mr. Bent, gives an instance of the intelligence of the chickadee. He says: "Among the dozen or more species commonly taken for banding in my Government-type sparrow trap, the black-capped chickadee was the only species with instinctive intelligence to remember its way out. This trap, with its entrance under inward-sloping wires, was successful through the failure of most birds to remember just how and where they came in and the confusion that resulted when escape was found impossible in any general direction, particularly upward. The chickadee, selecting a sunflower seed from among the mixed bait in the trap, went in, not to eat the seed there, but to get it out to where it could be opened on a branch. The little bird at its first visit would walk around the trap until the low entrance was discovered, then dart in, select a seed, and, if nothing disturbed it, head back whence it came and with little investigation find its way out. They rarely became confused as did the juncos, tree sparrows, and purple finches. After the first trip in and out the same individual would fly directly to the entrance and as directly out again after he had grabbed the seed. If I shifted the position of the trap on the same spot, or moved it to a new location, the trail was learned after one trial."

Voice.—The chickadee is a voluble little bird; when two or more are together they are full of conversation, exchanging bright, cheery remarks back and forth. The notes show great variety and extend over a wide range in pitch. Some of the minor ones are very high indeed, closely approaching the insectlike voice of the golden-crowned kinglet and the brown creeper; one, the familiar "phoebe" note, an "elfin whistle" Langille (1884) calls it, is a pure, prolonged tone so low that we can imitate it by whistling; others, lower, but high-pitched, remind us of short words or phrases given in a babylike voice.

The simplest of the notes mentioned above is uttered rather listlessly, thus differing from the kinglet's energetic delivery; it is sibilant but given with a hint of a lisp, suggested by the letters *sth*. It is a faint note, but it may serve to report one bird's whereabouts to another not far away. This note, emphasized and prolonged into *stheep*, is often given in flight, or when a bird is slightly disturbed. It may be doubled. By further emphasis and repetition into a sharp, rapid series, *si-si-si-si*, it serves as a warning or alarm note; we hear this form when a hawk comes near.

Of the "phoebe" whistle, Aretas A. Saunders (MS.) says: "There are two notes of equal length, the second tone lower in pitch than the first. The quality is that of a clear, sweet whistle. The pitch is commonly B-A or A-G, in the highest octave of the piano. Frequently the second note has a slight waver in the middle, as if the bird sang *fee-beyee* instead of *fee-bee*. Rarely a bird drops a tone and a half between the two notes." Not infrequently two birds will whistle the "phoebe" note antiphonally, the second bird picking up the pitch at the end of the first bird's song and then dropping a tone lower, i.e., B-A, and the response A-G, over and over again.

It is a matter for conjecture whether the phoebe note is a true song of the chickadee. It is heard oftenest in spring and early in summer, but we hear it also throughout the winter, sometimes in cold, inclement weather, and it is uttered by both sexes, according to Dr. Jonathan Dwight (1897). Perhaps the deciding point in determining a true song is the manner in which the bird delivers its notes rather than their beauty to our ears. With this in mind, an observation by Bradford Torrey (1885) seems significant. He says:

For several mornings in succession I was greeted on waking by the trisyllabic minor whistle of a chickadee, who piped again and again not far from my window. There could be little doubt about its being the bird that I knew to be excavating a building site in one of our apple-trees; but I was usually not out-of-doors until about five o'clock, by which time the music always came to an end. So one day I rose half an hour earlier than common on purpose to have a look at my little matutinal serenader. My conjecture proved correct. There sat the tit, within a few feet of his apple-branch door, throwing back his head in the truest lyrical fashion, and calling *Hear, hear me,* with only a breathing space between the repetitions of the phrase. He was as plainly *singing,* and as completely absorbed in his work, as any thrasher or hermit thrush could have been. Heretofore I had not realized that these whistled notes were so strictly a song, and as such set apart from all the rest of the chickadee's repertory of sweet sounds; and I was delighted to find my tiny pet recognizing thus unmistakably the difference between prose and poetry.

Francis H. Allen tells me that he has several times heard a chickadee similarly engaged, also early in the morning.

Among the several notes that lend themselves to syllabification is the well-known *chicka, dee-dee.* Aretas A. Saunders (MS.) says of it that it "is more variable than many suppose. While it is most commonly one *chicka* followed by three or four *dees,* it may vary from one to ten *dees,* and there are sometimes two *chickas.* The *chicka* is, as a rule, two tones higher than the *dees,* and the pitch is B on the *chicka* and G on the *dees,* in the next to highest octave on the piano."

Another pretty note may be written *sizzle-ee,* or, when it falls in pitch at the end, *sizzle-oo.* A single bird often gives this phrase over and over, sometimes alternating the two forms, and two birds may make a two-part song of them, singing back and forth. The prettiest note of all, and the most delicate, is a prolonged jingling—as if tiny, silver sleigh-bells were shaking.

Field marks.—The chickadee is a round, fluffy little bird, boldly marked with splashes of gray, black, and white in contrast to the streaks, lines, and pencilings characteristic of many of the smaller birds. The white side of the head, separating the black areas above and below it, shines out brightly and forms a good field mark even in the distance. The short bill and the fur-coat appearance of the plumage distinguish the chickadee from any of the warblers with their slender bills and sleek, elegant stylishness. And the invisible eye, hidden in black feathers, sets the chickadee apart from the kinglets, even when colors are obscured by the dark shadows of evergreens.

Enemies.—The smaller, fast-moving hawks often capture a chickadee, but the little bird is so watchful for danger and so quick in its movements that it sometimes escapes from an attack. Tertius van Dyke (1913) reports a narrow escape of a chickadee (aided by him, to be sure) from the strike of a sparrow hawk.

The northern shrike, too, is the chickadee's enemy, but it is not always successful. Some years ago I (Winsor M. Tyler, 1912) described a case in which a chickadee out-maneuvered a shrike thus:

Jan. 27, 1910. This afternoon (2 p.m.) I watched for five or ten minutes a Shrike attempting to capture a Chickadee. My attention was attracted by the Chickadee's notes, *si-si-si-si, dee-dee-dee,* and I found the bird hiding in an isolated red cedar tree, while the Shrike was doing his best to find him. The Chickadee made no attempt to leave the tree, but kept moving about, chiefly among the inner branches. The Shrike followed his prey as best he could through the network of fine twigs, but often lost sight of it, evidently, and, coming to an outside branch, sat quiet, listening.

When hard pressed, the Chickadee flew out and circled about the tree before diving in among the branches again. After these flights, sometimes he entered the tree low down, and then mounted to the very top by a series of short, rapid hops; sometimes, after flying to the apex of the tree, he passed downward to the lowest branches before flying again. Several times the Shrike hovered in the air, and holding his body motionless and upright, peered into the tree. Finally, although not frightened away, the Shrike gave up the chase.

Chickadee's nests are so carefully hidden away, and the entrance is generally so small, that cowbirds rarely find and enter them. There is, however, an instance of parasitism of unquestionable authority. Fred M. Packard (1936) reports: "On May 25, 1936 a Black-capped Chickadee's nest, containing four Chickadee eggs and two Cowbird's eggs, was found in a nesting box at the Austin Ornithological Research Station at North Eastham, Massachusetts. * * *

"The opening in this box was one and one-half inches in diameter, much larger than the usual entrance to Chickadee nests, and ample to permit the intrusion of Cowbirds."

Dr. Herbert Friedmann (1929) lists another recorded instance from Ravinia, Ill.; an egg was reported to be in a nest of the Carolina chickadee; but the locality would seem to indicate that it was the more northern species.

Harold S. Peters (1936) lists, as external parasites on this chickadee, a louse (*Ricinus* sp.), the larva of a fly *(Ornithoica confluenta),* and a mite *(Analgopsis passerinus).*

Fall.—It is certain that in fall a good many chickadees either migrate or at least wander about extensively. We meet them at this season in localities where they never breed, often in thickly built up sections of large cities. Speaking of the occurrence of chickadees on the Public Garden in Boston, Mass., Horace W. Wright (1909) says: "In the autumn Chickadees are much more in evidence [than in spring], as they quite regularly appear in the Garden and continue their stay into November; and, as already intimated, on two occasions two birds remained through the winter and were seen at intervals up to the end of March. Sometimes small flocks have appeared in October which numbered four, five, or six birds." In September, October, and November I have seen them also in smaller open places in Boston, such as a vacant lot surrounded by several square miles of city blocks.

Dr. Wilbur K. Butts (1931), during an able study of the chickadee by means of marked individuals, attempted to determine the extent of migration of the species at Ithaca, N. Y. Even with the aid of colored bands, the evidence of migration, except in minor degree, seemed not conclusive to him, as his following summaries show. He says:

In considering these evidences of a migratory movement, it should be remembered that even if birds appear to be more numerous during the winter, it is not proved that there really are more individuals present. Many birds are so much more conspicuous in winter than in summer that they may seem to be more abundant. The distributional records show that there is a movement of Chickadees, but it is not proved that there is a distinct north and south migration.

Bird-banding operations at some stations seem to indicate that there is an arrival of Chickadees in the fall and a departure in the spring, but the records have as yet no proof of a distinct north-and-south migratory movement. Published records show only two Chickadee recoveries at points other than the place of banding. These two were recovered at distances of only three and twenty miles. The records do show, however, that there are many permanent resident individuals. The records at most stations do not show whether there are more individuals present in winter than in summer, since at most stations few Chickadees are trapped in the breeding-season. Individuals which are recorded only during the winter months may really be present throughout the year. * * *

The records seem to indicate, also, that there are very few birds passing through Ithaca in the fall. Only four birds were recorded but once. It should be remembered, however, that transient visitants are much less likely to get caught than are the resident individuals. Accordingly, there may have been more individuals passing through than the records seem to indicate. All through the fall many unbanded birds, which may have been transients, were seen.

The evidence shows that there were but few, if any, arrivals from the South in the spring. * * *

Since some of the records in the North indicate a greater abundance of birds in fall and spring, it is possible that there is a migration of birds from the extreme northern part of their range, where we as yet have no records, and this may account for the increase in numbers of the Chickadee in the United States.

Additional evidence of southward migration is furnished by the following note by William Palmer (1885): "This bird has been very abundant here [near Washington, D. C.] during March and April, nineteen specimens having been taken, while many others were seen. Owing probably to the severe winter they were driven south, returning about the middle of March. The first specimens were taken on March 15, and others were taken every week until April 19, when six were shot and many others seen. The weather during April was fine and warm, and the birds were singing and appeared quite at home. But few *P. carolinensis* were seen until the last week in April, showing that they too had been driven much further south."

W. E. Saunders has sent us some notes on the migration of chickadees at Point Pelee from 1909 to 1920, from which it appears that the fall migration there is very irregular. On many days there would be none at all, and then for several days there might be as many as 300 or 400 of these birds. He says: "Usually there are none, but once in a while there is a flight, perhaps (probably) endeavoring to cross the lake; it takes some time to taper off this flight and return to the normal status of none at all. * * * I have always thought this chickadee matter very interesting, and can still remember the first big flight, when, after years of scarcity, all of a sudden chickadees were everywhere; it was fun to watch them down at the last trees, making ineffective little flights up into the air and then settling back into the trees. They had not enough of the migratory instinct to get across. These birds were, doubtless, from stock bred south of the Georgian Bay, and they had never crossed any large body of water."

Mr. Wallace (1941) cites two cases where banded chickadees have been taken at 50 and 200 miles, respectively, southwest of the point of banding; and he says that there are six returns recorded in Washington that might be regarded as long range.

Winter.—Chickadees, collected in small loose flocks, spend the winter roving about the woodland. The birds scatter out a good deal, so much so that they must often lose sight of one another, but they keep continually calling to one another, using their fine, lisping note or the louder *chickadee,* and thus indicating the direction in which the flock is moving. They seldom wander far from the protection of trees and shrubs but occasionally venture out a little way into a field or marsh if there are isolated bushes there in which they can perch and feed. As the flock moves along, each bird examines minutely bark, twigs, and branches, searching for tiny bits of food—spider's eggs, cocoons, or other dormant insect life. The flocks are not large, being seldom composed of more than a dozen birds, but they generally contain too many birds to represent only a single family.

Whenever we go out in the country we meet these cheery little roving flocks—pleasant companions who enliven the dreary, New England winter. Mr. Wallace's (1941) studies indicate that winter flocks "are remarkably constant in individual composition, the same individuals remaining together day after day through the winter, and, as far as survival permits, winter after winter."

DISTRIBUTION

Range.—North America in general, from the limit of trees south to the central United States; not migratory.

The range of the chickadee extends **north** to southern Alaska (near Holy Cross Mission, Knik, and Valdez); southern Yukon (Lake

Marsh); southeastern Mackenzie (probably Fort Simpson and Willow
River); northern Alberta (Smith Landing and Fort Chippewyan);
northern Saskatchewan (south end of Reindeer Lake); central Manitoba (Eckimamish River); probably northern Ontario (Fort Albany
and Moose Factory); southern Quebec (Godbout, Seven Islands, and
Natashkwan River); and Newfoundland (Nicholasville and St.
John's). The eastern limits of the range extend south along the Atlantic coast
from Newfoundland (St. John's) to Massachusetts (Nantucket); Long
Island (Huntington); and northern New Jersey (Passaic); and in the
mountains to western Maryland (Bittinger); southern West Virginia
(Cranberry Glades); and western North Carolina (Mount Mitchell).
South to west-central North Carolina (Mount Mitchell); eastern Ten-
nessee (Mount LeConte); central Illinois (Philo and Rantoul); central
Missouri (Marshall and Warrensburg); Kansas (Neosho Falls and
Wichita); southern New Mexico (probably Capitan Mountain); Ari-
zona (San Francisco Mountain); and northern California (Callahan).
The western limits of the range extend northward in Pacific coastal
areas from northern California (Callahan) to Alaska (Kodiak Island,
Katmai, and near Holy Cross Mission).

While there are records in winter north to the limits of breeding or
beyond, as Alaska (St. Michael) and central Quebec (Lake Mistassini)
there is sometimes a slight movement southward at this season. Winter
occurrences are south to southern North Carolina (Mount Pleasant);
southern Indiana (Bloomington and Carlisle); southern Kansas (Independence and Harper); and on the Pacific coast to Eureka, Calif.

Among more than 1,700 return records of chickadees banded in
Massachusetts, only two are for points outside of that State. One,
banded at Westfield on November 4, 1925, was found dead a short time
later (before December 31), at Stratford, Conn. The other, banded at
Amherst on October 7, 1932, was caught by a cat at Belvidere, N. J.,
on December 24, 1932. The files of the Fish and Wildlife Service contain the records of several thousand other banded chickadees, almost all
of which were recaptured at the points of banding.

The range as outlined is for the entire species, of which seven subspecies are currently recognized. The typical form (*Parus atricapillus
atricapillus*) is found in the Eastern United States, Canada, and Newfoundland, west to Missouri, Illinois, Minnesota, and western Ontario;
the long-tailed chickadee (*Parus atricapillus septentrionalis*) is found
chiefly in the Rocky Mountain region, breeding from the Kenai Peninsula of Alaska and central Mackenzie south to eastern Oregon and
northern New Mexico and ranging eastward to northern Manitoba,
western Minnesota, western Iowa, and eastern Kansas; the Oregon

chickadee *(Parus atricapillus occidentalis)* is found from southwestern
British Columbia south to northwestern California; while the Yukon
chickadee *(Parus atricapillus turneri)* occupies the Hudsonian Zone of
northern Alaska to the north and west of Cook Inlet. *P. a. bartletti*
has been described from Newfoundland; *P. a. practicus* from the central
Appalachian region; and *P. a. nevadensis* from northeastern Nevada.

Egg dates.—Alberta: 6 records, May 12 to 23.

Illinois: 17 records, April 20 to June 11; 9 records, May 2 to 16,
indicating the height of the season.

Kansas: 16 records, April 10 to June 3; 8 records, April 21 to
May 14.

Massachusetts: 27 records, May 7 to July 12; 13 records, May 20
to 29.

Nova Scotia: 5 records, May 21 to June 6.

Oregon: 57 records, April 13 to June 30; 28 records, May 8 to 18.

West Virginia: 13 records, April 22 to May 29.

PARUS ATRICAPILLUS PRACTICUS Oberholser

APPALACHIAN CHICKADEE

This form of black-capped chickadee, which is supposed to range from
eastern Ohio to southwestern Pennsylvania and southward through the
mountain region to North Carolina, is described by Dr. H. C. Oberholser (1937) as "similar to *Penthestes atricapillus atricapillus,* of
Canada, but smaller, particularly the tail; upper parts darker, more
grayish, less ochraceous, particularly in winter; wing-coverts and rectrices with narrower white edgings." Dr. Oberholser gives the range
as: "Resident and breeds chiefly in the Appalachian Mountains from
southwestern North Carolina, north through western Virginia, West
Virginia, southwestern Pennsylvania, to central eastern and northeast
central Ohio." Presumably the habits do not differ from those of the
typical race.

PARUS ATRICAPILLUS BARTLETTI Aldrich and Nutt

NEWFOUNDLAND BLACK-CAPPED CHICKADEE

John W. Aldrich and David C. Nutt (1939) found this chickadee
"abundant in all the thickets in eastern Newfoundland." They describe
it as "similar to *Penthestes articapillus atricapillus* but darker and more
brownish above, and darker buff on flanks and under tail-coverts.
White edgings to wing and tail feathers narrower. Bill larger. In
color nearer to *P. a. occidentalis* than to any other known race but

larger." It is their opinion "that a very well marked race is represented in Newfoundland with characters most pronounced in the eastern part of the island and specimens from the western part distinctly intermediate with *P. a. atricapillus.*"

I saw a few chickadees near Bay of Islands and along Fox Island River in western Newfoundland but did not collect any specimens.

PARUS ATRICAPILLUS SEPTENTRIONALIS Harris
LONG-TAILED CHICKADEE

HABITS

For nearly a hundred years the long-tailed chickadee has been recognized as a midcontinent race of our familiar little chickadee, ranging from Alaska to New Mexico in the Canadian and Transition Zones. It is described by Ridgway (1904) as "similar to *P. a. atricapillus,* but larger, with wing and tail averaging decidedly longer; coloration paler, with whitish edgings to greater wing-coverts, secondaries and lateral rectrices broader, more conspicuous."

P. A. Taverner (1940) has recently made an enlightening study of the Canadian status of this subspecies, based on a series of 99 specimens in the National Museum of Canada, including—

17 males and 14 females from southern Ontario, eastward to Nova Scotia; 19 males and 17 females from Manitoba, Saskatchewan and Alberta; 20 males and 12 females from the interior of British Columbia. Specimens from coastal areas of British Columbia referable to *P. a. occidentalis* were not included. These were all taken within two hundred miles of the international boundary and can reasonably be assumed to be of local breeding stock. They are from areas separated from each other by some eight hundred miles and include no specimens between. * * *

In these birds, laid out in comparable seasonal mass groups, a highly critical eye can detect a slight average color distinction as above postulated [by Ridgway], between the prairie and the eastern birds, but not enough to be readily detected and not consistent enough for the recognition of individual specimens. Every individual in one group can be matched in the other, and no single specimen can be confidently identified by this character, though winter and early-spring birds, before the wear and fading of nesting activity, show slightly more color differences than in later season.

His study of the tail measurements shows that "there is a large overlap in extreme measurements: the smallest *atricapillus* is only 0.2 inches (5.08 mm.) smaller than the smallest *septentrionalis*. The largest *septentrionalis* is only 0.05 inches (1.27 mm.) larger than the largest *atricapillus*." The wing measurements give "even less definite results. * * * There is a large overlap in extreme measurements; the smallest *atricapillus* is only 0.1 inch (2.54 mm.) smaller than the smallest *septentrionalis;* the largest *septentrionalis* is no larger than the largest *atricapillus*."

A study of Mr. Taverner's paper must convince the reader that *septentrionalis* is one of those millimeter races, based on averages, that many of the individuals of this race cannot be definitely recognized as such from the characters alone, and that his figures "open the question of the desirability of formal recognition of subspecies of which few or no individuals can certainly be referred to their proper race by physical characters without reference to the geographical origin."

In his notes from Montana, Aretas A. Sounders writes: "The only difference I have noted in the field between long-tailed and black-capped chickadees is that of habitat, the long-tailed being chiefly an inhabitant of willow thickets and cottonwood groves, not extending its range up into the evergreen forests of the mountains, as the blackcap does in the Adirondacks. Perhaps this is partly because the evergreen forests are inhabited by mountain chickadees." Other observers seem to agree that throughout its range the favored haunts of this chickadee are the open, sunny, deciduous woods, such as poplar, aspen, willow, and cottonwood groves, and that it seems to avoid the dense coniferous forests.

Nesting.—The nesting habits of this chickadee seem to be similar to those of its eastern relative. An unusually low nest was discovered by Harry S. Swarth (1922) in the Stikine River region "in a tract of rather open woods, mostly of small poplars. It was in a dead poplar stub about three inches in diameter, a mere shell of dead and decayed wood, hardly strong enough to hold the tightly packed and rapidly growing young, who did actually break through the wall at one place. The entrance hole was five inches from the base, the nest itself, flush with the ground. The lining appeared to be entirely of matted moose hair."

E. S. Cameron (1908) says that, in Montana, this chickadee sometimes "nests in small deep holes of high dead pines. On June 15, 1903, a pair of Chickadees were seen to be greatly excited over a strip of rag hung in a pine on Cottonwood Creek, Dawson County. They hovered about it, meditating an attack, but with each breath of wind the flag fluttered, and frightened away the birds which returned when the wind ceased. This strange behavior on their part induced me to investigate, when I found their nest of wool, hair, and grass in a very small hole below the rag. * * * The birds' fears were entirely allayed when I wrapped the offending rag around the branch."

Lee R. Dice (1918) found nests in process of construction in southeastern Washington early in April, "in the decayed wood of orchard or shade trees." He continues:

The process of nest excavation was watched for a short time on April 10, 1914. The nest was being excavated in the rotten heart of a pear tree, and entrance was obtained through the end of a stub about four feet from the ground. The male and female took part equally in the work, and the labors were continued throughout the day. A vigorous pecking could be heard while either bird was at work. The excavated material was carried in the bill a distance of ten yards or more from the nest before being dropped. It was not dropped in the same place each time, but was scattered over a wide area. Usually the birds alighted on some branch before dropping the debris, but sometimes it was dropped while the bird was flying. As soon as one bird left the hole the other entered immediately. Sometimes the bird outside had to wait a short time. Between 12 M. and 1 P.M. the average time each bird spent in the nest hole was thirty seconds and the shortest time four seconds.

Eggs.—The eggs of the long-tailed chickadee are indistinguishable from those of the black-capped chickadee. The measurements of 50 eggs in the United State National Museum average 15.7 by 12.2 millimeters; the eggs showing the four extremes measure **17.5** by 12.7, 15.1 by **12.9**, **14.2** by 11.9, and 15.2 by **11.2** millimeters.

Young.—Mr. Swarth (1922) watched the young being fed at the nest referred to above and remarks: "Both parents carried food to the nest assiduously after foraging expeditions that lasted from two to five minutes. In approaching the nest, the old birds came through the trees and bushes until within about eight or ten feet of their destination; then they dropped to the ground and hopped to the entrance [only 5 inches from the ground]. To the casual observer they disappeared at a point some distance from the nest, and it was not until they had been observed for some time that this subterfuge was detected. The staple food that was being brought to the young was a small green caterpillar infesting the poplars at that time; also a white grub, a green katydid, and many small mosquito-like insects."

The plumage changes, food, behavior, and voice of this chickadee are all similar to those of the familiar chickadee of the East and need not be mentioned here. But the following note from Claude T. Barnes is of interest:

"On January 4, 1924, at an altitude of 5,000 feet in the mountains near Salt Lake City, while wading through the deep snow of City Creek Canyon, I was attracted by the thin, oft-repeated *tchip* of half a dozen chickadees that were busy in the upper branches of some birch trees *(B. fontinalis utahensis)*. I noticed one take a peck at one of the numerous birch catkins, which, like Kaiser brown caterpillars, were suspended from the branches, and then instantly thereafter work with its bill against a limb, as if trying to get the kernel from a nut. In a second it made another peck followed by another working with its bill against a limb, and so on, hopping from twig to twig and constantly uttering its companionable *tchip*. Rarely did it sing *chick-a-dee-dee-dee*, though three or four times in an hour the familiar notes did come from the flock."

PARUS ATRICAPILLUS NEVADENSIS Linsdale
PALLID BLACK-CAPPED CHICKADEE

Dr. J. M. Linsdale (1938b) gives the above names to a local race of the long-tailed chickadee, which he says is "resident along streams in the Snake River drainage system south of the Snake River, in northeastern Nevada and southern Idaho." He describes it as "similar to *P. a. septentrionalis,* but coloration paler, with whitish edgings to greater wing-coverts, secondaries and lateral rectrices broader, more conspicuous, thus reaching the extreme in these respects for the species, but close to *P. a. turneri* from which it differs in larger size."

PARUS ATRICAPILLUS OCCIDENTALIS Baird
OREGON CHICKADEE

PLATES 52, 53

HABITS

This western form of our familiar blackcap occupies the northwestern coast from extreme southwestern British Columbia to extreme northwestern California. It is described by Ridgway (1904) as similar to *P. a. atricapillus* but decidedly smaller (except bill and feet) and coloration very much darker; back varying from deep mouse gray or very slight buffy slate-gray in spring and summer to deep hair brown or light olive in fall and winter plumage; sides and flanks (broadly) pale grayish buff in spring and summer, deep brownish buff, wood brown, or isabella color in fall and winter; whitish edgings of innermost greater wing-coverts, secondaries, and exterior rectrices more restricted than in *P. a. atricapillus.*"

Its haunts and habits are similar to those of our familiar eastern chickadee. W. E. Griffee tells me that it "is abundant all through the hardwood timber of western Oregon valleys but is very much less common in the coniferous timber, particularly during the nesting season."

S. F. Rathbun says in his notes that "it is a Transition Zone species and not to be found at any considerable altitude; the highest we have noticed it being 550 feet; it seems to prefer the lowlands," in western Washington.

Nesting.—Mr. Griffee says (MS.): "Probably nine-tenths of the nests are in dead willow, cottonwood, and alder trees and stubs, at least one of these three tree species being found wherever the Oregon chickadee nests. Nesting holes usually start with an irregular opening about 1¼ in diameter and are 8 to 10 inches deep. Often they are within 3 or 4 feet of the ground and rarely over 10 or 12 feet. Cavities, which are about 3 inches in diameter at the bottom, are invariably lined with a layer of green moss, often at least an inch thick. Upon this layer of moss is a thick lining of rodent fur, cow hair, and other hairy material.

"Nests containing incomplete sets practically never are occupied by the birds during the day, a coverlet of fur being drawn over the eggs while the birds are away. Incubating birds sit tightly and try to frighten the intruder by a hiss and flutter of the wings when an inquiring finger is poked into the entrance of the nesting hole."

Eggs.—The Oregon chickadee lays four to ten eggs. Out of 28 sets reported by Mr. Griffee, 18 sets consisted of eight eggs; there were only two of six, four of seven, three of nine, and only one of ten. The eggs are practically indistinguishable from those of the black-capped chickadee. The measurements of 40 eggs average 15.6 by 12.0 millimeters; the eggs showing the four extremes measure **17.0** by 12.0, 16.2 by **12.3, 14.6** by 11.7, and 14.8 by **11.5** millimeters.

The plumage changes, food, behavior, voice, and other habits are apparently similar to those of the closely related eastern race.

Mr. Rathbun observed some of these chickadees eating tent caterpillars, near Seattle, of which he writes in his notes: "It was toward evening, and seeing three of these birds very active in a lilac bush, we stopped to watch them. Near the top of the bush was a tent caterpillars' web of small size; as the worms were crawling toward it, some of them would be seized by the chickadees for food. During a space of less than five minutes the three chickadees captured and ate eight of the worms of large size. When one was caught the bird would beat it about a number of times and then, holding it with one foot on its perch, leisurely tear off pieces with its bill, which it then ate. The birds must have been feeding on the caterpillars for some time before we noticed them, for, on looking over the ground under the bush, many dead and mutilated worms were to be seen strew about."

PARUS ATRICAPILLUS TURNERI Ridgway

YUKON CHICKADEE

HABITS

According to the 1931 Check-list, this chickadee "breeds in the Hudsonian Zone of northern Alaska north and west of Cook Inlet."

Ridgway (1904) describes it as "similar to *P. a. septentrionalis* but slightly smaller, coloration grayer above and more extensively or purely white beneath, and white edgings of greater wing-coverts, secondaries, and outermost rectrices broader, more purely white; in spring and summer plumage the gray of upper parts without perceptible tinge of buff, except on rump and upper tail-coverts, where very faint, and white of sides and flanks very faintly, if at all, tinged with buff; in fall and winter plumage the buffy tinge on sides and flanks very much paler than in *P. a. septentrionalis.*"

Under the name long-tailed chickadee, with which this race was included by some of the earlier writers, Dr. E. W. Nelson (1887) writes:

Throughout the wooded region of Alaska, from the moist, heavily-wooded coast in the Sitkan and Kadiak region north throughout the entire Yukon and adjoining country, this bird is a common resident. Specimens were secured both at Cook's Inlet and Kadiak by Dr. Bean. I secured specimens from various places throughout the northern portion of the Territory, at times even along the barren sea-coast, where it only found shelter in the stunted alder or weed patches. Its visits to the coast, however, were mainly in roving parties during spring or fall. A few days of mild weather, at this season, are almost sure to bring some of these familiar birds about the coast settlements, and its familiar *dee-dee-dee* is a welcome sound on the clear frosty mornings which usher in the stinging blasts of winter, or announce the approach of spring. One meets it again while traveling through the silent snow-clad forests of the Yukon, as he tramps wearisomely on, until the mind is unconsciously affected by the lack of animation. At such times, as we move mechanically forward, the shrill, strident note of the Chickadee, as the bird eyes us from its swinging perch on a bush close at hand, breaks the silence and diverts the mind. Frequently the chorus of their Lilliputian cries arise from the bushes all about as the jolly company of harlequins swing and balance their tiny bodies and pass on as though too busily intent upon affairs of importance to stop. After their passage the forest resumes its cheerless silence once more, and the heavy breathing of the icy wind through the tree-tops or the sharp report of the contracting ice in the river are the only accompaniments of the toilsome march.

I have no information on the nesting habits, eggs, food, and other habits of the Yukon chickadee.

PARUS CAROLINENSIS CAROLINENSIS Audubon

CAROLINA CHICKADEE

PLATE 54

CONTRIBUTED BY EDWARD VON SIEBOLD DINGLE

HABITS

The Carolina chickadee, one of the four birds discovered by Audubon in the coastal part of South Carolina, is the low-country representative of the Boreal chickadee *(atricapillus);* yet *carolinensis* by no means confines itself to the Atlantic and Gulf coastal plains. It ascends the Blue Ridge Mountains probably higher than 5,000 feet, according to Brewster (1886), thus falling short by 1,500 or 1,600 feet of attaining the highest point in its range—Mount Mitchell, with an altitude of 6,684 feet. Brewster continues: "Common, and very generally distributed, ranging from the lowlands to at least 5,000 feet, and probably still higher. On the Black Mountains I found it breeding sparingly along the lower edge of the balsam belt, and thus actually mingling with *P. atricapillus.* In one place a male of each species was singing in the same tree, the low plaintive *tswee- dee- tswee - dee* of the *P. carolinensis,* contrasting sharply with the ringing *te - derry* of its more northern cousin. The fact that the two occur here together and that each pre- serves its characteristic notes and habits, should forever settle all doubts as to their specific distinctness."

Other observers have recorded the birds in summer at altitudes of 3,300, 4,400, and 5,000 feet. But the center of abundance is unquestion- ably the great swamp areas of the Coastal Plain, where the writer has found it to be one of our commonest birds. Any wooded territory attracts them, it seems, except possibly extensive pine woods. But even small towns and villages often have their chickadees, and the writer has frequently seen it as a backyard resident.

Except during the actual breeding period, chickadees are nearly always seen in small bands—family parties, as it were. Late in summer and in fall they are invariably associated with tufted titmice, yellow-throated and pine warblers, brown-headed nuthatches, and downy woodpeckers; later in the winter their ranks are increased by myrtle warblers and the two kinglets. In such foraging bands, the tufted tits appear as leaders, with the chickadees as next in command.

No bird has endeared itself to us as much as the chickadee; its gentle, confiding ways, soft colors, and saucy air, as well as its readiness to patronize feed trays, render it a universal favorite.

There is evidence that our chickadees, like other members of the titmouse family, remain mated for periods longer than one breeding season; Nice (1933) records a pair of Carolina chickadees in Ohio that were associated for three winters and two summers.

Nesting.—The Carolina chickadee is one of our early breeders; al- though much depends on whether the season is advanced or late, nest construction in the southern part of its range might begin as early as the first week or 10 days of February or as late as the end of March; in South Carolina excavations generally are begun in March, while in Ohio Wheaton (1882) says: "I have found the nest in this vicinity as early as the 18th of April, ready for the reception of eggs. The female sits very close, and is with difficulty driven from the nest."

The favorite nesting sites are fence posts and decayed stubs of small saplings. And like the chimney swift, the chickadee offers another ex- ample of a bird that has partly abandoned primeval nesting conditions in favor of man's more convenient replacements. The birds usually excavate their own burrows and select certain hardwoods or pines that are soft; but often peach and cherry stubs are used, and these have very hard outer bark. Dickey (MS.) lists 17 species of trees, all hardwood, that are used by *carolinensis;* to these the writer could add several pines and the peach. Woodpecker holes are sometimes used, as well as natural cavities in dead or live trees. Dickey writes that he has "known them to build in iron pipes used for clothes lines, pipes to support bridges, small bird houses, etc."

Both sexes excavate, but the female probably does the most in nest construction. The average height of the nest above the ground would be about 5 or 6 feet. Dickey mentions 1 foot as the minimum distance from the ground, while Erichsen's (1919) 22 feet must be considered the maximum.

According to Dickey, two weeks are required on an average to complete a burrow, but obviously this would depend on the depth of the excavation and the softness of the wood. In a peach stub, for example, after the hard shell has been pierced, the going would be easy. On the other hand, oak would be consistently harder to excavate. The same observer gives average measurements of the completed burrows and entrance holes, as follows:

```
Diameter of aperture ..................................1⅜ inches
Depth of cavity .......................................5 inches
Width of cavity at aperture ...........................2 inches
Width of cavity at nest enlargement ...................2⅜ inches
```

When the hollow has been excavated, nest-building is begun, as Dickey says, "with thick foundation of moss *(Hypnum)*—strips of yellow and brown bark, a few strips of yellow grass and grass culms or panicles, a little thistle down or milkweed pod down, and then such bird feathers as those of sparrows, bluebird or of the parent. The cup is well padded with silvery milkweed or thistledown, animal hair, red hair of the cow, gray fur of the cottontail rabbit and fur also from deer, mice, and other Mammalia."

Erichsen (1919) writes: "Simultaneous with the appearance of the down on the stalk of the cinnamon and royal ferns, which occurs during the middle of March, the chickadee begins nest-building, for this material is used largely by the birds in lining their nests. As far as my observations go, the birds, in gathering the down, always begin at the top of the stalk and work downward. The green moss that collects on the trunks of certain species of hardwoods is also used to a considerable extent, being always placed in the nesting hole first, and upon it the down is deposited."

A constant habit of this bird is to build up one side of the nest higher than the other, thus making a flap, which is used to cover the eggs when the parent is away.

Both sexes take turns in incubating.

Dickey, in describing a nest in a sugar-maple fence post says: "Over a series of at least 15 consecutive seasons a pair of birds bred annually at this habitat."

Eggs.—[AUTHOR'S NOTE: The Carolina chickadee lays five to eight eggs; six seems to be the commonest number. These are practically indistinguishable from the eggs of the black-capped chickadee, with similar variations. They are white, more or less unevenly marked with fine dots, spots or small blotches of shades of reddish brown. Often the spots are concentrated about the larger end. The measurements of 50 eggs average 14.8 by 11.5 millimeters; the eggs showing the four extremes measure 15.9 by 11.8, 15.7 by 12.4, and 12.7 by 10.4 millimeters.]

Young.—According to Dickey, "the period of incubation is exactly 11 days."

The same observer thus describes a newly hatched bird: "Length when spread out 6/8 of an inch. Color a rich pinkish white, say salmon hue. There were mere cilia of gray down on the head, back of wing stumps, lower back or rump. The conspicuous eyeballs slate blue, meas. 3 mm. diameter. Leg length 7/16 of an inch. Wing stumps ⅛ in. long, 1/16 in. wide. Bill ⅛ in. long; ⅛ in. wide at base; a light horn color. * * * It was revealed that they remain inside nests exactly 17 days. They are showy at that stage; well coated with plumage that resembles closely that of the adults, mouse-gray coats and black heads. They are animated enough to snap at and grasp one's fingers."

Plumages.—[AUTHOR'S NOTE: The plumages and molts in this chickadee parallel those of the black-capped chickadee. The young bird leaves the nest in practically full juvenal plumage, but with short wings and tail. In this plumage it is much like the adult, showing the distinctive wing edgings, but the black of the head and throat is duller, and the whole plumage is softer. A partial postjuvenal molt occurs in summer, involving the contour plumage and the wing coverts, but not the rest of the wings or the tail; this produces a first winter plumage, which is practically adult. Adults have a complete postnuptial molt in summer, but apparently no spring molt; the wash of pale pinkish buff on the flanks, and to a lesser extent on the back, characteristic of the fall plumage, disappears by wear and fading before nesting time, producing a grayer bird.]

Food.—Howell (1932) writes: "The food of this species was studied by Beal (1916, pp 24-26), who examined 210 stomachs. Animal matter composed about 72 per cent, and vegetable matter 28 per cent, of the total contents. Nearly half (44 per cent) of the food for the year consisted of moths and caterpillars. Bugs appeared to be next in favor among the insects, including stink bugs, shield bugs, leaf hoppers, tree hoppers, plant lice, and scales. Ants, bees, wasps, beetles, cockroaches, and katydids were consumed in small numbers. Spiders were eaten in considerable numbers, composing more than 10 per cent of the total food. The vegetable food consisted principally of seeds of poison ivy (10 per cent) and of other unidentifiable seeds (12 per cent). A small quantity of blackberries and blueberries was eaten."

Judd (1902) says that "seven Carolina Chickadees *(Parus carolinensis)* were taken during February, April, July, and August. Vegetable matter—mulberry seeds, pine seeds, and ragweed seeds—was present in four stomachs. All the birds had eaten insects. One had eaten 1 bee (Andrenidae), 2 ants, 3 insect eggs, 3 spiders, and 3 caterpillars (measuring worms, Geometridae and hairy Arctiidae, which are usually avoided by birds). One of the stomachs examined contained katydid eggs and two others eggs of the wheel-bug."

The writer has often watched chickadees early in spring feeding on the eggs of certain moths or other insects; these are encased in silky yellow coverings and attached to the under sides of leaves of the live oak. The birds hunt through the trees, inspecting the under sides of the leaves, all the while uttering their soft, conversational notes. The leaves are picked from the twigs and carried to a convenient branch. Then holding the leaf with its feet, the bird tears the silk away and devours the eggs.

Blincoe (1923) records it as feeding late in summer on the seeds of the redbud tree, "swallowing them as fast as they could be removed from the pods."

Brackbill (MS.) describes their manner of eating honeysuckle berries, which consists of holding the berry between the feet, as do blue jays, and hammering with their bills. Further, "examination of some of its discards showed them to be drilled through like beads, and but one seed remained in each. It seemed likely that some pulp and skin had been eaten, also."

Kalter (1932) observed that Carolina chickadees were removing and dissecting flowers of the leafcup *(Polymnia canadensis* L.), and "investigation of the flower heads of this plant showed that most of them were infected with the small striped brown larvae of one of the Noctuid moths. The work of these insects seemed to cause the blossoms to rot and turn brown."

Skinner (1928) says that, in winter, "they are easily attracted to dooryards and about our homes by hanging up bones with bits of meat and gristle attached, to a tree or bush. They will also eat cheese and suet, and pick up bread and doughnut crumbs."

Voice.—There is probably no native bird song more pleasing than the music of this chickadee. It has not the loud, ringing quality of the tufted tit's song, which comes to us from the blossoming dogwoods, half a mile away. Its voice is rather weak and the song a very simple one, but the notes are exquisitely mellow, soft, and satisfying.

Wayne (1910) writes: "The song period begins about the middle of February and the sweet notes are always welcomed as the herald of spring." Dickey (MS.) thus describes the notes: "Usually it is detected as it scolds cats, screech owls, or a human intruder, whereupon it will vent syllables like *dee-dee-dee-dee; chick-ah-dee-dee-dee-dee; sprittle-chick-ah-dee-dee-dee-dee; dee-dee-dee-pee-stick-dee; pee-tee-dee-dee-spee-teetle; spick-spick-ut-uh-dee,* and *phe-bee.*" Sometimes there is a marked liquid flow of notes prior to the *chickadee* series as *sputtle-dee,* but this is hard to put down on paper. Perhaps it is well simply to say that their run of outcries are buzzing exclamations.

"The song has been described by some writers as 'the pumphandle strain,' and that will suggest its nature very well. Indeed this does remind one of the not unpleasant, old-fashioned sounds made by a windlass well. *Spee-deedle-dee-deedle-dee* is what the chickadee seems to say. I have heard it repeatedly on fair days in midwinter; it increases in frequency as March is ushered in; is pronounced everywhere in spring and early in summer (the breeding period); and casually a subdued, shortened song is vented on crisp autumn days, too."

Aretas A. Saunders (MS.) has this to say about the song of *carolinensis:* "In my experience, the best way to identify a Carolina chickadee in the field is by its song. The song is enough different from the black-capped chickadee to name the bird instantly. The other call notes are not so easily distinguished.

"The song consists of two clear whistled notes, but each one is either introduced or followed by a shorter, lower-pitched, sibilant note. That is, instead of the bird singing a simple *fee-bee,* it sings *sūfee-sūbee* or else *feesu beesu.* These sibilant notes are like whispers rather than whistles, and I have known observers not to notice them and to think there was no essential difference in the song of this chickadee and the blackcap. The pitch and pitch interval of the clear, whistled notes are about the same as in the black-capped chickadee, one tone between them, and the notes pitched on B-A or A-G, in the highest octave of the piano. The sibilant notes are on a different pitch than the whistled ones, sometimes higher and sometimes lower. I have comparatively few records of the song of this species, however. Occasionally a bird sings three clear whistled notes, the second and third each lower than the preceding one.

"The season of singing is probably similar to that of the black-capped chickadee, but I have no extended notes except for the spring of 1908, when I was in central Alabama. Then I heard this species sing daily from my arrival early in March till the end of April. In May I heard the song frequently, but not daily, and heard it once or twice early in June. The other notes of this species are similar to those of the blackcap, the *chickadee* call being rendered somewhat faster."

The writer has noticed that the Carolina chickadee, when disturbed on the nest, utters a peculiar note—an explosive little sound like a sneeze. My first experience with this note is described (1922) in part as follows: "Late in the afternoon of March 28, I tapped on the tree; one of the birds was inside and gave a peculiar note, not a hiss such as Mr. Schorger heard, but more like a little sneeze. This was repeated every time I tapped. Several times the bird tapped on the interior of the cavity. Finally it put its head out of the hole and looked calmly at me as I stood about three feet away. I withdrew and it went back into the hollow. No eggs had yet been laid."

Dickey (MS.) describes the sounds as "hisses, serpent-like, and feared by unsuspecting boys." Also, when examining young birds out of the nest, "the parents darted close to my hat, hissed not unlike a black snake, and vented a variety of buzzing and liquid outcries."

The writer has never seen chickadees when they were engaged in hissing, but Pickens (1928) has, and he describes the "defense demonstration" as follows:

One of the most courage-taking sounds that I have encountered in my field studies is the hiss of the copperhead snake *(Agkistrodon mokasen)*. It lacks the animating interest we find in the ringing alarm of the rattlesnakes, and fills one with a kind of nausea. The reptile sounds as if it were inhaling a good part of the surrounding atmosphere and then discharging it in one sudden, explosive puff. There is nothing sedate and leisurely about it. Now the best imitation of that sound that I have heard is the explosive hiss of the brooding Carolina Chickadee *(Penthestes carolinensis)*. * * * In preparing for the hiss, the bird, as seen from above, appears to rise slightly on the legs as if to give a freer swing to the movements of the body, while the head is thrown back over the shoulders at a right angle, or even an acute angle. The attitude of the bird is one of tense rigidity. Then, as if with a great effort, the bird nods the head strongly forward. The whole body, with the wings and tail, seems affected. The tail moves, the expanding wings shoot out sideways and strike the surrounding wood inside the cavity, and as the head comes stiffly down the bird emits a strong hiss or puff strikingly like that of the copperhead. The head is brought down quite upon the surface of the lining in front of the bird, and while the noise appears to be produced in part by the stiff rustling of the feathers, and the reverberations within the hollow of the surrounding wood, much, or the greater part of the noise certainly comes from the mouth and throat, and the hiss sometimes dies out in a faint little vocal squeak. All combine to make a fearful noise, and while mimicry is of course an unconscious, or better, an unintentional occurrence, there is no mistaking what the noise is to be taken for.

According to other observers, this snakelike sound is also employed by the northern chickadee *(Penthestes atricapillus)*.

That the hissing note is not confined to North American chickadees is attested to by Jourdain (1929) ; he states that "the European Titmice produce warning noises in apparently exactly the same manner as the American Chickadee. I have frequently noticed this habit in the case of the British Great Tit *(Parus major newtoni)*, on at least one occasion in the British Coal Tit *(P. ater britannicus)*, and it is also characteristic of the British Blue Tit *(P. caeruleus obscurus)*. Mr. Pickens' description of the movements of the chickadee in producing this explosive hiss applies exactly to those of the Great Tit; but though well known to field-workers, there is little on record in the numerous books on British birds on the subject beyond a few references to 'hissing like a snake,' on the part of the setting Blue Tit."

Enemies.—Like all small birds, our chickadee has to be continually on the watch for small accipitrine hawks, cats, snakes, and small mammals; apparently the screech owl does not prey upon it to any extent, as the little bird tucks itself away at sundown in some hollow, too small for *asio* to enter.

That the cowbird occasionally imposes its domestic duties on the chickadee is shown by Friedmann (1938), who writes of "a nest containing five eggs of the chickadee and two of the cowbird, collected at Piney Point, St. Mary's County, Maryland, April 25, 1934, by E. J. Court, who tells me that he caught the female Cowbird on the nest, about half an hour after daylight."

Peters (1936) includes this bird in his list of avian hosts of external parasites; a Maryland specimen was found infected with lice of the species *Degeeriella vulgata* (Kell.), while mites [*Trombicula irritans* (Riley)], were taken from a South Carolina bird.

DISTRIBUTION

Range.—Southeastern United States; nonmigratory.

The range of the Carolina chickadee extends **north** to southeastern Kansas (Independence) ; central Missouri (Columbia and St. Louis) ; Illinois (Carlinville and Ravinia) ; Indiana (Indianapolis and Anderson) ; Ohio (Phelps Creek and East Liverpool) ; Pennsylvania (Washington and Doylestown) ; and central New Jersey (Princeton and Point Pleasant). **East** to the Atlantic coast in New Jersey, Virginia, North Carolina, South Carolina, Georgia, and Florida (Whittier). **South** to southern Florida (Whittier, Fort Myers, St. Petersburg, and Mulat) ; Louisiana (New Orleans, Bayou Sara, and Alexandria) ; and southeastern Texas (Houston and San Antonio). **West** to central Texas (San Antonio, Kerrville, Waco, Fort Worth, and Gainesville) ; Oklahoma (Wichita Mountains, Minco, Tulsa, and Copan) ; and southeastern Kansas (Independence).

The range as outlined is for the entire species, which has been separated into four geographic races. The typical Carolina chickadee *(Parus carolinensis carolinensis)* occupies all the range except Florida, where the Florida chickadee *(P. c. impiger)* is found, and the extreme western portion from northern Oklahoma south to the coast of Texas occupied by the plumbeous chickadee *(P. c. agilis)*. A northern race, *P. c. extimus,* is said to range from New Jersey west to Missouri and south to northern North Carolina and Tennessee.

Casual records.—This species has been recorded as an "accidental visitant" in western New York (Lancaster) ; one was taken at Ecorse, Mich., on July 17, 1899; and a specimen was collected at Keokuk, Iowa, on May 4, 1888.

Egg dates.—Arkansas: 9 records, April 11 to May 15.

Florida: 14 records, March 30 to April 27.

New Jersey: 11 records, April 12 to June 15.

North Carolina: 12 records, April 8 to May 12.

Texas: 45 records, Feb. 16 to May 20; 23 records, March 26 to April 20, indicating the height of the season.

PARUS CAROLINENSIS IMPIGER Bangs

FLORIDA CHICKADEE

HABITS

The Florida chickadee is a small, dark-colored race of the well-known Carolina chickadee. It is fairly common and well distributed over most of the Florida Peninsula, except perhaps the extreme southern part. I have found it almost everywhere that I have been in central Florida, mainly in the live-oak hammocks and around the edges of the cypress swamps.

Arthur H. Howell (1932) records it also in "open pine timber," and says: "A pair noted on the Kissimmee Prairie was occupying a small palmetto thicket, far from any large timber, a very unusual habitat."

Nesting.—Mr. Howell says that the nests "are placed in rotten stubs, usually 10 to 15 feet from the ground." A set of four eggs in my collection was taken by Oscar E. Baynard near Leesburg on March 30, 1910. The nest was about 5 feet up in a dead pine stub, about 5 inches in diameter, that stood on the edge of a small pond surrounded with pine trees. The cavity was about 7 inches deep; the nest was made of dry grass and lined with a few feathers and a considerable quantity of cattle hair and fur from a rabbit.

Frederick V. Hebard writes to me of a nest that was placed in the top of a 4-foot fence post along a road; "the nest was composed chiefly of dried grasses with a webbing of cypress bark strips and hairs, including two of a raccoon and one of a wildcat. The inside of the nest was softened with raccoon and fox-squirrel fur. The coon and wildcat hairs were probably taken from some of those trapped during winter."

Eggs.—Four or five eggs seem to be the usual numbers in the nests of the Florida chickadee, though very few data are available to the writer.

The eggs are practically indistinguishable from those of the Carolina chickadee. The measurements of 39 eggs average 15.1 by 12.1 millimeters; the eggs showing the four extremes measure **18.1** by 14.8, 17.8 by **15.3, 12.9** by 11.5, and 13.8 by **10.7** millimeters.

Except as affected by the difference in environment, the food, behavior, and voice of this chickadee are similar to those of the more northern race, and the plumage changes are apparently the same.

PARUS CAROLINENSIS AGILIS Sennett

PLUMBEOUS CHICKADEE

HABITS

The 1931 Check-list says that this southwestern race of *carolinensis* "breeds in the Lower Austral zone from northern Oklahoma to Refugio and Kendall counties, Texas." Mrs. Margaret Morse Nice (1931) says that it is rare in northwestern Oklahoma, but "resident in central Oklahoma from Tulsa and Hughes to Woodward and Jackson counties." In the region of Austin, Tex., George Finlay Simmons (1925) regards it as a "fairly common permanent and regular resident; appears to be more common during winter because of its preference for civilization at that season." Its haunts seem to be very similar to those of the Carolina chickadee—edges of woods, open woodlands, more or less open country, and, especially in winter, in towns and about houses.

It is slightly larger than specimens of *P. c. carolinensis* from the southern States, paler above and with whiter underparts.

Nesting.—Mr. Simmons (1925) says that, about Austin, the nests are placed anywhere from 1 to 23 feet above ground, commonly about 10 feet, "generally in natural cavities in dead elm, Chinaberry, Spanish oak, live oak, post oak, or blackjack tree or stump; in broken tops of leaning stumps or trees in decayed limbs; in old woodpecker hollows of telegraph pole or fence post; in decaying posts of barbed-wire fences along edges of woodlands; hollow iron hitching posts in town; bird boxes about farm houses and town houses." He says that in central Texas it seldom digs a hole of its own, unless forced to do so because of the scarcity of natural cavities.

He describes the nests as "composed of such warm materials as fine strips of bark (particularly of the cedar), soft green mosses, cowhair, plant fiber, wool, and feathers, with occasionally some rabbit fur, cotton, plant down, straw, bits of string, grass, horsehair, thistle down, and small buds. Lined with soft short cowhair, rabbit hair, plant down, and occasionally soft wool, plant fiber, cotton and feathers. Bottom of cavity filled with a good deal of green moss and occasionally with some cedar bark."

Eggs.—Mr. Simmons (1925) says that the set consists of three to eight eggs, most commonly six. These are apparently indistinguishable from those of other races of the species. The measurements of 40 eggs average 14.9 by 11.7 millimeters; the eggs showing the four extremes measure **16.5** by 12.4, 15.6 by **12.7,** and **13.5** by **10.5** millimeters.

Food.—Mrs. Nice (1931) writes: "In Norman the Chickadees were among the most charming of our feeding shelf guests, announcing their arrival with a cheery *peep,* enjoying everything we had to offer except raisins, but fondest of sunflower seeds and nuts, sometimes taking baths in the water dish in January. * * * These little birds are so friendly, so full of individuality and have so many different notes and pretty ways that they afford a most promising subject for a careful life history study."

Voice.—Mr. Simmons (1925) gives an elaborate account of the voice of the plumbeous chickadee, which would probably apply equally well to that of the other races of *carolinensis.* He says that it is "quite unlike that of the northern Chickadees; a much higher pitched and more hurriedly uttered *chickadee-dee-dee-dee,* characteristic of the Southern species, frequently running into *chick-a-dee-dee-dee-dee-dee-dee-dee; tweesee-dee-dee-dee-dee;* a clearly whistled *pseé-a-dee;* a low plaintive *tswee-dee-tswee-dee,* of four tremulous whistled notes, in sharp contrast to the clear, ringing notes *te-derry,* of the Northern birds; a low *sick-a-dee;* a short *chick-a-da;* a clearer *my watcher key, my watcher key;* a series of *day-day-day* or *dee-dee-dee-dee* notes."

PARUS CAROLINENSIS EXTIMUS (Todd and Sutton)

NORTHERN CAROLINA CHICKADEE

Todd and Sutton (1936) named this northern race, which ranges from New Jersey westward to Missouri and southward to northern North Carolina and Tennessee. They describe it as "similar to *Penthestes carolinensis carolinensis* (Audubon), but averaging larger, sex for sex; pale edgings of wings and tail averaging considerably more conspicuous; sides and flanks brighter reddish brown; and sides of head slightly grayer." The habits presumably are like those of the nominate race.

PARUS SCLATERI EIDOS (Peters)

MEXICAN CHICKADEE

HABITS

The above name now applies to the northern race of a Mexican species, which reaches the northern limits of its distribution in southeastern Arizona and southwestern New Mexico. Several specimens, now in the Brewster collection in the Museum of Comparative Zoology in Cambridge, were collected in the Chiricahua Mountains, Ariz., in March 1881, by Frank Stephens.

Mrs. Bailey (1928) gives the following records for New Mexico: "The Mexican Chickadee was taken in the San Luis Mountains July 19, 1892, and September 29, 1893, at about 7,000 feet (Mearns); and was found rather common among the pines of the Animas Mountains, 7,500-8,000 feet, August 1, 1908 (Goldman). These constitute the only State records of this Mexican species."

The Mexican chickadee *(Parus sclateri sclateri)* of the Mexican highlands is much like our Carolina chickadee in general color pattern, but it is larger, its coloration is darker, and its sides and flanks are olive-gray, with the white on the under parts restricted to a narrow median space, and with the black of the throat spreading fan-shaped over the chest.

The northern race, our bird, is characterized by the describer, James L. Peters (1927), as similar to the above, "but the grayish wash on the sides and flanks paler and grayer, lacking the olivaceous tinge; white area at the lower edge of the black throat and white abdominal median stripe less restricted."

Nesting.—There is a set of six eggs in the Thayer collection in Cambridge collected by E. F. Pope, near Benson, Ariz., on May 16, 1913. The nest of rabbit fur and wool, closely felted together, was in an 8-inch cavity, excavated by the birds, in a dead willow stub about 5 feet from the ground.

A set of six eggs, in the Doe collection in the University of Florida, was also taken by Mr. Pope, on April 4, 1911, in the same locality and similarly located; the nest was "composed of rabbit fur, and plant down, firmly felted together."

Eggs.—The eggs in the Thayer collection are short-ovate and only slightly glossy. They are white and are rather well covered, especially about the larger end, with fine dots and small spots of reddish brown, "hazel," and with a few underlying spots of "pale purple-drab."

The measurements of the above 12 eggs average 14.3 by 11.1 millimeters; the eggs showing the four extremes measure 15.3 by 11.4, 14.0 by 11.5, 13.5 by 11.0, and 15.3 by 10.6 millimeters.

Plumages.—Young Mexican chickadees, in juvenal plumage, are similar to the adults, but the black of the head is duller, and the plumage is softer, shorter, and less firm. The postjuvenal molt of young birds and the annual postnuptial molt of adults seems to occur mainly in August, beginning late in July and continuing into early September, according to what few molting specimens I have seen. Birds in fall plumage, adults, and young being practically indistinguishable, are slightly more strongly tinged with olive than are the faded spring and summer birds.

Voice.—Dr. Frank M. Chapman (1898) published the following short note on the voice of the type race, as observed by him at Las Vegas, Veracruz: "The call of this Titmouse is a rapid, vigorous, double-noted whistle repeated three times, and not at all like the notes of *Parus atricapillus.* In its conversational 'juggling' notes there is, however, a marked similarity to the corresponding notes of that species."

DISTRIBUTION

Range.—Highlands of Mexico from Veracruz and Oaxaca, north to southern New Mexico and Arizona; nonmigratory.

The range of the Mexican chickadee extends **north** to southern Arizona (Mount Lemmon and the Chiricahua Mountains); and southern New Mexico (San Luis Mountain). **East** to southwestern New Mexico (San Luis Mountain and Animas Mountain); Puebla (Teziutlan); and Veracruz (Orizaba, Los Vigos, and Jalapa). **South** to central Veracruz (Jalapa); Oaxaca (La Parada); and central Guerrero (Omilteme). **West** to eastern Guerrero (Omilteme); Durango (Ciénaga de las Vacas); western Chihuahua (Pinos Altos); and southeastern Arizona (Mount Lemmon).

Two forms of this species are recognized but their respective ranges cannot now be clearly defined. The subspecies found in Arizona, New Mexico, and northern Mexico is *Parus sclateri eidos*.

Casual records.—A specimen of this species has been taken in the Davis Mountains of western Texas.

Egg dates.—Arizona: 3 records, April 4 to May 29.

PARUS GAMBELI GRINNELLI (van Rossem)

GRINNELL'S CHICKADEE

HABITS

This northern race of the white-browed chickadees *(gambeli)* is thus described by Mr. van Rossem (1928): "In relative proportions of wing and tail *Parus gambeli grinnelli* most closely resembles *Parus gambeli gambeli* (Ridgway), from which it differs in smaller size and darker coloration. On interscapular region it is of the identical shade of *Parus atricapillus atricapillus* (Linnaeus)."

Its range includes northern British Columbia, eastern Washington, east-central Oregon, and northern Idaho. Just where it intergrades with the mountain chickadee of the Rocky Mountains and the short-tailed chickadee of northern California does not seem to be definitely known.

The remarks by Dawson and Bowles (1909) on the mountain chickadee, as they found it in eastern Washington, evidently apply to this race. Mr. Dawson found two nests "placed in decayed stumps not above three feet from the ground. One, in a wild cherry stub in northern Okanogan County, contained fresh eggs on the 18th day of May. Their color had been pure white, but they were much soiled thru contact with the miscellaneous stuff which made up the lining of the cavity: moss, cow-hair, rabbits' wool, wild ducks' down, hawks' casts, etc."

At another nest, containing young, "it was an unfailing source of interest to see the busy parents hurrying to and fro and bringing incredible quantities of provisions in the shape of moths' eggs, spiders, wood-boring grubs, and winged creatures of a hundred sorts. Evidently the gardener knew what he was about in sheltering these unpaid assistants. Why, when it comes to horticulture, three pairs of Chickadees are equal to one Scotchman any day."

The measurements of eight eggs average 16.1 by 12.2 millimeters; the eggs showing the four extremes measure **16.3** by **12.3, 14.7** by 12.2, and 16.2 by **12.1** millimeters. They are apparently indistinguishable from those of the mountain chickadee.

PARUS GAMBELI ABBREVIATUS (Grinnell)

SHORT-TAILED CHICKADEE

PLATE 55

HABITS

The 1931 Check-list gives the range of this race of the mountain chickadee as "higher mountains of central and northern California, southern Oregon, and northwestern Nevada south to Mt. Sanhedrin and Mt. Whitney." It thus occupies a range intermediate between the ranges of three other races, but it does not seem to be intermediate in characters and is therefore a good subspecies. Dr. Grinnell (1918) gives its characters as "tone of color on sides, flanks and back the same as in *inyoensis,* though not quite so pale, namely, in fresh plumage, cartridge buff. Tail much shorter than in either *gambeli* or *inyoensis;* and bill averaging smaller than in any of the other three races."

W. E. Griffee writes to me that "this chickadee is common throughout the ponderosa pine and lodgepole pine country of eastern Oregon, particularly in the lodgepole areas."

As to their haunts in the Lassen Peak region, Grinnell, Dixon, and Linsdale (1930) state: "In the higher portions of the section chickadees were observed to frequent lodgepole pines, white firs, hemlocks, yellow pines, and junipers. At lower altitudes, in winter, the birds were observed also in blue oaks and valley oaks. Wherever found, this bird foraged about the ends of branches and over twigs in the outer parts of the foliage of the trees. Apparently the more open portions of the woods, or their marginal portions, were most favorable for the species."

Nesting.—The same authors report several nests found in the above region. Most of the nests were in low stumps in clearings, in open spaces, or on the edges of the woods, either in natural cavities of crevices or in rotting or burnt stubs, so that in most cases the birds had little or no excavating to do. Two nests were in old woodpeckers' holes. Most of the nests were less than 2 meters above the ground; the lowest was only 165 millimeters up; and the highest was nearly 5 meters from the ground. The only lining mentioned was rabbit fur.

Chester Barlow (1901) found a nest under the baseboards of a cabin in which he was camping. The bird had entered through a rough hole in the boards, and "the nest had been built on a joist under the cabin in a space ten inches long and seven and a half inches wide. This had been filled with cow-hair, squirrel fur and hemp picked up from about the dairy, and when the nest was removed it presented a solid mat 2½ inches thick and of the dimensions given. Near the center of the mat a round cavity 2½ inches across and 1½ inches deep held the eight eggs."

J. E. Patterson has sent me a photograph of a nest that was in the under side of the bole of a prostrate pine log, only a few inches above the ground.

Mr. Griffee says in his notes: "Nesting cavities usually are 4 to 8 feet above ground and situated in lodgepole pines when that species is available. Often they will choose a live lodgepole tree, even when punky aspen stubs are available. Nesting pines often have heart rot, which makes the excavating easier than it looks from the outside, but nevertheless the work of excavation must be several times as arduous as that usually performed by the Oregon chickadee. Entrance holes are about 1½ inches in diameter and often go straight back as much as 4 or 5 inches to the heart of the tree before turning down for 8 to 12 inches. The bottom of the cavity, often irregular in shape because of an intruding knot, is lined with more or less shredded bark upon which is piled a lot of rodent fur. As the fur is short and not felted together compactly, the nest will not hold its shape when removed from the cavity.

"In my experience, the short-tailed chickadee always stays on the nest from the time the first egg is laid. Probably this is necessary because of the great abundance of chipmunks, which are small enough to run into a chickadee nesting hole and make a meal of the eggs, if the parent bird were not on the job at all times. The Oregon chickadee, which nests where chipmunks are much less common, and makes a smaller entrance to its nesting cavity, apparently is not so much bothered by chipmunks and so does not hesitate to leave its nest unguarded until incubation begins."

Eggs.—The eggs of the short-tailed chickadee apparently do not differ materially from those of other races of the species. They are mostly plain, pure white, but usually some of the eggs in a set are more or less finely speckled with reddish brown. The numbers I have seen recorded run from five to nine in a set. The measurements of 40 eggs average 16.1 by 12.3 millimeters; the eggs showing the four extremes measure **17.0** by 11.9, 16.5 by **13.2**, and **14.7** by **11.4** millimeters.

Young.—Grinnell, Dixon, and Linsdale (1930) noted one case where two broods were raised in a season in the same nest; probably two broods are often raised. At a nest that they watched the young were fed 11 times within half an hour, between 8.59 and 9.30 A.M., at intervals varying from one to seven minutes, but usually at intervals of three or four minutes. Such food as could be seen consisted of green caterpillars. Both old birds helped in the feeding and in keeping the nest clean, carrying away the excrement sacs.

Mrs. Wheelock (1904) gives the period of incubation as 14 days. She says that the young remained in the nest nearly three weeks, which seems to be an unusually long time for such small birds; and for fully two weeks longer they were begging to be fed. She observed that "the nestlings were fed by regurgitation until four days old, when fresh food was given."

Food.—Strangely enough, nothing specific seems to have been published on the food of any of the races of the mountain chickadee; if there has, I have been unable to find it. But its feeding habits are similar to those of the other chickadees; it has repeatedly been observed examining the twigs, foliage, and crevices in the bark of trees, where it doubtless finds a variety of insect food; and it is fair to assume that its food does not differ very materially from that of other members of the genus. Grinnell and Storer (1924) have seen one thoroughly examining the interior of a rotted-out cavity, where it probably found insect food of some kind.

Behavior.—Grinnell, Dixon, and Linsdale (1930) describe in some detail the intimidation behavior of this species when the nest is invaded:

> When a slab of rotten wood was removed the bird lunged, at the same time spreading its wings convulsively, and then gave a prolonged hissing sound—just that order of procedure. The bird repeated this performance nineteen times by count before it suddenly flew from the nest at the close approach and light touch of the observer's hand. The body had been kept closely depressed into the nest cavity. The lunges were rather inane—the bird simply struck out, in one direction and then another. At the moment of the lunge, the black-and-white striping of the head brought her into abrupt and conspicuous view of the observer peering into the cavity—reinforcing the surprise effect of the sounds produced. At times, the hissing sound was produced, the wall of the cavity was struck, and the white of the head moved, all at the same instant. * * * During the winter chickadees regularly made up portions of the companies of birds of several species that foraged together through the day. Some of the individuals that moved to low altitudes in winter joined circulating bands of bush-tits.

Grinnell and Storer (1924) write: "After the nesting season the chickadees and several others of the smaller birds are wont to associate with one another in flocks of varying size. Such a gathering was seen in Yosemite Valley on July 30, 1915. Included in the openly formed yet coherent aggregation were the following species: Mountain Chickadee, Black-throated Gray Warbler, Western Chipping Sparrow, Sierra Creepers, Warbling Vireo, and Cassin Vireo. The birds were foraging through black oaks, incense cedars, and young yellow pines, each kind of bird of course adhering to its own particular niche and own method of getting food."

PARUS GAMBELI BAILEYAE Grinnell

BAILEY'S CHICKADEE

HABITS

This race of the white-browed chickadees occupies the higher mountains of southern California, from Tulare and Monterey Counties to San Diego County. It was named for that distinguished and popular ornithologist, Mrs. Florence Merriam Bailey, who has done so much for western ornithology.

Dr. Joseph Grinnell (1918) gives as his diagnosis of it: "Tone of coloration on sides, flanks and back distinctly plumbeous—more exactly, on sides and flanks the 'smoke gray' of Ridgway (1912, pl. 46), and on back near the 'mouse gray' of the same authority (pl. 51). The tail in this race is short as in *abbreviatus,* but the bill is long and heavy, averaging thicker through than in any of the other three races."

Like other races of the species, Bailey's chickadee finds its favorite haunts, during the breeding season at least, in the coniferous forests of the mountains, from the lower borders of the pines up to 10,000 feet or higher, or perhaps as far as the evergreen forest extends. In the San Bernardino Mountains, Dr. Grinnell (1908) found these chickadees in the tamarack pine belt as high as 10,600 feet; and in August they were common in the pinyons and chaparral, and as far down the desert slope as Cactus Flat, at 6,000 feet.

Nesting.—J. Stuart Rowley writes to me: "I have found these chickadees nesting in cavities and woodpecker holes rather abundantly throughout the higher mountains of southern California. They nest as high as 35 feet up and down to within a foot of the ground, as a rule, but on June 9, 1935, while I was collecting on Mount Pinos, Ventura County, I saw a chickadee go down a squirrel hole underneath a dead pine stub in a little clearing. Upon investigating, this bird was seen on a nest on the ground in the excavation under the stub; the nest contained five eggs ready to hatch. This is the only nest of a chickadee I have ever found which was actually below the level of the ground."

In the San Bernardino Mountains, Dr. Grinnell (1908) reports:

A nest found June 17, 1905, near the mouth of Fish Creek, occupied a vertical slit in a dead black-oak stub. The nest was not more than three feet from the ground and was made of soft, downy plant fibers, and contained six newly-hatched young. Another nest was found June 21 on a ridge near Dry lake. This was twenty feet from the ground in a dead fir stub, and was ensconced behind the loosened bark. It consisted of fur, apparently from the woodrat and chipmunk, and contained five eggs in which incubation was well advanced. Another nest containing seven young was found the same day in a cavity of a pine stub even with the surface of the ground. A fourth nest in the same locality contained six small young. In this case the nest was a felted mass of deer hair and woodrat fur, intermingled with a few feathers. It was in a knot-hole of a dead fir sapling, two and one-half feet from the ground. In 1906, at Dry lake, June 15, a set of five slightly incubated eggs of this species was taken from an old sapsucker hole twenty feet above the ground in a dead tamarack pine. The nest was a large mass of reddish deer hair.

There is a set of seven eggs in my collection, taken by Wright M. Pierce near Bear Lake in these mountains on May 19, 1923, from a cavity on the under side of a large, dead, fallen yellow pine.

Eggs.—The eggs of Bailey's chickadee are evidently similar to those of the type race, the mountain chickadee, as described under that form, sometimes pure white, but oftener more or less lightly spotted with fine dots of light browns. I have no record of such large sets as mentioned under the mountain chickadee, but they may occur. The measurements of 40 eggs average 16.2 by 12.7 millimeters; the eggs showing the four extreme measure **17.7** by **13.5**, and **14.6** by **11.6** millimeters.

Voice.—Ralph Hoffmann (1927) gives a slightly different account of the voice of this chickadee from that quoted under the mountain chickadee. He writes:

A visitor from the East misses the familiar Black-capped Chickadee from the rich bird life in the lowlands of southern California. Let him, however, climb a few thousand feet up any of the mountain ranges, among the yellow pines, and there will be, if not his eastern friend, at any rate a close relative. The Mountain Chickadee is so close to the eastern bird, so like in voice, habits and appearance, that it will take a few moments to discover the difference. The bird clings head downward to an outer twig, hammers a seed open on a limb, lisps *tsee-dee-dee* to its fellows and is apparently the same active, cheery mite. The sweet whistled call is more often made up of three (sometimes four) notes than that of the Eastern bird. Sometimes the three notes come down the scale to the tune of 'Three Blind Mice.' At other times the last two are the same pitch *tee-dee-dee*. Occasionally the bird either leaves off the third note or adds a fourth. As the chickadee gleans from twigs, it utters a hoarse *tsick tsick dee dee* or a husky *tsee dee*, and other little gurgling or lisping calls, and a sharp *tsik-a* when startled or excited.

PARUS GAMBELI ATRATUS (Grinnell and Swarth)

SAN PEDRO CHICKADEE

In naming and describing this Lower California subspecies, Grinnell and Swarth (1926) remark:

The race of Mountain Chickadee of the Sierra San Pedro Martir, as compared with related subspecies, exhibits an appreciable darkening of the plumage in the direction not of brown but of slate. This darkening is most apparent on the flight feathers, which are slaty black as compared with the more brownish-hued quill feathers of other races; but it shows also in more leaden-hued flanks and upper parts. This general leaden tone of coloration is quite apparent in fresh plumaged birds, but it is a character that tends to be lost even when the feathers become only slightly worn.

Together with this darkening there is restriction in the area covered by the one conspicuous white marking on this bird, the superciliary stripe, which marking extends forward in fresh plumage to nearly or quite meet its fellow on the forehead. The white on the head of *atratus* is not only less in area occupied, but it is shallower; and birds in breeding plumage, when it is reduced or effaced by wear, come to bear a curious resemblance about the head to *Penthestes atricapillus*.

They gave the range of this form, "so far as known, only the main plateau of the Sierra San Pedro Martir"; and they state that it "adheres closely to the coniferous belt of the Transition and Canadian life-zones." The 1931 Check-list extends its range to include the Sierra Juárez, of northern Lower California.

It probably does not differ materially in its habits from other races of the species.

The measurements of 6 eggs average 16.5 by 12.6 millimeters; the eggs showing the four extremes measure **16.8** by **12.7**, 16.5 by **13.0**, and **16.2** by **11.7** millimeters.

PARUS GAMBELI GAMBELI Ridgway

MOUNTAIN CHICKADEE

PLATE 57

HABITS

The species *Parus gambeli* occupies a wide territory in western North America, from British Columbia to Lower California and from the Rocky Mountain region westward to the Pacific coast region, in all suitable mountain ranges. The type race, the subject of this sketch, is confined to the Rocky Mountain region, from Wyoming and Montana southward to Arizona, New Mexico, and central western Texas.

It is well named the mountain chickadee, for, during the breeding season at least and for much of the remainder of the year its favorite haunts are the coniferous forests of the mountains, from 6,000 up to 11,000 feet, but mainly at the higher levels, 8,000 to 10,000 feet. Below the coniferous forests it is largely or wholly replaced by the long-tailed chickadee.

In fall the mountain chickadees, with their young, range up to timberline or even beyond; in fall and during winter they often range down to the foothills and valleys, where they are sometimes seen together with the long-tailed chickadees in the fringes of cottonwoods and willows along the streams.

Mrs. Bailey (1928) says that, in New Mexico, "they may be met with almost anywhere in the forested mountains. In Santa Clara Canyon, where we found them in the oaks, nut pines, and junipers of the south slope, down along the creek, in the turns where the sun came in, they were in the alders and birches together with migrating warblers, vireos, and flycatchers. But they are found in the high, dark, coniferous forests as well, and it is here that their cheery notes are most gratefully heard."

In his paper on the subspecies of the mountain chickadee, Dr. Joseph Grinnell (1918) says: "Among the four subspecies of *Penthestes gambeli* here recognized, color alone is sufficient for distinguishing *P. gambeli gambeli*. The flanks, sides of body and back in this form are pervaded with a distinct tinge of cinnamon—more exactly, the 'pinkish buff' of Ridgway (1912, pl. 29). In addition, this race shows the greatest length of tail, and slenderest bill."

Nesting.—The mountain chickadee does not seem to be at all particular about the choice or location of its nest. It prefers, however, to place its nest in a natural cavity in a tree, or in an old woodpecker hole, and I believe that it does not excavate its own nest cavity if it can find one already made for it. Its nest has been found at heights ranging from 2 to 80 feet above the ground, the extreme heights being very rare; apparently very few nests are more than 15 feet from the ground, and many are less than 6 feet up. J. K. Jensen (1923) says that, in New Mexico, he often finds this chickadee nesting in bird boxes, and he has "found the nests in cavities in pine stumps, in quaking aspens and under rocks." Later (1925) he writes:

"May 15, 1925, I made a trip ten miles southeast of Santa Fe intending to examine a number of bird boxes. One of the boxes contained a set of six eggs of the Mountain Chicadee *(Penthestes gambeli gambeli)* and three eggs of the Gray Titmouse *(Baeolophus inornatus griseus)* with the Chicadee incubating. I took out the six eggs of the Chicadee and left those of the Titmouse. May 22, the Chicadee was incubating four Titmouse eggs, all of which hatched. June 8, I again visited the box and found the Chicadee busy feeding four young Titmice."

This chickadee is a very close sitter, reluctant to leave its nest, and it has developed to a very high degree the intimidation reaction to the approach of an intruder, a habit shared by other species of chickadee. This consists of a loud hissing noise and a rapid fluttering of the wings, when the nest is invaded; it might be enough to frighten away some smaller enemy, but to man it serves only to illustrate the devotion of the brave little bird to its eggs or young; the heartless egg collector seldom rewards the devoted mother for her bravery.

The nest is made of soft mosses and the fur and hair of mammals, being warmly lined with finer material of the same kind, much like the nests of other chickadees.

Eggs.—The mountain chickadee seems to lay very large sets. Sets of less than six are probably incomplete; and from that the numbers run up to 12, sets of 9 being common. There are 16 sets of eggs of this chickadee in the collection of the University of Colorado Museum; in this series there are three sets of 7, seven sets of 9, three sets of 10, two sets of 11, and one set of 12 eggs.

The eggs are normally ovate in shape, with variations toward rounded-ovate. The shell is smooth and practically lacking in gloss. The ground color is pure, dead white, with much variation in the extent of the markings. In most sets a small or a large proportion of the eggs are entirely unmarked; and in some sets all the eggs are spotless pure white. Some eggs are faintly marked all over the entire surface with fine dots of pale or reddish brown. In others these small spots are more or less concentrated about the larger end. An occasional set is brilliantly marked with a ring of bright reddish brown or orange-rufous spots or small blotches.

The measurements of 40 eggs average 15.6 by 12.3 millimeters; the eggs showing the four extremes measure **16.5** by **12.9,** and **13.8** by **11.5** millimeters.

Young.—I have no information on the period of incubation for this race.

Dean Amadon has sent me the following note on a nestful of young mountain chickadees that he observed at 9,800 feet on the east slope of Snowy Range, Medicine Bow Mountains, Wyo., about 20 feet from the ground in a natural crevice of a large lodgepole pine: "Both parents were feeding the young very frequently at the time, which was 7 P.M., just before dark. Once, when the two parents appeared with food at the same time, they crouched on limbs near the nest, opening and quivering their wings, as do young birds when begging for food. The young were noisy enough to be heard for about 30 feet from the nest tree; I was told that they had left the nest and were not seen two days later, on July 8. Nest was in rather dense pine stand, but only 40 feet from the clearing made by a main road."

Claude T. Barnes tells me that five tiny fledgings, in a nest that he examined, "hissed in the manner of a snake" when he reflected light into the nest. The nest was in a quaking aspen, which, "twisted by winds and snow, had cracked, making a cozy hole about 4 inches deep and 3 inches in diameter."

Plumages.—In the juvenal plumage, young birds are much like adults.

366 BULLETIN 191, UNITED STATES NATIONAL MUSEUM

but the white stripe over the eye is more imperfect, less distinct, and grayer; the black of the crown and throat is duller; and the edgings of the greater wing coverts and tertials are tinged with pale buff. The body plumage is softer and fluffier, less compact. The annual molt seems to occur mainly in August, though I have seen very few molting birds. Fall birds have the white superciliary stripe broader and more distinct, and the gray portions of the plumage slightly more buffy than in spring birds; in spring birds the superciliary stripe is reduced to a broken series of white streaks.

Voice.—Aretas A. Saunders sends me the following note on the song of this chickadee, as heard by him in Montana: "The song of the mountain chickadee is similar in quality to that of the black-capped chickadee, a sweet, clear whistle, but it usually consists of three notes of equal length, each lower in pitch than the preceding, so that it is like *fee-bee-bay*. The bird occasionally responds to an imitation and comes to the observer, but not so readily as the black-cap does. The song is rather infrequently used."

Claude T. Barnes says in his notes: "Two chickadees, which from the white superciliary stripe I took to be *gambeli*, flitted about the maple trees uttering every second or so a single note *chip*. Once in a while one would issue a burring sound like *trrrrrrrrp*. Overcome with curiosity at my immobility, they edged their way by little flits and various maneuvers behind tree trunks until they were within six feet of me, when, evidently being satisfied, they as casually worked their way from me."

Edward R. Warren (1916) writes: "They seemed to say 'chick-a-dee-a-dee-a-dee', not 'chick-a-dee-dee' as the Black-caps do. And the tone was also different, but I cannot describe it."

Field marks.—Although similar in general appearance and behavior to our more familiar black-capped chickadees, this species can be easily recognized by the usually conspicuous white stripe that runs from the bill over the eye and into the black cap. Its song is different, as described above, and its ordinary chickadee note is somewhat hoarser and more deliberate. Also, it is oftener found in the coniferous forests than is *atricapillus*.

DISTRIBUTION

Range.—Mountains of the Western United States, Canada, and northern Baja California; nonmigratory.

The range of the mountain chickadee extends **north** to northern British Columbia (Atlin and Nine Mile Mountain); Alberta (Smoky Valley and Banff); and central Montana (Gold Run and Fort Custer).

East to eastern Montana (Fort Custer and Red Lodge) ; eastern Wyoming (Wheatland and Laramie) ; Colorado (Golden, Pikes Peak, and Fort Garland) ; New Mexico (Willis and Capitan Mountain) ; and western Texas (Davis Mountains). **South** to southwestern Texas (Davis Mountains) ; southwestern New Mexico (Pinos Altos Mountain) ; southern Arizona (Santa Catalina Mountains) ; and northern Baja California (San Pedro Mártir Mountains). **West** to Baja California (San Pedro Mártir Mountains and Sierra Juárez) ; central California (Barley Flats, Big Trees, Marysville, and Weed) ; Oregon (Pinehurst and Fort Klamath) ; Washington (Mount Rainier and Spokane) ; and British Columbia (Summerland and Atlin).

The range as outlined is for the entire species, which has been separated into at least six subspecies. The typical mountain chickadee *(Parus g. gambeli)* is found in the Rocky Mountain region from Wyoming and Montana south to western Texas, New Mexico, and Arizona ; Grinnell's chickadee *(P. g. grinnelli)* occupies the northern parts of the range from British Columbia south to central Oregon and northern Idaho ; the short-tailed chickadee *(P. g. abbreviatus)* is found from southern Oregon south to central California and northwestern Nevada ; Bailey's chickadee *(P. g. baileyae)* is found in the higher mountains of southern California ; the San Pedro Chickadee *(P. g. atratus)* is found in the mountains of northern Baja California ; and the Inyo chickadee *(P. g. inyoensis)* occupies the mountain areas of eastern California chiefly in Mono and Inyo Counties.

Egg dates.—California : 82 records, May 4 to July 11 ; 42 records, May 22 to June 13, indicating the height of the season.

Colorado : 33 records, April 5 to June 23 ; 17 records, June 3 to 11.

Oregon : 15 records, May 20 to June 12 ; 8 records, May 30 to June 6.

PARUS GAMBELI INYOENSIS (Grinnell)

INYO CHICKADEE

This is a pale race of the white-browed, or mountain, chickadees found in the more arid mountain regions of eastern California. Dr. Grinnell (1918) describes it as "the palest colored race of the four ; sides, flanks and back, in unworn plumage, pervaded with pale buff— the 'cartridge buff' of Ridgway (1912, pl. 30). Wear or fading, or both, removes most of this buff tone, so that the resulting effect, in spring and summer birds, is of an ashy tone of coloration, distinctly lighter than in any of the other three subspecies, in same stage. It seems probable that there is a paler tone to the underlying plumage

368 BULLETIN 191, UNITED STATES NATIONAL MUSEUM

parts and that this becomes revealed by loss of the superficial pigment-bearing portions through the gradual progress of feather abrasion. *Inyoensis* shows nearly as long a tail as does *gambeli*. Its bill is somewhat smaller."

He gives as its range "the higher mountains of eastern California lying east and southeast of Owens Valley, from the vicinity of the Mono Craters and the White Mountains, in Mono County, south to the Panamint Mountains, in Inyo County."

I cannot find anything in print about the haunts, nesting, eggs, food, or other habits of this subspecies, which are probably similar to those of mountain chickadees elsewhere.

The measurements of 9 eggs average 16.8 by 12.8 millimeters; the eggs showing the four extremes measure 17.1 by 12.9, 17.0 by 13.0, 15.7 by 12.8, and 17.0 by 12.5 millimeters.

PARUS CINCTUS ALASCENSIS (Prazák)

ALASKA CHICKADEE

HABITS

The Alaska chickadee is our representative of an Old World species, widely distributed in northern Siberia and Russia, that has crossed Bering Strait and become established, as an American subspecies, in the Hudsonian Zone of northern Alaska and northwestern Mackenzie. Closely related races occur in eastern Siberia *(P. c. obtectus)* and in northern Europe *(P. c. cinctus)*. The range of our subspecies extends, so far as known, from the Kowak River and St. Michael, Alaska, on the west to the Anderson River, Mackenzie, on the east. Dr. E. W. Nelson (1887) wrote: "Its range does not appear to extend to the south along the Upper Yukon, as a considerable series of Titmice, brought me from that region by the fur traders, does not contain a single example. From the vicinity of Nulato, thence down the Yukon, and to the north and northeast, this form appears to be as abundant as the Hudsonian Titmouse, whose range it shares in this region."

Olaus J. Murie (1928) writes of the haunts of this chickadee in the Old Crow River district, Yukon, as follows:

The habitat of the Alaska Chickadee was spruce and willow woods covering the valley of the Old Crow River, about a mile in width, but much more in some places. The edge of this valley rises abruptly about 75 feet above the stream to the level of the flat tundra, which stretches away for many miles on either side. The tundra is covered with numerous ponds and lakes, and except for a few small groups of spruces here and there it is practically treeless, although near the mouth of the river, where it enters the general wooded area of the Porcupine River district, there is a more general distribution of forest. The wooded valley of the Old Crow and some of its tributaries, therefore, carry the spruce woods in the form of long sinuous belts through a tundra region. These narrow belts of forest are the home of the Alaska Chickadee, apparently to the exclusion of other Chickadees. *Penthestes hudsonicus* was not collected on the Old Crow nor was it identified among those observed. * * *

A consideration of the circumstances under which the Alaska Chickadee has been observed tends to show that it prefers the edges of forest tracts or regions where spruce forest is broken up, as contrasted with more extensive, continuous forest areas. * * * Grinnell says, 'The Alaskan Chickadee was never seen in company with the other species and was an inhabitant of the spruce tracts along the base of the mountains rather than in the river bottoms.' Other records show that *alascensis* was found even in the willows beyond the spruce woods. The range of this bird borders the northern tree limit, where habitat conditions mentioned here may be found.

Joseph S. Dixon (1938) found it "well distributed in the aspen and spruce forests," in Mount McKinley National Park. "People living in the region told us that these chicadees disappear in the spring and are rarely seen all summer, but that in the fall they again gather about the cabins to be fed."

Our Alaskan bird differs from the Siberian race in having a smaller bill and slightly darker coloration. It resembles the Hudsonian chickadee in a general way, but the sides of the neck are white instead of gray, and the coloration is paler throughout.

Nesting.—The first nest reported of the Alaska chickadee was that found by Roderick MacFarlane (1891) in the Anderson River region in northern Mackenzie, of which he states: "On 1st June, 1864, a nest of this species, containing seven eggs, was found near Fort Anderson, in a hole in a dry spruce stump, at a height of about 6 feet from the ground. It was composed of a moderate quantity of hare or rabbit fur, intermixed with a sprinkling of dried moss. The female parent was snared on the nest, but the male was not seen. The contents of the eggs were tolerably fresh."

There is a set of six eggs in the Thayer collection, taken by Bishop J. O. Stringer near the Peel River on June 30, 1898; the nest was in a hole in a tree stump. The European race is said to make its nest in natural cavities in trees, or in old woodpecker holes. Dr. E. W. Nelson (1887) says that it "has been known to eject the rightful owner of a cavity and seize upon the site for its own nest. Its eggs are usually placed upon a mass of hairs of the lemming and hare, combined with fine moss or vegetable down."

Eggs.—Dr. Nelson (1887) says that "it lays from seven to nine eggs, which are grayish-white, with reddish-violet and reddish-brown spots often collected at the larger end. The eggs are broad in proportion to their length."

The eggs in the Thayer collection are ovate, with hardly any gloss. The ground color is pure white and is finely speckled, more thickly around the larger end, with small dots of reddish brown.

The measurements of 31 eggs average 16.3 by 12.1 millimeters; the eggs showing the four extremes measure **17.3** by 12.7, 16.5 by **13.2,** and **15.0** by **11.0** millimeters.

Voice.—Mr. Murie (1928) says: "The characteristic call of this Chickadee generally consisted of two notes, which I described variously in my field notes as 'dee-deer,' 'chee-ee,' or 'pee-vee,' with emphasis on each syllable and a tone and accent which seemed to imply a peevish or complaining state of mind. Nelson describes it as '*pistéé-téé,* uttered in a hissing tone.' I imagined this call differed from that of the Hudsonian Chickadee, but in the absence of the latter for comparison at the time I cannot rely too greatly on this impression."

Field marks.—The Alaska chickadee most closely resembles the Hudsonian chickadee, but it is slightly larger, its general coloration is paler, its crown is grayer, less brownish, the sides of its neck are white instead of gray, and it lacks the rich-brown flanks of *hudsonicus,* the latter being paler and grayer. It can be distinguished from any race of the black-capped chickadee by the gray instead of the black crown and by the absence of white edgings on the tail feathers.

So little is known about our Alaskan subspecies that it seems worthwhile to include the following notes on the European race, kindly contributed by B. W. Tucker: "In the forest belt of Arctic Europe the Lapptit *(Parus cinctus cinctus),* the racial representative of the Alaska chickadee in that region, is one of the characteristic small birds. It has been described as more characteristic of the pine forest than of the birch and alder, but in Finnish and Norwegian Lapland I found it chiefly among birch or mixed birch and pine on the borders of the pine forest proper. In habits this species does not differ from the black-capped tits. In the latter part of June I found it chiefly in family parties of parents and fledged young, the latter in one or two cases still being fed by the old birds, but I also found a pair still feeding young in the nest on June 21. The nest in question was in an old woodpecker hole at about eye level in a dead pine trunk on the edge of a swamp, woodpecker holes being, it is stated, the favorite nesting site of this tit. Whether it will also excavate its own hole, like some of its allies, seems not to be recorded.

"The common note of the Lapptit may be represented as a low-pitched, grating *tchaa-tchaa* or *tzaa-tzaa,* in which the *a* sound must be given a pronounced nasal quality, as in *twang,* but more exaggerated. It is often quite indistinguishable to my ear from the typical note of the willowtit, but at other times it is obviously softer and less harsh, and easily distinguished. Sometimes it is repeated rapidly in a way that would doubtless recall the chickadee to an American observer but that to a Britisher recalls the marshtit, for in Europe oddly enough it is the marshtit that has (among others) a rapid *chicka-bee-bee-bee* note and not the willowtit, although the latter is more closely allied to the chickadee and indeed is currently regarded as a form of the same species. The call note is a hoarse little *tzeep* or *tzip* and *tzee-ip* and the same note, or duplications of it, commonly precedes the *tzaa—tzeet-tzaa-tzaa, tzitzi-tzaa-tzaa,* etc. It has also a very shrill keening note, again like the willowtit. The song also recalls the song of the willowtit, as opposed to the marshtit, in being distinctly warbling, and I have described it in my notes as a sustained, low, liquid, ripply or bubbling warble."

DISTRIBUTION

Range.—Arctic regions of northern Asia and northwestern North America; nonmigratory.

In northern Asia the range of this chickadee extends eastward from the Yenisei River to the coast of Bering Sea and south to Lake Baikal. In North America the species is found **north** to northern Alaska (Kowak River and Altana River); northern Yukon (Old Crow); and northern Mackenzie (Richards Island and Fort Anderson). **East** to northwestern Mackenzie (Fort Anderson). **South** to northwestern Mackenzie (Fort Anderson); and central Alaska (Twelvemile Creek, probably Dishna River, and St. Michael). **West** to western Alaska (St. Michael and Kowak River).

Three races of this species are recognized, the typical form of northern Europe *(P. c. cinctus);* the form of eastern Siberia, Kamchatka, around the shores of the Okhotsk Sea *(P. c. obtectus);* and the form found in North America known as *P. c. alascensis.*

Egg dates.—Alaska: 2 records, June 10 and 24.

Arctic Canada: 1 record, June 30.

Mackenzie: 1 record, June 1.

Siberia: 1 record, June 1.

PARUS HUDSONICUS HUDSONICUS Forster

HUDSONIAN CHICKADEE

HABITS

The type race of these brown-capped chickadees was described and named many years ago from specimens taken on the west coast of Hudson Bay, at Severn River. For nearly 100 years it remained the only recognized form of the species. The characters by which other recognized subspecies have been separated will be mentioned under the respective races. This type race has the widest breeding range of the three races recognized in the 1931 Check-list, from northwestern Alaska to Hudson Bay and south to central Manitoba and central Ontario, whence it wanders farther south in winter.

Dr. Joseph Grinnell (1900a) says of its status in the Kotzebue Sound region of Alaska: "At our winter camp on the Kowak this species was common up to the middle of September. After that date and up to the first of April, but one or two at a time were seen and then only at long intervals. Early in September groups of four to seven were noted nearly every day in the spruces around our cabin. * * * Those chickadees observed during the winter were all in the dense willow thickets along Hunt River. They were there quieter and, by nature of their retreat, hard to find. It may have been that at the advent of cold weather all the chickadees left the spruces and betook themselves to the shelter of the willow-brush; but I am rather inclined to believe that there was a partial migration to the southward. By the first of May the chickadees were back again roving through the woods in pairs."

Lee R. Dice (1920) says that in the interior of Alaska "they occur in willows and alders and in white spruce and paper birch forest."

I cannot find that the Hudsonian chickadee differs materially in any of its habits from the better-known Acadian chickadee, to which the reader is referred.

Nesting.—Dr. Samuel S. Dickey (MS.) tells of a nest probably of this race that he found while exploring along the Moose River, west of James Bay. It was in "a singular glade, along the moist north terrace of Moose Island. It was hedged in with black spruce trees of moderate size and a natural fence of speckled alder and mountainholly shrubs *(Nemopanthus mucronata)*. The green moss carpet that lay beyond was seen to contain in its midst several short, weathered, barkless spruce stubs, and in the side of one of them a dark hole loomed up. It was about the size of a 25-cent piece. With a stout pocket ax I parted the hard resistant wood opposite the entrance. Thus I could view the interior. It contained a compactly woven nest, in whose cup lay a clutch of six somewhat incubated eggs. The nest was better composed than are those of the eastern chickadees. Its foundation was a mass of dead and also green cedar moss *(Hypnum cristatum)*. Upon this was the soft bed of fur of the snowfoot hare. The eggs were nicely adjusted in the cup in the center of this mass. Further examination of this nest showed that at its base was decayed moss and hair of former nests of other years. Evidently the much worn cavity and entrance had served this pair for many seasons.

"The eggs were light creamy white in ground color and were sprinkled nearly all over the entire shell surface with light reddish brown. They resembled more closely the run of eggs of the winter wren (*Nannus hiemalis*) than of specimens from other eastern chickadees."

The stub was 30 inches high, and the entrance to the nest was 18 inches above the bog surface; the cavity was 6 inches deep.

A. D. Henderson has sent me two photographs of nesting stumps of this chickadee. One was an old tamarack stump in a muskeg; the entrance hole was only 5½ inches above the moss, and the nest was practically at ground level. The other was a stub in an old cutting, 13 inches high, and the bird was seen to enter through a hole in the ax cut.

Eggs.—The eggs are apparently similar to those of the Acadian chickadee. The measurements of 22 eggs average 15.3 by 12.3 millimeters; the eggs showing the four extremes measure **16.3** by 12.2, **15.4** by **12.7**, **14.9** by 12.4, and 15.2 by **11.7** millimeters.

Fall.—Frank L. Farley writes to me from Camrose, Alberta: "This species is partially migratory in this latitude. It is a common summer resident of the spruce forests along the foothills of the Rockies and in much of the territory north of the Saskatchewan River. Numbers of them, at the approach of winter, wander south and east to scattered areas of spruce, which persist on the northern exposures of the larger rivers in central Alberta. Here they remain until early in March. It has been noted that these visitors always feed in the higher branches of the spruces, while the black-capped chickadees hunt the lower parts of the trees. During very severe cold spells, when the thermometer shows 50° below zero, I frequently find dead blackcaps in the woods, no doubt as a result of intense cold or inability to secure food, but I have never known the Hudsonian to succumb at such times. They are, no doubt, the hardier of the two species."

Numerous reports of periodic southward migrations of Hudsonian chickadees have been recorded. The latest one comes to me in a letter from O. E. Devitt, of Toronto, who writes: "In October 1937 a rather remarkable influx of these northern titmice occurred in this area. They were first noted at Nancy Lake, near King, on October 29, by R. D. Ussher; several turned up at Ashbridges Bay, Toronto, on October 31, and on this date I saw several near Bradford and collected a male. This specimen was later submitted to P. A. Taverner, of Ottawa, with the view that it might be the Acadian race. However, it was identified by him as the '*nigrescens*' type of the brown-headed chickadee (*Penthestes hudsonicus hudsonicus*). Individuals remained about Nancy Lake well on into the winter."

DISTRIBUTION

Range.—Northern North America; not regularly migratory.

The range of the Hudsonian chickadee extends **north** to northern Alaska (Hunt River, Tanana, White Mountains, and Bern Creek); Yukon (Robinson Camp); Mackenzie (Fort Goodhope, Lake Hardisty, and Fort Rae); northern Manitoba (Lake Du Brochet and Mosquito Point); northern Quebec (Chimo); and Labrador (Okkak). **East** to Labrador (Okkak, Davis Inlet, and Cartwright); Newfoundland (Paynes Cove, St. John's, and Makinsons Grove); Nova Scotia (Dartmouth and Seal Island); New Hampshire (Washington); and southeastern New York (Big Indian Valley). **South** to New York (Big Indian Valley); possibly Massachusetts (see text); possibly Pennsylvania (see text); southern Ontario (Brule Lake and Sayma Lake); northern Michigan (Blaney); northern Wisconsin (Mamie Lake); northern Minnesota (Sandy Lake and Deer River); northern Montana (south fork of Teton River); and southern British Columbia (Schoonover Mountain). **West** to British Columbia (Schoonover Mountain, Salmon River, and Ninemile Mountain); and Alaska (Houkan, Fort Kenai, Nushagak, Nulato, Kowak River, and Hunt River). The species has been reported in the mountains of eastern Pennsylvania (Laanna and Pocono Lake) during the summer, and it may be found to breed there.

While not regularly migratory there appears to be an occasional fall movement that extends the range in winter south to southern Michigan (Lansing); northern Illinois (Waukegan Flats); southern Minnesota (Fairmont); and northern North Dakota (Upsilon Lake); Massachusetts; and New York.

As outlined the range is for the entire species, of which four subspecies are recognized. The typical Hudsonian chickadee *(P. h. hudsonicus)* is found from northern Alaska and Mackenzie southwestward to Ontario; the Columbian chickadee *(P. h. columbianus)* is found from Montana and Alberta west through British Columbia and Alaska to the Kenai Peninsula; and the Acadian chickadee *(P. h. littoralis)* occupies that part of the range that, in general, is east of Michigan and Ontario. The Cascade brown-headed chickadee *(P. h. cascadensis)* is apparently confined to the northern Cascade Mountains in Washington.

Egg dates.—Alaska: 1 record, June 9.

Alberta: 4 records, May 17 to June 13.

Labrador: 5 records, June 8 to 12.

Manitoba: 5 records, June 2 to 15.

Nova Scotia: 26 records, May 16 to June 9; 14 records; May 29 to June 5.

PARUS HUDSONICUS COLUMBIANUS Rhoads
COLUMBIAN CHICKADEE

This extreme western race of the Hudsonian chickadee ranges from the Kenai Peninsula in Alaska, through the Rocky Mountain region of western Canada, southward to southern British Columbia, Alberta, and northern Montana, but the limits of its range are not accurately outlined.

According to Ridgway (1904), it is "similar to *P. h. hudsonicus,* but slightly darker and less brown above, especially the pileum and hind neck; chin and throat more decidedly black; bill relatively larger."

Nothing seems to have been published on any of the habits of this race, which are probably similar to those of the other races. The type specimen was taken at Field, British Columbia, in the heart of the Canadian Rockies, at an elevation of about 5,000 feet.

PARUS HUDSONICUS LITTORALIS Bryant
ACADIAN CHICKADEE

PLATES 58, 59

HABITS

The eastern race of the Hudsonian chickadee breeds in the spruce and balsam forests, north to the limits of these forests, east of Hudson Bay, in Ungava, Labrador, Quebec, Newfoundland, and Nova Scotia. The 1931 Check-list says that it breeds south to Maine, "the mountains of northern Vermont and central New Hampshire, and the Adirondacks of New York." But there is some evidence to indicate that it may breed, at least occasionally, in some of the mountains farther south. It has been seen in June in Plymouth County, Mass., and at least twice during that month in the Pocono Mountains in Pennsylvania.

As to the Massachusetts evidence, Dr. Arthur P. Chadbourne (1896) wrote many years ago: "While walking through some dense old-growth pine woods *(Pinus strobus* and *P. rigida) * * * I was greeted by the snarl *chee-dè-e-e-e-e-ah* of a Hudson Bay Titmouse. . . . The woods in which I saw the Chickadee were only a few rods from a large cedar swamp, said to be a couple of miles wide, which is seldom visited except by lumbermen in winter; and in many portions the original growth of huge white cedars *(Cupressus thyoides)* and hemlock *(Abies canadensis)* has never been cut. In this old timber one seems to be in northern Maine or New Hampshire, instead of in Massachusetts;—the subdued half twilight of the damp cool forest, with its rocks and fallen trees, covered with a rich carpet of green moss and ferns might well tempt this and other northern birds to make it their summer home."

The Pennsylvania evidence is equally suggestive. J. Fletcher Street (1918) found a pair of these chickadees at Pocono Lake on June 17, 1917. "The location was at the edge of a sphagnum swamp amid a dense grove of dwarf spruces. When discovered the birds evidenced considerable excitement and came and scolded within three feet of me." Regarding the other Pennsylvania record, Thomas D. Burleigh (1918) writes:

In company with Richard C. Harlow, Richard F. Miller and Albert D. McGrew, I spent three weeks in the field in the spring of 1917 about La Anna, Pike County, Pa., and June 3, while searching a large sphagnum bog for a nest of the elusive Northern Water-Thrush, two brown-capped chickadees were seen. * * * They showed a preference for a certain part of the bog that we had been floundering through but although several suspicious looking holes were found, we could detect no signs of their nesting. I returned to the spot the next day, and had no difficulty in finding the birds again. This time I spent two hours trailing them but with no success other than leaving with the conviction that they were mated and if not as yet nesting here, would undoubtedly do so. Not satisfied, however, all of us returned the following day and made another attempt but with no more luck though we again found them at the same place. * * * The situation in which they were found was typical of that much farther north, being indeed a northern muskeg in every sense of the word, with lichen covered tamarack, deep beds of sphagnum moss and scattered pools."

The localities in which these birds were found in Pennsylvania would match almost exactly the favorite haunts of the species in the north woods of Canada, coniferous forests of spruces, firs, cedars, pines, and larches, especially in the vicinity of peat bogs and muskegs, sometimes mixed with a few small paper birches and mountain-ashes, with a ground cover of sphagnum moss, Labrador tea, and other northern plants.

The only place where I have ever found the Acadian chickadee really common was on Seal Island, Nova Scotia. This island is situated about 15 miles off the southwest coast and is about 4 miles long; it is divided in the middle by a low stretch of sandy beach and marsh, from which the land rises at both ends and is heavily wooded with a dense forest of small spruces and firs, sometimes growing so closely together as to be nearly impenetrable. These forests, nourished by the fog banks that envelop that coast almost constantly, were rich and luxuriant, thickly carpeted with soft mosses and ferns, the fallen trees, as well as the trunks and branches of the standing trees, supporting a flourishing growth of various mosses and lichens. In these dense and shady retreats, where the trees were often dripping with moisture, were the favorite haunts of Bicknell's thrushes and Acadian chickadees, the two most conspicuous birds. It was the first week in July and the young of both species were on the wing. We saw the chickadees feeding their young, and, through the kindness of John Crowell, the owner of the island, we were allowed to collect a few specimens.

Courtship.—At Averill, Vt., on May 24, 1915, Frederic H. Kennard watched a pair of these chickadees in what seemed to be courtship behavior. His notes state that "the male was very thoughtful and attentive to his little mate, whom he fed frequently. She kept up an almost continuous twittering call, and would flutter her little wings and ruffle her feathers on his near approach. We saw him give her several green cankerworms and many other small bugs; and I saw them copulate once."

Nesting.—W. J. Brown writes to me that the Acadian chickadee is fairly well distributed in the County of Matane on the south shore of the Gulf of St. Lawrence, where he has found some ten nests. The lowest nest was one foot from the ground in an old spruce stub in a bog, and the highest elevation was about 8 feet. Out of the ten nests under observation, two had the entrance hole on the top of the stub, facing all kinds of weather, while the others had the hole at the side of a dead stub. All the nests were made of rabbit hair, with some feathers, well put together.

Philipp and Bowdish (1919) record three nests found in New Brunswick as follows: "On June 5, 1917, a nest was found, nearly or quite completed, in a natural cavity in a cedar stump about two feet from the ground. On June 16 the bird was sitting hard on five eggs, and was persuaded to come out only with great difficulty. As she laid no more, this was apparently her full laying. On June 24 a nest containing seven quite small young was found in a knot hole in a small live spruce. On June 13, 1918, another nest with young was found in a cavity in the top of a dead and rotten stub, about ten feet from the ground. This nest was very near the site of the 1917 nest with young, very possibly belonging to the same pair of birds."

Mrs. Eleanor R. Pettingill (1937), with her husband, Dr. Olin S. Pettingill, Jr., had an interesting experience with a family of Acadian chickadees on Grand Manan, New Brunswick. The nest was about 10 feet from the ground in a hole, made perhaps by a hairy woodpecker, in a tall dead spruce stump. The nest contained seven young that were "fitted compactly together on a comfortable bedding of birch-bark shreds and bits of moss. The base of the nest was about 6 inches below the entrance."

Aaron C. Bagg (1939) discovered a nest containing young in Somerset County, Maine. He writes:

For some moments the two chickadees flew about nearby, uttering faint scolding notes of alarm and continued to gather insects from the ends of spruce boughs. It was not until I had seated myself and remained quiet that one of the birds flew to a clump of spruce trees, a lone birch and a cedar. Presently the chickadee dropped down low behind the cedar for an instant. Suspecting it might be the nest, I approached and discovered the nesting cavity hidden in the cedar. Fifteen inches above ground the cedar, not over six inches in diameter, divided into two upright branches at an easy angle. Where they joined on the inside, a space fully ten inches in length, the secret lay—an ideal cavity with a narrow opening. Within the nest were young birds well feathered, nearly ready to leave. When I revisited the nest on July 5, they had departed. Search of the vicinity failed to discover any of the fledglings or of their parents. The nesting cavity contained finely shredded cedar peelings and bits of decayed cedar. But the bulk of the nest consisted of moss and deer hair.

Several other nests have been described by other observers, all in very similar situations and made of similar materials. The cavity is often filled with dry or green mosses, bits of lichens, fine strips of the inner bark of cedars and the down from ferns; but the main part of the nest, where the eggs are hatched, is a well-felted bag composed of deer hair and the soft fur of rabbits or other small mammals, making a warm bed for the young.

Eggs.—The Acadian chickadee has been known to lay four to nine eggs to a set, but apparently the two extremes are uncommon. The eggs vary in shape from ovate to short-ovate, and some are rather pointed. They have very little or no gloss. They are white and more or less sparingly and unevenly sprinkled with fine dots or small spots of reddish brown, "hazel"; occasionally the spots are concentrated in a ring about the larger end.

The measurements of 40 eggs average 16.0 by 12.2 millimeters; the eggs showing the four extremes measure 17.4 by 11.6, 15.8 by 12.9, 14.7 by 12.7, and 15.3 by 11.4 millimeters.

Young.—We have no definite information on the period of incubation, which is probably about the same as that of other chickadees, or about two weeks; other young chickadees usually remain in the nest 14 to 18 days.

The Pettingills (1937) watched their family of Acadian chickadees on Grand Manan for an entire day, from sunrise to sunset, each taking turns, with the following results:

Both sexes shared equally in the feeding. Frequently they arrived together and one stood by awaiting its turn to feed while its mate entered the hole with food. On several occasions one bird passed the food to its mate returning from the nest who immediately re-entered the nest to carry it below. * * *

During the course of the day the birds fed their young 362 times. The first feeding took place not long after break of day, at 4:46 A.M. One bird was already on the nest, where it had spent the night, when its mate arrived with food. The brooding bird left the nest and permitted its mate to enter and feed. They left the vicinity of the nest together. Before 6 A.M. they fed their young 34 times. During the day the average feedings were 24 times per hour. The last feeding took place at 7:40 P.M. when the bird, returning with food, entered and remained in the nest to brood.

Plumages.—I have seen no very young nestlings of this species, but Mrs. Pettingill (1937) says that the young, when "approximately three days of age," were naked except for a few wisps of down on their developing tracts, and that their eyes were only partially opened.

The juvenal body plumage is acquired before the young leave the nest, but the wings and tail are not fully grown until later. The color pattern is much like that of the adult, but the colors are duller and paler, and the plumage is softer and less compact. Dr. Dwight (1900) describes it as "above, brownish mouse-gray, the pileum pinkish drabgray. Wings and tail dull slate-gray whitish edged, the coverts edged with pale wood-brown. Below, including suborbital region and auriculars dingy white and washed on the sides and crissum with pale cinnamon, the chin and throat dull black."

He says that the first winter plumage is "acquired by a partial post-juvenal moult, beginning early in August in eastern Canada, which involves the body plumage and wing coverts, but not the rest of the wings nor the tail, young and old becoming practically indistinguishable." In the first winter plumage the pileum is "darker and the back browner, contrasting but slightly with the cap; the flanks, sides and crissum rich Mars-brown; the black on the throat deeper and the white of the sides of the head and lower parts clearer."

Adults have a complete postnuptial molt in July and August, replacing the decidedly worn, ragged, and somewhat faded plumage of the breeding season with the fresh and more richly colored autumn plumage.

Food.—These and other chickadees are among the best conservators of the forest trees that we have. They are very active at all seasons, inspecting the trunks, branches, and twigs of the trees in search of the minute insects that are so injurious and are too small to be noticed by the woodpeckers and other large birds; nothing escapes the chickadees' keen little eyes. The food of all the species is very similar in character, varying only with the latitude of the habitat of each and the kind of trees it frequents. The Acadian chickadee is essentially a bird of the northern coniferous forests and is especially useful in protecting the spruces, firs, and pines in these woods. All summer it may be seen carefully inspecting the branches of these trees even to the outermost twigs, often hanging head-downward to search among the bases of the needles, looking for caterpillars, moths, beetles, and other insects with which to feed its large and growing family. And in the winter it continues the good work by prying into crevices in the bark and searching the branches and twigs for hibernating insects, pupae, or egg clusters; many of the insects thus destroyed are among the worst enemies of the conifers.

Lucien M. Turner says in his Ungava notes: "It is not uncommon to find their beaks covered with gum from the spruce and larch. I accounted for it by supposing that during the summer months, when the gum exudes plentifully and is so soft, many insects adhere to it, and when winter comes the birds search for just such places to obtain the insects."

While visiting New England in fall and winter, and probably at other seasons, this chickadee apparently feeds to some extent on various seeds; it comes occasionally to feeding stations and seems to be fond of fatty foods.

Horace W. Wright (1917) received a letter from Richard M. Marble, of Woodstock, Vt., in which he states that an Acadian chickadee fed at a feeding station from November well into January. Mr. Wright saw some of these birds feeding frequently "upon stalks of golden rod and aster"; and he quotes William Brewster as having seen them "pecking at gray birch seed-cones."

He (Wright, 1914) saw them "picking seeds on the ground" and "picking at the green undeveloped berries of a red cedar."

Behavior.—Judging from my limited experience with them on their breeding grounds, I should say that Acadian chickadees are just as tame and confiding as our little blackcaps; we had no trouble in watching them at short range, and they fed their nearly full-grown young within a few feet of us. They are less active than our familiar chickadees, more deliberate in their movements, and less noisy. They were traveling about in small family parties. Some observers have referred to it as shy, but others have found it almost tame enough to be caught by hand. Oliver L. Austin, Jr. (1932), found that, in Labrador, "while occupied with their nesting duties, they are very quiet and unobtrusive." He continues:

They keep out of sight and are seldom noticed, even by one looking for them. I had to hunt, and hunt persistently, to get three specimens at Sandwich Bay, July 16, 1928. But the moment the young leave the nest, usually during the last two weeks in July, the Chickadees alter their demeanor, and the woods suddenly seem overrun with them. Small bands of young and old together, probably parents with their broods, meander inquisitively through the spruce and larch forests amid the clouds of mosquitoes and black flies. Their tameness, in contrast to their previous reticence, is surprising. Their buzzing statements of facts greet you on all sides. They seem to follow you about. Hunting industriously for aphids, they explore every nook and cranny of the larch branch within two feet of your face. Perched upside down, rightside up, in all manner of conceivable and inconceivable attitudes, they regard you perkily with their bright beady eyes, burst suddenly into their commonplace *atser-day-day-day*, and flutter past your ear to the next promising branch. At this season you could almost catch them with a butterfly net.

W. J. Brown tells me of an usually tame Acadian chickadee that he saw. An old trapper had a nest of this bird about 15 feet from his back door in a natural cavity in a balsam fir. He had tacked a small branch directly under the entrance hole for a perch. When he tapped the side of the hole the chickadee came out and alighted on his hand to be fed. The man said that he had fed the bird in this way several times a day for the past ten days and that it would perch on any finger held out to it.

Acadian chickadees may usually flock by themselves, especially in their summer haunts, but they are often seen to join the merry little winter parties of black-capped chickadees, kinglets, nuthatches, and small woodpeckers that roam through the woods at that season. William Brewster (1938) watched such a gathering at Lake Umbagog in January. He says of the behavior of the Acadians: "For a time they kept high up in the tops of some tall balsams working among the cones, apparently extracting and eating the seeds. The Nuthatch was with them here for several minutes, but the Black-cap chickadees remained lower down. The Hudsonians differed from the Black-caps as follows: —they were much less noisy (often passing minutes at a time in absolute silence); they seldom hung head downward; they hopped and flitted among the branches more actively and ceaselessly, spending less time in one place; their shorter tails were less in evidence; they flirted their wings much more with a more nervous, tremulous motion very like that of Kinglets."

Mr. Wright (1917) noted that "Golden-crowned Kinglets have proved to be the closest companions of these Northern Chickadees on many occasions. Indeed, they seem to be their natural associates. Black-capped Chickadees are rather their incidental companions, with whom they occasionally come in touch, but do not habitually move."

Voice.—My impression of the ordinary note of the Acadian chickadee was that it resembled the corresponding note of the black-capped chickadee, but it was easily recognizable as not so sharp, clear, or lively as that of our more familiar bird; it was fainter, more lisping, hoarser, and more nasal; I wrote it in my notes as *chicka-deer-deer*, or *chicka-deer*. But I like Mr. Austin's rendering, *atser-day-day-day*, as quoted **above.**

William Brewster (1938) describes it as "a sharp *che-day, day,* very different from any note of the common Chickadee. * * * The ordinary chirp is much louder and more petulant. Another note frequently heard is a sharp *chip, chee-chee, chee* sometimes preluded by a sharp *che-chit* or *chee-chit-chit.*" Again (1906) he writes it "a nasal, drawling *tchick, chee-dày, dày.*"

A number of observers have heard this chickadee give a sweet, warbling song of three or four notes, and considerable has appeared in print about it. Other equally keen observers have failed to hear it. Aretas A. Saunders writes to me: "I am inclined to think that the brown-capped chickadees have no notes that correspond to the 'phoebe' note of the black-capped chickadee. I have seen quite a bit of the Acadian chickadees in the Adirondack Mountains, and Hudsonian chickadees in Montana, but have never heard a song of any kind from them."

Mr. Brewster (1906), after mentioning some published accounts of the song, writes: "I have never heard anything of the kind from the Hudsonian Chickadee, although I am reasonably familiar with that species, having had abundant opportunities for studying its notes and habits in the forests of northern New England where I have met with it on many different occasions and during every month of the year excepting April."

If two such experienced and keen observers have failed to hear the song, it must be of rather rare occurrence.

Townsend and Allen (1907) add to the discussion and quote Dr. Townsend's description of a song, heard at Cape Breton Island in August 1905: "It was a low, bubbling, warbling song, which I vainly attempted to describe in my notes. It began with a *pset* or *tsee;* followed by a sweet but short warble."

Francis H. Allen (1910) gives a number of references to published accounts of the song, and then adds his own observation, made on Mount Moosilauke, N. H., September 29, 1909: "I observed it for some time at close range and heard it sing again and again. The song was a short one but took two or more forms, one of which I set down at the time as bearing some slight resemblance to the syllables *wissipawiddlee,* though this rendering conveys no clear impression of its warbling quality. The final syllable was sometimes trilled and sometimes pure. It seemed to me that the song corresponded exactly to the *phoebe* song of the Black-capped Chickadee *(P. atricapillus),* but it was also strangely suggestive of the song of Bicknell's Thrush!"

Field marks.—The Acadian chickadee bears a general resemblance to our common chickadee, but it can be easily recognized by its brown instead of black cap and by the rich chestnut-brown of the sides and flanks; the black throat patch seems somewhat duller or less conspicuous. Its behavior and its voice are different, especially the latter, which is easily recognized.

Enemies.—Chickadees have to be on the watch for all the mammals and birds that prey on small birds, such as small hawks and squirrels, but their eggs and young are usually safe from many nest robbers in their snug retreats. Mrs. Pettingill (1937) writes: "Once during the day a red squirrel appeared in a near-by birch sapling. The Chickadees, on discovering him, were beside themselves with fright. * * * Both birds began to call noisily and to jump from one branch to another, keeping at a safe distance from the animal, but threatening him by making fake darts in his direction. The fact that one of them feigned injury came as a surprise. Perching at first upright on a branch, it suddenly but slowly toppled over backward until it clung upside down on the branch, wings fluttering helplessly. It did not drop to the ground but let go and alighted near-by. This time, on another branch, it seemed to fall over sidewise, nevertheless holding its legs stiff and not letting go."

In the nest examined by Mr. Bagg (1939) were found an adult *Protocalliphora,* a blood-sucking fly, and several pupae probably of this species, as well as the larvae of some less harmful species of insects. These fly maggots may be, at times, sufficiently numerous to kill not only the very young birds but those nearly fully fledged.

Fall.—Most of these northern chickadees remain on or near their breeding grounds all winter, but on certain seasons, at very irregular intervals, there has been a well-marked southward migration into New England and perhaps farther south. Two of the largest incursions were in 1913 and 1916, of which Horace W. Wright (1914 and 1917) has written full accounts. In November 1904 he saw only four birds, but in four different localities. But in the 1913 flight he had the records of over 40 birds, seen by himself and others, in 15 different towns or distinct localities. The 1916 flight seems to have been even heavier and more widely extended, reaching as far south as Staten Island, N. Y. The birds began to appear in October and some remained almost through January, the crest of the wave coming between November 9 and December 10. He referred the birds of the 1916 flight to the supposed Labrador race, *nigricans,* which is now regarded as the first winter plumage of the species; as all the birds taken seemed to be of this race, it suggests that these southward flights may be made up mainly of immature birds.

Some of these birds evidently spent the winter of 1916 and 1917 in

New England, or not much farther south. Mr. Wright (1918) gives another full account of the return flight in the spring of 1917; the latest record seems to be of a bird seen at West Roxbury, Mass., on May 18.

PARUS HUDSONICUS CASCADENSIS A. H. Miller

CASCADE BROWN-HEADED CHICKADEE

Dr. Alden H. Miller (1943b), who is responsible for the above names, says that this race "differs from *Parus hudsonicus columbianus* by darker, much sootier pileum (near Chaetura Drab in fresh plumage rather than Bister or Sepia); interscapular area somewhat darker and gray of sides of neck darker and more extensive proximally in auricular area; chestnut of sides darker (Prout's Brown rather than Cinnamon Brown). Size much as in *columbianus,* although measurements of the small sample available suggest somewhat greater average dimensions for the Cascade population * * *.

"The race *cascadensis* is even darker and duller on the pileum than is *P. h. littoralis* of the eastern seaboard and it is larger and notably longer-billed as are *P. h. hudsonicus* and *P. h. columbianus.* The contrast in coloration between *cascadensis* and *columbianus* is almost as great as that between *P. h. hudsonicus* and *Parus cinctus alascensis,* which, although evidently closely related, breed side by side in the Kowak Valley of Alaska.

"Range. *Cascadensis* is known at present only from the northern Cascade Mountains in the vicinity of Monument 83 on the United States-Canadian boundary in northwestern Okanogan County, Washington."

PARUS RUFESCENS RUFESCENS Townsend

CHESTNUT-BACKED CHICKADEE

HABITS

The visitor from the Eastern States is accustomed to seeing roving bands of chickadees, kinglets, creepers, and other small birds trooping through the winter woods and is not surprised when he finds just such jolly companies of friendly little feathered mites foraging through the dark coniferous forests of the humid Northwest coast. The kinglets and the creepers are so much like their eastern representatives that he does not recognize the difference, as he sees them in life; they are just familiar friends, kinglets and creepers. But the chickadees are different; they do not fit into memory's picture of our New England woods; their caps are not so black as those of eastern birds, and the rich chestnut of their backs and sides is strikingly new. We get the thrill of a new bird, seen for the first time. But, as we watch them we see that they are still chickadees, with all their manners, activities, and cheery notes, just old familiar friends in more richly colored garments, but just as sociable, friendly, and intriguing; they win our affection at once.

The chestnut-backed chickadee, of which there are three recognized subspecies, occupies a long narrow range from the Sitka district of southern Alaska southward along the humid coast belt to a little south of Monterey Bay in California. Dr. Joseph Grinnell (1904), in his interesting paper on the origin and distribution of this species, says that its range is very "narrow, only within the confines of Oregon and Washington exceeding one hundred miles and elsewhere usually much less, save for one or two isolated interior colonies." The type race, the subject of this sketch, occupies the greater part of this range, from Alaska southward to Marin County, Calif., where it intergrades with the Nicasio chickadee *(P. r. neglectus)*. The interior colonies referred to are in suitable coniferous forest environments in Idaho and western Montana, west of the Continental Divide. As to the possible origin of the chestnut-backed chickadee, Dr. Grinnell (1904) calls attention to a certain degree of resemblance, as to appearance and habitat, between it and the Hudsonian chickadee; and he suggests that the two species may have been derived from common ancestry, the dark, rich coloring of *rufescens* having evolved under the influence of the humid coast belt in which it lives; though no intermediates between the two are now known to exist, these may have been eliminated by the existence of insurmountable natural barriers and thus the two have become separate species. It is an interesting theory!

The favorite haunts of the chestnut-backed chickadees are the heavy, dark forests of firs, spruces and pines, dense cedar, tamarack, and hemlock woods, and, in California, the redwood forests. In the woods about Seattle and Kirkland, Wash., where we found this and the Oregon chickadees in 1911, there was then some of the primeval forest of lofty firs still left, but much of it had been lumbered and overgrown with second-growth firs of two or three species, with a considerable mixture of hemlock and a very handsome species of cedar; there was also some deciduous growth consisting of large alders and maples, with flowering dogwood in full bloom and a wild currant with pink blossoms.

Dr. Samuel S. Dickey writes to me that on the coast of southern Alaska "it is a bird that rather inclines to remain much of the time in the forests of gigantic evergreens, the Alaska cedars, Sitka spruces, western hemlocks and the firs. But not infrequently it will rove into glades and bogs, and it often comes down to the edges of the sea beaches, and only a stone's throw from cabins and totem poles of the native Indians."

Nesting.—The only nest of this species that I have seen was shown to me by D. E. Brown near South Tacoma, on May 14, 1911, while we were hunting through some of his favorite collecting grounds, smooth, level land with a fine growth of firs and cedars scattered about; the local species of firs were most abundant and were growing to perfection in the open stand, where they were well branched down to the ground. The chickadee's nest was 5 feet from the ground in the trunk of a large dead pine, in a cavity evidently excavated by the birds in the rotten wood behind the bark; since it contained one fresh egg, it was not closely examined.

The nests of the chestnut-backed chickadee have been placed at widely varying heights, according to various observers, but all seem to agree that most of the nests are less than 10 feet above ground. Thomas D. Burleigh (1930) writes of the nests that he has found about Tacoma: "The usual situation was in a fir stub, varying in height from a foot and a half to nine feet from the ground, although one nest was twelve feet from the ground in a knot hole in the trunk of a large dead oak at the edge of a stretch of open prairie, while another was five feet from the ground in a cavity in the thick bark of a large Douglas fir in a short stretch of open woods."

J. H. Bowles (1909) has published an excellent account of this chickadee, in which he says:

At the approach of the nesting season the Chestnut-backs retire to the most arid section of the country to be found, the more exposed it is to the sun the better, and it is only in such locations that one may ever expect to find them during the breeding season. The nesting site is chosen about the middle of April, most often in the dead stub of some giant fir or oak. On one occasion only have I found the nest near water, this being in a small willow on the edge of a swamp.

The birds almost invariably dig their own hole, but I once found a nest in the winter burrow of a Harris Woodpecker. One peculiarity about them, which greatly increases the difficulty of finding their nests, is that they almost never start the hole for themselves. Instead they select some place where a fragment of the wood or bark has been split away, or else they will often take the oval hole made by the larva of one of our largest beetles. These holes are not altered at the entrance in any way and, as the dead trees are full of them, it is extremely difficult to locate the one containing the nest.

He says that these chickadees sometimes nest in loose colonies; in one locality he "found no less than seven occupied nests inside a very small area, some not more than fifty yards apart." The lowest nest he found was only "two feet up in a tiny fir stub," but he says that "it is nothing unusual to find them fifty feet up in the giant fir stubs, remnants of long past forest fires." Dawson (1923) says that he has "found nests as high as eighty feet in a fir stub; and in two instances in a dead tree wholly surrounded by water."

As to the nest itself, Mr. Bowles (1909) writes: "The cavity is usually about seven inches in depth, seldom any more, tho occasionally much less. Almost any soft substance to be found in the vicinity is used to make up the nesting material, but there is always a substantial foundation of green moss. Cotton waste from factories, hair of cows, squirrels, rabbits and goats, and small feathers are most often used, one very beautiful nest in my collection being composed almost entirely of feathers from the Kennicott Screech Owl *(Otus asio kennicottii)*. No matter how large the bottom of the cavity may be, it is always packed tight, and I have sometimes removed a nest that would easily fill both hands."

Mr. Burleigh's (1930) nests contained similar materials, including horsehair, feathers of a Steller's jay, rope fiber, and white fur of a cat.

Eggs.—The chestnut-backed chickadee most commonly lays a set of six or seven eggs, sometimes only five, frequently eight, and sometimes as many as nine. Mr. Bowles (1909) says that "the eggs vary greatly in both shape and size, some being shaped like a quail's egg, others like a murre's egg." But most of the eggs that I have seen are ovate or short-ovate, though some are slightly pointed.

The ground color is pure white, and they are sparingly sprinkled with reddish brown or light red dots, sometimes with "sayal brown" or "snuff brown"; the markings are sometimes concentrated about the larger end of the egg, but oftener they are irregularly distributed; some eggs are evenly sprinkled with fine dots, and some are nearly or quite immaculate. The measurements of 40 eggs average 15.3 by 12.0 millimeters; the eggs showing the four extremes measure **16.2** by 12.2, 14.9 by **12.6**, **14.4** by 12.0, and 15.9 by **11.3** millimeters.

Young.—The exact period of incubation does not seem to have been determined for this species. Dawson (1923) and Bowles (1909) both state that incubation begins when the first egg is laid, as the sizes of the embryos in a set of eggs vary considerably. Perhaps the bird does not incubate all through the laying period, but she covers the eggs when she leaves the nest, which keeps them warm, and furthermore, the nest is usually fully exposed to the heat of the sun, which helps the progress of embryo development.

The chickadees are very brave in the defense of their nest and resort to the common chickadee habit of hissing and fluttering their wings in a startling manner when an intruder looks into the nest.

Undoubtedly both parents assist in the care and feeding of the young, though we have no definite data on the subject. They seem to lose all fear of the human intruder in their anxiety to defend their young, and Dawson (1923) says: "Not infrequently, if the young are kindly treated, the parent bird will venture upon the hand or shoulder to pursue its necessary offices."

Plumages.—I have seen no very young chickadees of this species. In the juvenal plumage, which is mainly acquired by the time the young bird leaves the nest, except that the wings and tail are not fully grown, the color pattern is the same as in the adult; the chestnut of the back, however, is duller, and that of the sides and flanks is duller and paler; the plumage is also softer and less blended. A partial post-juvenal molt, involving the contour plumage and the lesser wing coverts, but not the rest of the wings or the tail, takes place in August; by the first week in September the young bird has acquired a first winter plumage that is practically indistinguishable from that of the adult. Adults have one complete postnuptial molt in August and September. The birds show some signs of wear and fading before summer, but assume the darker and more richly colored plumage in fall.

Food.—Prof. F. E. L. Beal (1907) studied the contents of 57 stomachs of the chestnut-backed chickadees, taken in every month except March, April, and May, and found the food to consist of nearly 65 percent of animal matter and 35 of vegetable. Caterpillars constituted 18 percent of the animal food, taken in nearly every month, even in December and January; the largest amount, 53 percent, was taken in August. Hemiptera, leafhoppers, treehoppers, and olive and other scales were the most important item of food, amounting to about 25 percent. "Wasps were eaten to the extent of 13 percent of the food, but no ants were found. Beetles amount to less than 2 percent of the food, but nearly all are noxious; weevils appeared in one stomach." No trace of flies or grasshoppers was found. Spiders amounted to 7 percent for the year but amounted to nearly 16 percent in August.

"The vegetable portion of the food consists of fruit pulp 8 percent, seeds nearly 20 percent, and miscellaneous matter 7 percent. Fruit pulp was found only in a few stomachs taken in fall and winter and was probably waste fruit. The seeds eaten were mostly those of coniferous trees."

Dr. Dickey (MS.) writes: "When they have wearied themselves in taking food from the trunks of trees, they will pass to huge crumbling logs, peck at green moss pads for certain items, and flit into and glean the tangled branches of such shrubs as salal, elderberry, dwarf blueberry, depauperized paper birch, alders, dogwood, etc. By mid-March, hordes of small winged gnats arise from the newly unfolding buds of the elderberry bushes, and such items are cherished by the tits. I noticed that, after the birds had fairly bounced the 'bugs' out of such cover, then they would arise and, craning their heads back and forth and thrusting forward their bodies, cleanse the air of this kind of provender. They lower themselves to boulders and rocks, and cleanse boats on dry docks of hiding insects, nor will they hesitate to peck at 'barnacle scales'."

Behavior.—The chestnut-backed chickadees are almost exact counterparts of our familiar eastern chickadees in traits of character and behavior—fearless, sociable, and full of friendly curiosity. Taylor and Shaw (1927) describe their behavior very well, as follows:

> Establish yourself in an inconspicuous position in the general vicinity of a flock and make a squeaking sound with the lips on the back of the hand. Presently a tiny chestnut back will appear in the needle clumps not far away, calling excitedly and seeking the author of the unusual call note. If you remain quiet and continue the squeaking you may soon find that the trees about you are alive with chestnut-backs, buzzing about and hurling imprecations at you as if you were a new kind of owl. Incidentally in the group of excited birds you may catch sight of a number of other species.
>
> Chestnut-backed chickadees are sociable bodies, indeed, even gregarious. Seen characteristically in flocks of 4 or 6 to 20 of their own kind, they approve, if they do not actively cultivate, loose association with several others, including western golden-crowned kinglets, red-breasted nuthatches, Shufeldt juncos, mountain chickadees, and lutescent and Townsend warblers. Of these the kinglets are most often found in their company.

Dr. Dickey, in Alaska, found them associated in March with winter wrens, brown creepers, red-breasted nuthatches, sooty song sparrows, and Oregon juncos. "They are quick to react to noises in their haunts; they come hurrying out of plant cover, a gleam in their beady eyes; and they dangle upon dried seed heads and flower clusters of several kinds of shrubs or undergrowth of this wild region. They will swing up and down on bending branches, vent squeaks and low chirps, varied with buzzing 'dizzes.'"

Voice.—The chestnut-backed chickadee seems to have a great variety of notes, perhaps of conversational value, most of which bear little resemblance to the *chick-a-dee* note of our blackcap, though Dawson (1923) says that this becomes *kissadee,* and Taylor and Shaw (1927) say that "when scolding us at short range they interjected numerous fine *tseek a dee dees* into their conversation."

Taylor and Shaw found some of the notes to be very similar to "certain calls of the western golden-crowned kinglet, so as to be distinguishable with difficulty. Several much-used expressions were caught and set down in our field books as follows: *Toot seet seet see!* repeated several times; this was sometimes varied to *tsweet tsweet tsweet!* One note is like *whist*, uttered once or repeated as many as three times. This triple note sometimes sounds like *twit twit twit*. The principal call note heard during one exceedingly foggy, rainy day early in September was *tseet tseet!* or *tseet tseet tsew*, a very kingletlike utterance. This was quite certainly a flock location call, for the birds continued it when we were no longer in view."

Both Bowles (1909) and Dawson (1923) refer to a song resembling that of the chipping sparrow. The latter says of it: "When the emotion of springtime is no longer controllable, the minikin swain mounts a fir limb and raps out a series of notes as monotonous as those of a Chipping Sparrow. The trial is shorter and the movement less rapid, so that the half dozen notes of a uniform character have more individual distinctness than, say, in the case of the Sparrow: *Chick chick chick chick chick chick*. Another performer may give each note a double character, so that the whole may sound like the snipping of a barber's shears: *Chulip chulip chulip chulip chulip.*"

Field marks.—While traveling through the treetops in loose flocks, as is its customary habit, this chickadee might easily be mistaken for one of the other western chickadees. But at lower levels and at short range its chestnut back and sides are quite conspicuous. In juvenal plumage the young of this and the Hudsonian chickadee look somewhat alike, but the former is considerably darker. The chestnut-backed chickadee frequents, as a rule, more heavily timbered and drier country than the Oregon chickadee, but there are exceptions to this rule. Its voice is also different from that of the others.

Enemies.—In addition to the ordinary enemies of all small birds, there is, according to Mr. Bowles (1909), another unusual enemy, which "is no other than the common black-and-yellow bumble bee. This insect has a veritable mania for living in holes in trees, and a chickadee nest appears to be the acme of its desires. It seems to like the nesting material and prefers the nest before the eggs are laid, but will often drive the bird away from an incomplete set, pulling up most of the nesting and leaving the eggs underneath."

Fall.—S. F. Rathbun (MS.) says: "In October there appears to be a movement to the lowlands of those individuals that have spent the summer in the higher altitudes; and one who may happen to be in the mountains at that period will see, each day all through the month, numbers of these active little birds trooping by, this continuing well into November. It is common throughout the winter in the sections adjacent to tidewater, and also breeds in such localities, for the species can be found at all seasons in all parts of the region [around Seattle], although there is little doubt that the majority of the birds spend the summer in the more elevated districts, judged from the numbers that come from such in fall."

Winter.—The chestnut-backed chickadee is a permanent resident throughout its range. Alfred M. Bailey (1927) says that "they are to be noted the year around, throughout the whole of southeastern Alaska," where "they are probably the most numerous of the winter birds. * * * These cheery little creatures are often the only signs of bird life to be seen in the winter woods, and their quiet, comrade-like call, as they drift from one tree to another, can often be heard when the birds are obscured by the falling snow."

DISTRIBUTION

Range.—Pacific coast region from Prince William Sound, Alaska, south to southern California and east to western Montana; not migratory. The range of this species extends **north** to Alaska (Resurrection Bay, Glacier, and Skagway); and northern British Columbia (Flood Glacier). **East** to British Columbia (Flood Glacier, Blackwater Lake, and Kootenay); western Montana (probably Glacier National Park, Clark Fork, and Fort Sherman); northeastern Oregon (Blue Mountains and Powder River Mountains); and California (Mount Shasta, McCloud, Hayward, and Cambria). **South** to southern California (Cambria). The **western** limits extend northward along the coast from southern California (Cambria) to the Kenai Peninsula, Alaska (Resurrection Bay).

As outlined the range is for the entire species, of which three subspecies are recognized. The typical form *(Parus rufescens rufescens)*, occupies all of the range south to central California; the Nicasio chickadee *(P. r. neglectus)* is confined to coastal areas of Marin County, Calif.; and Barlow's chickadee *(P. r. barlowi)* is found on the coast of California in the general area between San Francisco Bay and Monterey Bay.

Egg dates.—California: 58 records, March 12 to June 7; 30 records, April 23 to May 16, indicating the height of the season.

Washington: 30 records, April 7 to June 10; 16 records, May 9 to 24.

PARUS RUFESCENS NEGLECTUS Ridgway

NICASIO CHICKADEE

In a short and narrow coastal region of middle California, the humid Transition Zone of Marin County, there lives a subspecies of the chestnut-backed chickadees that seems to be strictly intermediate in coloration between the other two races, one north and one south of it. Mr. Ridgway (1904) describes it as "similar to *P. r. rufescens* but with much less of chestnut on sides and flanks, which exteriorly are pale gray, the chestnut also paler and duller." Dr. Joseph Grinnell (1904), in discussing this group, remarks that "this southward paling of the lateral feather tracts seems to be parallel to the relative decrease in the humidity of the regions occupied." And this paling is carried still farther, with the practical disappearance of the chestnut sides in the next race to the southward, *barlowi*. The Nicasio chickadee seems to occur in its purity only in Marin County; it intergrades with *P. r. rufescens* in Sonoma County to the northward; and San Francisco Bay and the Golden Gate seem to form an effectual barrier between it and *P. r. barlowi* to the southward.

In support of his theory that the two species *Parus hudsonicus* and *P. rufescens* were derived from common ancestry, Dr. Grinnell (1904) calls attention to the fact that "the young of *barlowi* has the sides paler rusty than *neglectus, neglectus* slightly paler than *rufescens,* but *rufescens* has the sides slightly more rusty than *hudsonicus,* a sequence which accords well with the present theories of origin." His hypothesis is based, of course, on the generally accepted theory that immature individuals more closely resemble the ancestral form than the adults do.

We have no reason to think that the habits of the Nicasio chickadee are very different from those of the chestnut-backed chickadees elsewhere. The eggs are characteristic of the species, as described under the preceding form. The measurements of 39 eggs average 15.7 by 12.3 millimeters; the eggs showing the four extremes measure **17.6** by 12.2, 16.5 by **13.0,** 14.3 by 12.0, and 15.2 by **11.9** millimeters.

PARUS RUFESCENS BARLOWI Grinnell

BARLOW'S CHICKADEE

PLATE 56

HABITS

Farther south along the coastal area of middle California, from San Francisco Bay to a little south of Monterey Bay, we have this paler, less rufous-sided race of the chestnut-backed chickadees. In his original description of this race, which he named in honor of Chester Barlow, Dr. Grinnell (1900b) characterizes it as "similar to *P. rufescens neglectus,* but the sides pure smoked gray without a trace of rusty."

The San Francisco Bay region seems to form the northern barrier to the distribution of this race farther northward, and climatic conditions apparently prevent its extension farther south, a certain degree of humidity being required by this species. Dr. Grinnell (1904) remarks that "even the Santa Cruz District with its gray-sided *barlowi* has very much greater rainfall and cloudiness than regions immediately to the southward and interiorly. Too abrupt aridification with accompanying floral changes apparently forms the present barrier to further distribution in these directions."

One would hardly expect Barlow's chickadee to differ materially in its habits from the other two races of the species, and this seems to be the case, though differences in environment may cause it to select unorthodox nesting sites, as the following quotations will show. Dudley S. De Groot wrote to Milton S. Ray (1916) of three nests found in Golden Gate Park: "A nest found April 7, 1916, which contained six badly incubated eggs lying in a thick bed of rabbit fur, was located eight feet up in a hole in the side of a log cabin. Another was in a small cavity fifteen feet up in a eucalyptus and contained young almost ready to fly. The third nest was remarkable for its situation, being placed in a pipe leaning against an out-building. The nest was about one and a half feet down the pipe, which was only three inches in diameter, and contained, in very cramped quarters, young birds about half grown."

Joseph Mailliard (1931) located a nest in the same park that was in "the large mandibular foramen on the inside of the left mandible of the huge Sulphur-bottom Whale skeleton under the shed!"

The eggs of Barlow's chickadee are practically indistinguishable from those of the chestnut-backed chickadee. The measurements of 40 eggs average 15.5 by 11.9 millimeters; the eggs showing the four extremes measure **17.3** by 12.2, 15.2 by **12.7**, and **14.2** by **11.2** millimeters.

PARUS BICOLOR Linnaeus

TUFTED TITMOUSE

PLATES 60, 61

HABITS

As we travel southward, weary of the rigors of the northern winter and anxious to meet spring halfway, one of the first southern birds to greet us from the still leafless woods is this cheery little tomtit. Long before we reach the land of blooming jessamine, hibiscus, and oleanders, we may hear its loud, whistling *peto, peto,* welcoming us to his home in the southland.

To the novice, these notes may at first seem to bear a resemblance to the three-syllabled notes of the Carolina wren or to the spirited whistles of the cardinal, which one hears so frequently all through the southern States. I have sometimes been puzzled, when hearing them for the first time each season, but one soon learns to recognize them, for all three are quite distinct. Being a rather noisy bird and rather somberly colored, the tufted titmouse is generally heard before it is seen, though it is not particularly shy. We may look for it with best success in the deciduous woods.

In Pennsylvania, near the northern limit of its range, according to Dr. Samuel S. Dickey (MS.), it is oftener found in beech timber, where its coloration harmonizes and where it finds congenial openings in trunks and branches for nesting purposes. "But it will inhabit a variety of cover in modern times, and is found among oaks, tulip poplars, yellow locusts, sycamore, and thickets of mixed saplings, as well as orchards."

In the Middle West and southward it frequents the river-bottom forests in spring and summer but wanders about at other seasons in more open areas, among the shade trees and about houses in the villages. In the Gulf States and Florida it is often found in the live oaks, which shade the streets of villages and towns, but its favorite haunts are the mixed hammocks and the smaller cypress swamps that are scattered through the flat pine woods; it is seldom seen in these flat woods outside of these little cypress heads.

Courtship.—After wandering about all through fall and winter in small flocks by themselves, or mixed with other species, they begin their courtship activities early in spring and prepare to separate into pairs. Dr. Dickey (MS.) says that "males pursue and chase females among branches and often end up in brush piles. They will glide between avenues of trees along the courses of streams. Sometimes pairs thus continue up the forest-clothed flanks of slopes and cliffs. Males are combative, and are seen clasping and falling among vegetation. They will end up on the forest floor, there to part company and to continue their advances to the female of their choice."

Nesting.—As I have never been fortunate enough to find a nest of the tufted titmouse, I must rely on the observations of others. Dr. Dickey (MS.) writes to me, of the nesting habits in Pennsylvania and West Virginia, as follows:

"Naturally tufted tits breed inside cavities, mostly in trees. They utilize both live and dead growth, often cavities that are surrounded with hard resistant wood. A number like to breed in knot holes, slits left where lightning has struck, and long weathered squirrels' holes.

Not a few pairs inhabit the abandoned holes of downy, hairy, red-bellied, red-headed, and pileated woodpeckers and the cavities of the flicker. I have three records of their breeding in crude wooden bird boxes in town yards; and one instance was a hollow metal pipe, 4 inches in diameter, beside the yard of a farmhouse."

He thinks this bird shows a preference for beech trees for nesting sites, but he has found nests in white, red, and blue oaks, tupelos, sycamores, pines, hemlocks, apple trees, mulberries, water and sugar maples, yellow locusts, white ashes, and chestnuts. "It will come out from cover and nest in fence posts along roads and borders of fields, and occasionally it selects some stub or post in an open pasture. The run of pairs prefer the woods in which to breed, but not a few enter and nest in orchards, groves, parks, and even shade trees along community streets. Nests are found at both low and high elevations; they range from 3 feet up to as many as 85 or 90 feet. They will continue to use the identical cavity for years, if unmolested.

"Nest building begins late in April, although birds are seen to carry odd leaves and trash into holes even as early as late in March. They begin by carrying in strips of bark and dead deciduous leaves; those of white oak and maple are common. Then they add sprays of green moss and dry grass, and round out the interior with pads of hair from cattle, rabbit, deer mouse, and others, and bits of rags, strings, or cloth."

In South Carolina, according to Wayne (1910), "this species deposits its eggs in natural cavities of trees or in the deserted holes of the smaller woodpeckers and does not appear to excavate a hole for itself. It seems to have a preference for hollows in chinquapin and dogwood trees, and the hole ranges from four to forty-five feet above the ground. While nest-building, the birds carry large quantities of material at every trip and one generally accompanies the other to and from the site. The nest is composed of wool, cotton, hair, leaves, fibrous bark and snake skins, the last material being indispensable to this species, as it is to the Crested Flycatcher. * * * The birds are the closest of sitters and have to be removed from the nest before it can be examined. Only one brood is raised and these follow the parents for many months."

Mr. Wayne (1910) also tells of an unsuccessful attempt of a pair of these titmice to nest in a tuft of Spanish moss. The nest was built in a very large mass of the hanging moss *(Tillandsia usneoides)* and five eggs were laid, but a violent rainstorm occurred and the nest and eggs were blown out. The bird was undismayed, rebuilt the nest again in the same bunch of moss, and laid three eggs; but she was disappointed again, for another storm came up before the set was completed, and the nest and eggs were found on the ground the following day.

M. G. Vaiden, of Rosedale, Miss., reports an unusually lofty nest of the tufted titmouse that was located in a cavity of a black locust near there some 97 feet above the ground. Another nest was found in a gatepost about 8 feet up; it was composed of horsehair and a few feathers.

The nesting cavities occupied by this titmouse vary greatly in size and shape, which means that in some cases a large quantity of material has to be collected to fill up extra space. C. S. Brimley (1888) mentions a nest that he found in a hollow in a small dogwood, near Raleigh, N. C. "The opening of the hollow was about two feet from the ground, and the hollow reached to the earth, but for half the distance three sides of it were gone. So the birds had piled up moss, leaves, etc., from the ground right up into the hole and then lined the nest at the top with white cat fur and a few pieces of snakeskin, the eggs being at least eighteen inches from the bottom of the nest."

The material used to fill up large cavities consists largely of leaves, preferably those that are damp enough to pack well without crumbling, but not too wet; these are picked up near a brook, or in some damp place in the woods. Lucy H. Upton (1916) made an interesting observation on the use of damp leaves by a titmouse that she was watching: "Having chosen a damp brown oak leaf from the ground, it flew with it into a bare tree, and, holding the leaf with its claw firmly against the branch, it drew itself to its full height, raised its head like a Woodpecker, and with all the might of its tiny frame gave a forcible blow to the leaf with its bill. This process was kept up nearly half an hour. * * * At last its purpose seemed to be accomplished. It rested, and lifted the leaf by the petiole. We then saw that the hammering had made it into a firm brown ball nearly as large as an oak gall."

The bird flew away with the leaf and probably placed it in its nest.

Freda L. Hood (1916) adds by way of explanation, that these birds "line their nests with a pulpy substance not unlike a sponge. They carry a large number of these damp leaf-balls to their nest-hole and there pull them into shreds. * * * The Titmouse uses this sort of lining for its nest only when they build in damp weather. They do not seem to be able to use dry leaves in this manner."

R. B. McLaughlin (1888) adds that about moist places "she gets a supply of green moss and mixes in a modicum of dirt. After she has accumulated the desired amount of such materials, we will find her at the bed of the flying squirrel (*Pteromys volucella*), or some other mammal which collects the thin inner bark of trees. and she does not hesitate to appropriate as much as she needs. Then she is off for the farmer's barn, and any bunch of cornsilks about his granary is used.

Again she is over where he curried his horse or butchered his pig, in quest of hair."

But the titmouse is not content with picking up stray hairs, or even bunches of fur from dead animals, and often becomes bold enough to collect this needed nesting material from living mammals, including human beings.

J. Harris Reed (1897) noticed a tufted titmouse that was apparently trying to drive a red squirrel away. "The squirrel was lying flat on the upper side of a large sloping limb, and the Titmouse would approach cautiously from behind and catch at its tail. It was not long before I noticed that the bird had collected quite a mouthful of the hairs, with which it flew off to a hole near by where it was deposited."

Ward Reed (1927) writes: "While walking through the woods looking for Crows' nests about the first of May, I came upon an unusual sight. On a branch of a tree a few feet from the ground sat a Woodchuck *(Marmota monax)*, while bobbing up and down above it a tufted Titmouse *(Baeolophus bicolor)* was engaged in plucking hair from its back. On a near-by twig the bird's mate was perched, with its mouth already full of hair, and in a few minutes they flew away together."

Mrs. Vitae Kite (1925) generously allowed an aggressive titmouse to help himself to some of her silvery locks. "Without the least warning he lit squarely on top of my head, giving me such a start that it was with great difficulty I controlled myself and sat still. At first I thought he was trying to frighten me away but soon changed my mind, when he began working and pulling at my hair with all his might. Now my hair has been very white for many years, but I still have plenty of it, and was more than willing to divide with this little bird, so I steadied myself and 'held fast' while that energetic 'Tom' had the time of his life gathering 'wool' to line his nest, for that was what I now felt sure he was doing. He didn't seem to have much luck with the coils on top, so he worked around over my ear, where there were short loose hairs, and I could hear and feel him snip-snip as he severed them—not one by one, but in bunches, it seemed to me."

Even man is not immune to such attacks, for E. Irwin Smith (1924) had a similar experience. He was seated on a stump on the edge of some woods, with his hat off, when he noticed a titmouse flitting about his head. "It flew back into the bushes, only to return and flutter above my head as before. Yet the third time it came back, but this time, instead of flying away again, it lit on my head, and, in a very diligent manner, began to pick the hairs therefrom. The pricking of its sharp little toes on my scalp and the vigor of the hair-pulling was a trifle too much for my self-control, and I instinctively moved my head. Away it flew, but only for a moment, and then it was back at work, harder than before."

Other somewhat similar cases have been reported, but the above will suffice to illustrate this strange habit.

Eggs.—Four to eight eggs may be found in the nest of the tufted titmouse, but oftener there are either five or six. The eggs vary from ovate (commonly) to elongate-ovate, and there is practically no gloss. The ground color is usually pure white, but often creamy white, or rarely pale "cream color." They are generally more or less evenly speckled all over the entire surface with very small spots or fine dots; often these markings are thickest at the larger end, where they are sometimes concentrated into a wreath; rarely this concentration is at the small end. The markings are in various browns, "hazel," "cinnamon-rufous," "vinaceous-rufous," "burnt sienna," or "chestnut"; some eggs have a few underlying shell markings of "lilac-gray" or "drab-gray." The measurements of 50 eggs average 18.4 by 14.1 millimeters; the eggs showing the four extremes measure **20.7** by 13.5, 18.5 by **14.7, 16.8** by 14.0, and 17.0 by **12.7** millimeters.

Young.—Dr. Dickey (MS.) tells me that in several nests that he watched the period of incubation proved to be "exactly 12 days"; and he says that young remain in the cavity 15 or 16 days. A young bird, 4 days old, had a light salmon-pink body, with eyes only partly open, and was naked except for "feather tufts of dusky grey down" on the top of the head, at the base of the skull and in the middle of the back. When 6 days old, the "body had blue-gray down and rows of conspicuous slate-blue pin-feather shafts"; the eyes were now open. Two days later, "the gray down was falling away from head and sides; the back mouse-gray; the flanks under back of wings tinged with light brown; pin-feather scabbards of wings not entirely unsheathed, but fast disintegrating." When ten days old, the young were well feathered and closely resembled the adults, but they remained in the nest five days more.

Mrs. Margaret Morse Nice (1931) writes: "In the Wichita Reserve June 6, 1926, we discovered we had fastened our tent to a black jack in a cavity of which five fully feathered titmice were housed; happily the parents accepted the situation with equanimity. I watched the nest from 2 to 4 p.m. the first day, from 10:40 to 12:10 the next. Despite the hot weather mother Tit brooded 3 and 8 minutes the first day, 8 and 15 the next, father in the meantime giving the food he brought to her. Both birds kept their crests depressed, both often twitched their wings—the female more than her mate—and both used a great variety of notes. During the first two hours 18 meals were given, during the last hour and a half, seven."

I cannot find it definitely so stated, but apparently incubating and brooding devolve mainly, if not wholly, on the female. Both sexes help to feed the young for some time after they leave the nest, and *both* young and old travel about together in a family party during summer, until they all join the mixed parties of their own and other species that roam the woods during fall and winter.

Plumages.—The young nestling is mainly naked, except for a scanty covering of dusky, or bluish gray, down on the head and back. The development of the first plumage is outlined above. In full juvenal plumage, when it leaves the nest, the young is much like the adult, but all its colors are duller and less distinct, and the plumage is softer, less compact. The crest is not fully developed; the forehead is dusky rather than black and not so clearly defined against the gray of the crest and the white of the sides of the head; and the sides and flanks are tinged with pinkish buff, instead of the richer brown of the adult. A partial postjuvenal molt takes place in August, or later, which involves the contour plumage and the wing coverts, but not the rest of the wings or the tail. In this first winter plumage, young and old are practically indistinguishable; the crest is distinct, the forehead is black, the sides of the head are more decidedly white, and the sides and flanks have become a deep "russet" or "Mars brown." There is apparently no spring molt. Adults have one complete annual, postnuptial molt in August. Adults in fresh fall plumage are more or less tinged with olive-brownish on the back and with pale buffy brownish on the chest. The sexes are practically alike in all plumages, but the colors of the adult female are usually somewhat duller than those of the male.

Food.—The 186 stomachs of the tufted titmouse examined by Professor Beal (Beal, McAtee, and Kalmbach, 1916), were irregularly distributed throughout the year, and were considered by him too few "to afford more than an approximation of the bird's economic worth." However, the results show that, so far as his investigation goes, the bird is beneficial and has no bad food habits to offset the good it does.

The food consisted of 66.57 percent animal matter and 33.43 percent vegetable. He says that the food "includes one item, caterpillars, which form more than half the animal food, and two items, caterpillars and wasps, which are more than half of the whole food." Beetles make up 7.06 percent, of which only one-tenth of 1 percent are useful species; the cotton-boll weevil was found in four stomachs. Ants are eaten occasionally, and other hymenopterous food, bees, wasps, and sawfly larvae, amounted to 12.5 percent. Other items include stink bugs, treehoppers, scales, only one fly, eggs of katydids, egg cases of cockroaches, spiders (found in 40 stomachs examined in May, 12.67 percent, only a trace in June, and in 3 stomachs in July, 16.33 percent, evidently a makeshift food), and a few snails. Caterpillars are the largest item, 38.31 percent of the whole food for the year. No grasshoppers or crickets were found.

Of the vegetable food, corn was discovered in one stomach, evidently taken on trial. Fruit was eaten to a moderate extent (5.15 per cent), mostly in midsummer, and included raspberries, blackberries, and strawberries, which might have been of cultivated varieties, but probably were not. The wild fruits were such as grow by the wayside and in swamps, as elderberries, hackberries, blueberries, huckleberries, and mulberries. Seeds of various kinds, as sumac—including poison ivy—bayberry, or wax myrtle, aggregate 4.07 per cent. It is difficult to draw the line between broken seeds and mast in stomachs of the tufted tit, but, together considered as mast, these form more than two-thirds of the vegetable food. While largely composed of acorns, there is no doubt that chinquapins and beechnuts and many smaller seeds enter into its composition. As thus defined, mast amounts to 23.4 per cent of the whole food, comprising 95 per cent of that eaten in November, 50.42 per cent in January, and 55.97 per cent in February; in fact, it is the principal vegetable food eaten from August to February. That such small birds should crush such hard nuts as acorns and chinquapins is surprising, but the broken fragments found in the stomachs well demonstrate their ability.

M. P. Skinner (1928) writes:

During the winter at least [in North Carolina], the favorite food of Titmice is the acorns supplied by the innumerable shrub oaks, post oaks and turkey oaks. From January to March, I found them hunting acorns, occasionally on the ground, but generally in the trees themselves. Quite often they knocked the acorn from its twig and then flew down to the ground after it. Titmice do not open their bills wide enough to admit the whole acorn, but they sometimes pick it up by its stem, or more often they simply spear the nut with their sharp, closed bill and fly up to a limb it that way. Once on a suitable limb, the acorn is firmly held between the bird's two feet and strong downward blows are rained upon it. This hammering is rapid and very effective, so that it does not take long to scale off the shell, and then the soft interior meat is eaten in small pieces. * * * At times they spring out after insects flying by them, and sometimes they tear the tent nests of caterpillars to pieces. On February 11, 1927, near the Mid Pines Club, a Titmouse picked up an oak apple an inch or more in diameter, carried it in its bill to the crotch of a tree and there dug through its half inch of tough material to feed on the hundred or so small white grubs in the center.

Dr. H. C. Oberholser (1896) saw one hammering away at a half-punctured cocoon of a Polyphemus moth. B. J. Blincoe (1923) saw one feeding on cultivated Concord grapes. Dr. Dickey (MS.) has seen it catch flying insects, including a small butterfly or moth; the wings of Lepidoptera are torn off and only the soft body is eaten. He includes wild cherries and service-berries in the food. Others have added dogwood berries and those of the Virginia-creeper. In winter, titmice will come readily to feeding stations to eat suet and bread and doughnut crumbs; a dish of water will also attract them. Mabel Gillespie (1930) says that the berries of the Japanese honeysuckle, alder seeds, and the seeds of tuliptree pods are favorite foods.

A. L. Pickens writes to me: "They are among the friendliest of all our southern birds, exceeding the Carolina chickadee by far. I have taught several individuals to take food from my hand. The great drawback is that they are so thrifty that they empty a food box and store all the surplus food before the more backward chickadees, wrens, and nuthatches arrive. For the last two forms I was able to overcome this difficulty by using a block instead of a box for the food. In this block I bored holes with a small auger. Then at the bottom of the holes I placed bits of nuts, and the wrens and nuthatches, with their longer beaks, were able to reach deeper than the titmice and so retrieve the food."

Behavior.—This lively little titmouse is one of the most popular of the southern birds, with its active, vivacious manners, as it flits about in the foliage of the trees, often hanging head downward from some terminal cluster of leaves, or clings to the trunks and branches, searching in the crevices of the bark for its insect food. It attracts attention and endears itself to us with its tame, confiding manners, as it is not at all shy, but comes freely into our orchards and gardens, even close to houses, and partakes of our hospitality at our feeding stations; it appears utterly fearless of human presence. As Edmund W. Arthur (Todd, 1940) says:

We should probably ascribe to him without hesitation the first place in our hearts. He presents many claims to the rank of first nobleman of the forest realm. His presence is genial and pleasing, his plumage attractive, his alertness conspicuous; and his habits are good. * * *

Each pair of tufted titmice has a domain of its own during mating season. Over this the birds exercise a jealous sway, at least in so far as errant titmice are concerned. Enter upon this domain and without too much fuss begin to whistle the titmouse challenge. Directly you will excite vigorous replies from the lord of the manor. If you persist—and you probably will—he will approach to within a few feet of you. If you carry in your hand a hat or a sizable piece of dark cloth or a box, his lordship seems to think you have another bird in captivity. He will shake himself as if with rage, or in defiance, and drop, scolding, almost within arm's length, where as long as you continue to answer him, he will remain to scold and protest.

At other times, too, these inquisitive birds show their curiosity by reacting to the sound of human voices. Dr. Dickey tells me that they are "seen to react to the voices and noises made by road workers, drillers, and farmers. They hurry forward from shelter in twos or threes. Even when a visitor calls at the door of a house and starts

to talk, then the titmouse arrives, evidently curious at a stranger in
its habitat. I sometimes hesitate to wonder if such birds do not dis-
criminate between the natives and strangers, for they have a sagacity
that is hard to fathom."

Mabel Gillespie (1930) gives them credit for great intelligence and
individuality about her banding traps. She says that they quickly
learned how to find their way out of the traps, "with no time lost in
searching about for the entrance." They repeatedly entered the trap,
picked up some food, and went out again immediately, time after time.
She says that she could not confuse them, as she often did other birds,
by running toward the trap; for "approaching danger seems only to
stimulate their keenness and composure, for they most containedly and
successfully seek the exit at the first hint of hazard." She thinks that
this ability to find the exit so quickly is due to accuracy of memory, and
relates the following incident to illustrate it: "During one night there
was a fall of very soft snow, with a succeeding drop in temperature.
The traps were all removed but one lest they should become frozen in
the ice crust. After the freezing the outline of each trap was clearly
visible in the crust. A Titmouse was seen to fly to the ground at the
spot directly in front of the outlined mark of an entrance funnel. This
showed that the bird clearly remembered the location of the funnel. Then,
however, just as it was about to run forward, it appeared to realize
that the trap was not there. The food was directly in front of the
bird with no intervening obstruction. Yet the bird hesitated, looked
about, and observed that another trap was in its accustomed place.
It flew to this trap and entered for food."

The above incident does illustrate accuracy of memory, but it also
indicates suspicion of food under unusual conditions, or a sense of
security in taking food from traps, based on past experience.

The tufted titmouse is quick and active in all its movements, flitting
upward among the branches or gliding down between them, but it seldom
indulges in long flights; its short flights from tree to tree, or across an
open space, are undulating, irregular, much like that of a chickadee, it
seems to me; but Dr. Dickey (MS.) calls it "rather precise; the short,
rounded wings and well spread tail, with vibrating vanes, press the
atmosphere." It reminds him somewhat of the flight of the blue jay.

Voice.—The notes of the tufted titmouse are many and varied, mostly
loud and generally pleasing; it is a noisy bird. Aretas A. Saunders has
sent me the following excellent notes on the subject: "The loud, whistled
call of the tufted titmouse, commonly translated as *peto, peto,* is in about
the same status as song as the *phoebe* whistle of the chickadee. That is,

it is used by both sexes and, apparently, at almost any season of the year. Also, like the chickadee, the birds respond to an imitation and come to the imitator very readily.

"The song is loud, clear, and lower-pitched than the chickadee's *phoebe*. It is also quite variable; I have a number of records and no two of them are alike. The song consists of a two-note phrase, repeated over and over three to eleven times, according to my records. The two-note phrase is more frequently with the first note high and the second low. The interval between may be one, one and one-half, or two tones. The pitch of the notes varies in different songs, or different individuals, from A″ to A‴, that is, between the highest two A's on the piano. The majority of songs in my records are between E‴ and C‴.

"Sometimes the two-note phrase sounds like *peto,* at other times like *wheedle* or *taydle.* When the pitch goes up, instead of down, the phrase is commonly written *daytee;* the same pitches and pitch intervals are common but it often sounds like *toolee,* and sometimes the first note is short, and it is like *tleet* or *tlit.* I have recorded all these variations in the field, writing down what each particular song sounded like to me at the time it was heard.

"An occasional phrase slurs down, like *teeoh,* and there are rarely phrases of three notes, such as *wheedleoh,* or of one note, *whee,* each repeated a number of times. Sometimes a song begins or ends with notes unlike the rest, as *tidi, waytee, waytee, waytee,* etc., or *wheedle, wheedle, wheedle, whee, whee.*"

Dr. Dickey (MS.) mentions a number of slightly different interpretations of some of the above notes, and adds some that are quite different, such as *piper-tee, piper-tee, piper-tee; ah-peer, ah-peer; chee-chu, chee-chep*; and *wheep-did-er-ee,* ending with *purty-purty-purty.*

Nuttall (1832) devotes considerable space to the voice of the tufted titmouse, and aptly remarks that "though his voice, on paper, may appear to present only a list of quaint articulations, * * * yet the delicacy, energy, pathos, and variety of his simple song, like many other things in nature, are far beyond the feeble power of description." He mentions a very lively and agreeable call of *'whip-tōm-killy-killy*; and then, "in a lower, hoarser, harsh voice, and in a peevish tone, exactly like that of the Jay and the Chickadee, *dăy-dăy-dăy-dăy,* and *day-dăy-dăy-day-dáit;* sometimes this loud note changed into one which became low and querulous. On some of these occasions he also called *'tshica dee-dee.* The jarring call would then change occasionally into *kai-tee-did did-dit-did.*"

Several other observers have noted the resemblance of some of these notes to the notes of the Carolina chickadee. The single whistled call sounds like the whistle of a man calling his dog. It can readily be seen from a study of the above interpretations how easy is it for a novice to confuse the voice of the titmouse with that of the Carolina wren, the chickadee, or even the cardinal. All observers agree that the titmouse is a loud and persistent singer for nearly all the year; it is a joy to hear it tuning up in January, when so many other birds are silent. The song increases in frequency and intensity when the nuptial season approaches in February; early in spring its oft-repeated *peto* note is given so constantly that it may become monotonous and even tiresome. No wonder that the bird is locally known as the "Peter bird."

Field marks.—The tufted titmouse may be recognized as a small gray bird, less than English sparrow size, with a prominent, blackish crest, and chestnut-brown flanks. The colors are duller in the female than in the male, but otherwise they are much alike. Mr. Skinner (1928) suggests that "its big black eyes show a strong contrast to its trim gray plumage. * * * When the crest lies back on the crown, its long feathers stick out behind so that it is noticeable then as well as when erect."

Enemies.—Titmice are doubtless subject to attack by the ordinary enemies of all small birds, cats, hawks, owls, and snakes, but published records are not plentiful. The enterprising cowbird finds and enters the nesting cavity to deposit its unwelcome egg occasionally. Dr. Friedmann (1929) records four cases, and probably others have occurred since, but sometimes the entrance hole is too small for the parasite to enter.

Harold S. Peters (1936) lists, as external parasites on the tufted titmouse, two lice *(Myrsidea incerta* and *Philopterus* sp.), a mite *(Trombicula irritans),* and a tick *(Hoemaphysalis leporis-palustris).*

Fall and winter.—Mabel Gillespie (1930), referring to the vicinity of Glenolden, Pa., writes: "During the late spring, summer, and early fall, Titmice tend to disappear. This disappearance indicates a period of retirement during nesting and the subsequent annual molt. At this season the birds are in the secluded depths of woods and are unaccustomedly silent. In the fall they appear in small groups, which, as far as they can be counted, vary from two to at least six. Presumably there is more or less wandering at this time, but the tendency apparently is to choose a favorable location in which to spend the winter, and then to remain within a rather limited area. * * * In winter small groups suggesting family units occupy very definite and limited areas, never overlapping."

This last statement hardly agrees with the observations of several others; for instance, Dr. Dickey (MS.), referring to Pennsylvania and West Virginia, says: "Particularly in autumn and winter, tufted tits are rovers. They tend to assemble with such birds as Carolina chickadees, cardinals, various sparrows, several local woodpeckers, Carolina wrens, goldfinches, tree sparrows, and juncos. Bands of such species enter patches of weeds, flit along the courses of streams, cross country roads and highways, and peer forth from cover at farm yards. I was interested, during my many trips among these birds in fall and winter, to learn that often individuals roost, or spend dark drab days, inside orifices of woodpeckers and in natural cavities of posts and stubs. Not long ago I came upon a tit; it was drowsy and almost could be taken in the hand. Whether the species invariably roosts in such manner at night, I do not know, but I have read of campers routing the birds from holes in stubs."

Several other observers have reported winter wanderings of titmice in association with such other species of winter gleaners as are named above. Mr. Skinner (1928) says that, in North Carolina in winter, "sometimes these Titmice seem to join with Chickadees, Juncos or White-throated Sparrows. With Fox Sparrows, Field Sparrows, Blue Jays, Cardinals and Myrtle Warblers, their association is probably only accidental and very temporary."

Tufted titmice are practically permanent residents in even the more northern portions of their range, being regularly found in winter as far north as New Jersey, Pennsylvania, Indiana, and Illinois. Though largely woodland birds at all seasons, gleaning their food from the trunks and branches of trees, or rustling among the leaves on the ground, they are more inclined in winter to roam about in the open, or visit the neighborhood of houses, along with the chickadees and blue jays, to pick up scraps of refuse, or visit the well-stocked feeding stations. On the feeding shelf the tit seems to be the dominant character; only the blue jay refuses to make way for him.

DISTRIBUTION

Range.—Eastern United States; not migratory. The range of the tufted titmouse extents **north** to central Iowa (Ogden and Independence); southern Wisconsin (Maxomanie and probably Racine); southern Michigan (Grand Rapids and Detroit); probably southern Ontario (London and Toronto); New York (Hamburg, Potter, and Goshen); and northern New Jersey (Mahwah and Englewood). The **eastern** limits extend south along the coast from New Jersey (Englewood), to southern Florida (probably Royal Palm Hammock). **South** to southern Florida (probably Royal Palm Hammock, Fort Myers, Tallahassee, and Choctawatchee Bay); Louisiana (New Orleans); and southeastern Texas

(Houston and Giddings). **West** to eastern Texas (Giddings, Corsicana, Decatur, and Gainesville); Oklahoma (Norman, Arnett, and Copan); eastern Kansas (Wichita, Junction City, and Manhattan); and central Iowa (Ogden).

During summer the species has been recorded from eastern Nebraska (Red Cloud, Lincoln, and Neligh), from northern New York (Long Lake), and from Maine (Orono), while during fall or winter it has been recorded from southeastern South Dakota (Vermillion), Minnesota (Fosston, Hutchinson, Minneapolis, and Northfield), Connecticut (New Haven and Norwalk), and eastern Long Island (Easthampton).

Egg dates.—Florida: 5 records, May 2 to 9.

Maryland: 5 records, April 26 to May 26.

Oklahoma: 6 records, April 16 to May 27.

South Carolina: 7 records, April 18 to 30.

Texas: 9 records, March 26 to April 20.

PARUS ATRICRISTATUS ATRICRISTATUS Cassin

BLACK-CRESTED TITMOUSE

HABITS

The above name was originally applied to the species as a whole, which is to be found over much of eastern Texas and eastern Mexico, but the species has been split into two subspecies, and the subject of this sketch is now restricted in its distribution to the southern portion of the range, from the Rio Grande River southward through eastern Mexico to Coahuila, San Luis Potosí, and northern Veracruz.

George B. Sennett (1878 and 1879) seems to have been the first to make us acquainted with the black-crested titmice of the Rio Grande Valley. He says in his first paper: "These lively and sweet singers were everywhere abundant, especially in old lagoon-beds, now largely grown up with the mesquite and lignum vitae." We found these sprightly and attractive little birds to be common everywhere around Brownsville, in the heavy timber along the resacas, in the open groves of deciduous trees, and in the shade trees in the town. Their behavior and their delightful songs were strikingly like those of the familiar tufted titmouse.

Nesting.—Mr. Sennett (1879) was also the first to find the nest of this bird. His first nest, found in 1877, contained young, but on April 20, 1878, his assistant brought him a nest containing five young and an addled egg, probably the first one ever collected. He says of this nest:

The nest was situated some six feet from the ground, in a hollow limb of a half-dead willow, which was leaning on some brush, and was discovered by the bird's flying into its opening. It lay some ten or twelve inches from the opening, and is composed chiefly of wool intermixed with strips of soft inner bark, and now and then bits of snake-skins; the whole being much firmer and thicker than is usual with nests that are built in hollow stubs. All other nests found with young were situated higher, with one exception; the distance varying from four to twelve feet from the ground. I found them to occupy usually the abandoned holes of the Texas Woodpecker, *Picus scalaris;* but split forks of trees were sometimes put in use. They prefer living trees to dead ones, and in every case in my experience the opening had to be enlarged, sometimes with difficulty, before examination of the nest could be made. The localities mostly selected for nesting are groves or open timber free from undergrowth, whether in old lagoon beds, which receive the overflow from the river, or on the driest knolls. They do not avoid human habitations, as two nests were found on the ranch in ebony-trees, near buildings much frequented. The parents guard their treasures well, and are much disturbed when the nest is invaded; though not until they see that their nest is actually being handled do they give any cry of alarm, or other intimation of uneasiness than their near presence.

Others have referred to this bird's use of pieces of cast-off snake-skin in its nests, which seems to be a common practice with the species.

Eggs.—The black-crested titmouse probably deposits a set of five or six eggs ordinarily, perhaps sometimes as many even as seven, or as few as four.

Of the single egg, referred to above, Mr. Sennett (1879) says: "The ground color is clear dead white; distributed unevenly over the whole surface, and not very sparingly, are flecks and blotches of fawn-color of various shades, the sides having rather more than either end." A set of four fresh eggs he describes as follows: "The ground color is pinkish-white. The spots of reddish-brown are small and few in number, and scattered over the greater part of the egg, but at the larger end they are large and numerous, covering nearly the whole end, though in no case forming a ring."

The measurements of 50 eggs average 17.0 by 13.5 millimeters; the eggs showing the four extremes measure **18.9** by 13.5, 16.2 by **14.4, 15.0** by 13.4, and 15.1 by **12.7** millimeters.

Young.—The period of incubation does not seem to be known. Mr. Sennett (1879) found that both sexes share the duties of incubation, for he took a male on the nest, and noticed that other males had bare and wrinkled bellies. Apparently two broods are reared in a season.

Plumages.—According to Mr. Sennett (1879), the "young just from the egg are nude, with the exception of a few long, dark, downy feathers on the back, nape, and over the eyes."

Ridgway (1904) describes the young in juvenal plumage as "essentially like adults, but black of crown and crest much duller (the feathers **often narrowly tipped with grayish**), less sharply defined laterally and posteriorly against the gray, and anteriorly invading the forehead almost (sometimes quite) to base of culmen; throat and chest pale gray; color of sides and flanks much paler (cinnamon-buff instead of rufous-cinnamon); back sometimes suffused with sooty or blackish."

What few molting birds I have seen indicate that the postnuptial molts of adults, and probably the postjuvenal molt, take place mainly in August; September birds seem to be in fresh plumage.

Food.—Little seems to be known about the food of this titmouse, and practically nothing has been published on it. Austin Paul Smith (1910) writes: "Having but one true Titmouse, the Black-crested *(Baeolophus atricristatus),* we especially appreciate him, though he is omnipresent, even into the heart of the city [Brownsville]. They inspect any object of size, that may arouse suspicion of harboring caterpillars or other insects. They are very fond of the caterpillar of the butterfly *(Libythea bachmanni)* which so persistently attacks our hackberry trees, as to have surely defoliated them this summer, but for the combined efforts of the Titmouse and Sennett Oriole."

Voice.—Mr. Smith (1910) says further: "The Black-crested Tit is rarely silent, the usual notes being a continuation of sounds like 'pete-chee-chee-chee'; more rarely 'peter-peter.' By April the young have appeared on the scene."

DISTRIBUTION

Range.—South-central Texas and northeastern Mexico; not migratory. The range of the black-crested titmouse extends **north** to central Texas (Chisos Mountains, San Angelo, and Lomita). **East** to central Texas (Lomita, Austin, Corpus Christi, and Brownsville); and Veracruz ("highlands"). **South** to Veracruz ("highlands"); and San Luis Potosí (Tamazunchale and Valles). **West** to San Luis Potosí (Valles); western Tamaulipas (Victoria and Montemorelos); western Nuevo León (Monterey and Lampazos); and southwestern Texas (Chisos Mountains).

The range outlined is for the entire species, which has been separated into two subspecies, the typical black-crested titmouse *(Parus atricristatus atricristatus),* occupying the southern portion of the range, north to the Rio Grande Valley, while Sennett's titmouse *(P. a. sennetti),* is found in Texas.

Egg dates.—Texas: 68 records, March 7 to May 26; 34 records, April 3 to May 2, indicating the height of the season.

PARUS ATRICRISTATUS SENNETTI (Ridgway)

SENNETT'S TITMOUSE

HABITS

More than 50 years elapsed after the species was discovered before this northern race of the black-crested titmouse was named and described, as distinct subspecifically from the race found in the Rio Grande Valley and in eastern Mexico. Ridgway (1904) describes it as "similar to *B. a. atricristatus,* but decidedly larger; upper parts much clearer gray, with little, if any, olive tinge; adult female with crest feathers more often and more extensively tipped with gray, and both sexes with forehead more often tinged with brown or rusty, sometimes deeply so." He goes on to say in a footnote that "any pronounced rusty tinge to the color of the forehead indicates, in the writer's opinion, admixture of *B. bicolor* blood." And he suggests that the two subspecies described by Sennett, from Bee County, Tex., are merely hybrids between the two species, *bicolor* and *atricristatus.*

John Cassin (1852), who first described the species and published the first colored plate of it, says that it was discovered in Texas by John Woodhouse Audubon, and it was described by Cassin in the Proceedings of the Academy of Natural Sciences of Philadelphia, vol. 5, p. 103, 1850. The only information he had regarding its habits came from Dr. Samuel W. Woodhouse, from whose journal he quoted as follows:

While our party was encamped on the Rio Salado in Texas, near San Antonio, in March, 1851, I observed this handsome little chickadee for the first time. It was busily engaged in capturing insects among the trees on the bank of the stream, and like the other species of its family, was incessantly in motion and very noisy. At our camp at Quihi, on the eighth of May, I again found it very abundant among the oaks. The young males, which were then fully grown, much resembled the adult females, both wanting the black crest which characterizes the male. Afterwards I noticed this species, occurring sparingly, along our route, as far as the head waters of the San Francisco river in New Mexico. [The birds seen in New Mexico were probably the gray titmouse, *P. inornatus ridgwayi.*]

I observed it almost entirely in trees bordering streams of water. * * * It occurred in small parties, appeared to be very sociable and lively in its habits, and in general appearance and in nearly all its notes which I heard, it so very much resembled the common crested chickadee of the Northern States as scarcely to be recognized as a distinct species at a short distance.

The distribution now given for this subspecies in the 1931 Check-List is the "Lower Austral Zone of central Texas, from Tom Green and Concho counties east to the Brazos River, and from Young County south to Nueces and Bee counties."

George Finlay Simmons (1925) lists as its haunts, in the Austin region, "woodlands along creeks; scrub oaks and cedars on hillsides; oak groves or mottes in open or semi-open country; city shade trees; ravines, gullies, and canyons among the hills; oak-clad crests of hills; telegraph poles along railroad rights-of-way."

Mrs. Bailey (1902) says that "Mr. Bailey found the black-crest one of the most abundant birds of the Upper Sonoran zone, flying about conspicuously among the junipers, nut pines, and scrub oaks."

Nesting.—Like others of the genus, Sennett's titmouse builds its nest in natural cavities in trees, stumps, or posts, in old woodpecker holes, or in bird boxes. Mr. Simmons (1925) says that the nest may be placed anywhere from 3 to 22 feet above ground, averaging about 10 feet; he says the commonest locations are "hollows in live oaks, next commonest in fence posts and bird boxes, then boxed fence posts, elms, hachberries, cedars, telephone poles and post oaks." He found one nest on the top of an old mockingbird's nest in a well-sheltered tree.

He says that the nest consists of "a mass of rubbish composed of cowhair, rabbit fur, green lichens, cedar bark, green moss, cotton, feathers, and oak blossoms; and occasionally small bits of inner bark and bark fiber, grass, wool, soft down, leaves, rootlets, a stick or two, hemp string, tissue paper, onion skins, and felting materials." It is "lined with soft short cowhair, rabbit fur, opossum hair, wool, cotton, and occasionally horsehair, soft down, feathers, and snake skin." The bottom of the cavity is filled with green moss to a depth of from 2 or 3 inches in one case to as much as 36 inches. He and others have reported that pieces of cast-off snakeskin are usually found in the nests; these and the tissue paper and onion skin may be used to give resiliency or ventilation to the nest; this is evidently a characteristic habit of the species, as it is with the crested flycatcher, under which it is more fully discussed.

Eggs.—The eggs of Sennett's titmouse vary in number from four to seven; of 25 sets, recorded by Mr. Simmons (1925), 5 were sets of seven, 12 of six, 5 of five, and 3 of four eggs each. The eggs are apparently indistinguishable from those of the other black-crested titmouse, under which they are more fully described. Albert J. Kirn writes to me that he once found a nest containing twelve eggs; and once he found a nest with two eggs of the titmouse and two of the dwarf cowbird, which was afterwards deserted. The measurements of 40 eggs average 17.9 by 14.1 millimeters; the eggs showing the four extremes measure **19.3** by 14.3, 18.0 by **15.0**, **16.1** by 14.0, and 18.4 by **12.6** millimeters.

Food.—Although no careful analysis of the food of this titmouse seems to have been made, it is probably similar to that of the closely related tufted titmouse, about two-thirds insects in various forms and about one-third vegetable matter. It seems to be very fond of cater-**pillars** and searches the limbs and trunks of trees for hidden insects, their larvae and their eggs; scales and spiders are probably eaten to some extent, as well as berries, wild fruits, and some soft-shelled nuts and acorns. H. P. Attwater (1892) says that "the favorite food of the Black-crested Titmouse during winter is the pecan nut; they hold them on the horizontal limbs, or place them in the cracks of the bark, and break them open by knocking with their bills, like Woodpeckers."

Behavior.—The behavior of both races of the black-crested titmouse is so much like that of the more familiar tufted titmouse that one would hardly recognize the difference between the two species at a little distance. They are both friendly, confiding, cheery, busy, active, and noisy little birds that attract our attention and our interest. Their elevated crests give them a jaunty appearance that is very pleasing. During the breeding season they are usually seen in pairs; after the young are on the wing, rather early in the season, they may be seen traveling about in family parties, and in the winter in loose companies, when they are often seen about human habitations and in towns. Mr. Simmons (1925) says that they become attached to one locality; "one pair nested for six consecutive years in a hollow of an old persimmon tree."

Illustrating the confiding nature of this bird, Henry Nehrling (1893) relates the following experience that came to him while he was watching a white-eyed vireo's nest:

While I stood there in perfect silence, with my gaze steadfastly fixed on the pretty lichen decorated domicile, a Black-crested Titmouse came very close to me. It first perched on a small bush, then it flew to the ground, and finally, growing very bold, clung fast to my trousers. When I moved, it flew back to the bush, contemplating me curiously, but finally, convinced of my good will, it returned and clambered up and down my back, pecking me, and again vigorously thrusting its bill into my clothes. It was obviously looking for insects, especially wood-ticks which in such places creep over ones clothes in great numbers. Whenever I made a noticeable movement, it fled a little distance, but invariably returned. Finally when I went and seated myself on a prostrate tree, it followed me again. It became so bold, that it not only climbed up and down my back, but fearlessly crept over to my shoulders and arms, and even onto the hat. This Titmouse stayed near me as long as I remained in that part of the woods, and pursued me a short distance, screaming loudly *Wait-wait-wait-wait,* while I continued my way through the forest. Never before have I seen such boldness and confidence exhibited by a wild bird.

Voice.—Mr. Simmons (1925) says that the song is "quite similar to that of the Eastern Tufted Titmouse," consisting of "a cheery, abbreviated *Peté, Peté, Peté, Peté;* a series of monotonous whistles, *hew, hew, hew, hew, hew, hew, hew, hew;* a whistled *tseee ep;* a rasping, scolding *eck-eck.*"

Enemies.—Mr. Simmons (1925) lists this bird as a local victim of the cowbird.

Field marks.—The long crest, usually erect, will mark this species as one of the crested titmice. The jet-black crest of the male and the dark crest of the female, much darker than that of the other crested titmice, will mark the bird as a black-crested titmouse; the subspecies are hardly recognizable in the field. This species has a white forehead, often tinged with brownish in the northern subspecies, whereas the tufted titmouse has a black forehead. The females and young have more or less admixture of gray in the crown and crest.

PARUS INORNATUS SEQUESTRATUS (Grinnell and Swarth)

OREGON TITMOUSE

This northern race of the plain tits seems to occupy a very narrow range in Jackson County, Oreg., and Siskiyou County, Calif., between the Coast and Cascade Ranges. The describers, Grinnell and Swarth (1926), state:

[It] differs from *Baeolophus inornatus inornatus,* to which it is nearest geographically, in slightly smaller size and in grayer, more leaden color throughout, with but a trace of the brownish tinge that shows clearly on the upper parts of *inornatus;* lower surface less purely white, more suffused with gray. Similar to *B. i. griseus,* but smaller, with especially shorter tail, and darker in color, much less ashy in tone. Similar to *B. i. affabilis* but bill much smaller, and coloration not quite so deeply leaden, especially as to wing and tail feathers. * * *

Careful examination of the Museum's series of all the races here concerned has convinced us that both the Lower California and Oregon forms are deserving of names. It is a curious fact that, though the intervening forms are different from either, these two subspecies, so far apart geographically, should be strikingly alike in the matter of their relatively dark, brown-less coloration. The outstanding difference between them lies in the bill. The Oregon bird is smaller billed even than typical *inornatus;* the San Pedro Martir race is large billed, like *murinus.*

The Oregon titmouse does not seem to differ materially in any of its habits from its more southern relatives.

The measurements of eight eggs average 17.8 by 13.2 millimeters; the eggs showing the four extremes measure 18.1 by 12.4, and 17.5 by 14.0 millimeters.

PARUS INORNATUS INORNATUS Gambel

PLAIN TITMOUSE

PLATE 62

HABITS

This is, indeed, a *plain* titmouse, without a trace of contrasting colors in its somber dress; *inornatus,* unadorned, is also a good name for it. But it is a charming bird, nevertheless, with its jaunty crest, like a miniature jay, its sprightly manners, and its melodious voice. Its gray coat blends well with the trunks and branches of the oaks among which it forages. It is the western counterpart of our familiar eastern tufted titmouse, which it resembles in appearance, behavior, and voice and for which it might easily be mistaken, unless clearly seen.

The species, of which there are at least nine subspecies, occupies a wide range in western North America, from the Rocky Mountain region to the Pacific coast, and from Oregon to Lower California. The type race is now restricted to northern and central California.

The favored haunts of the plain titmouse are the oak-clad, sunny slopes of the foothills, where the foliage of the evergreen oaks provides shelter and a good food supply all the year around; and here it is practically resident at all seasons. It seldom seems to range above 3,500 feet.

In the Lassen Peak region, according to Grinnell, Dixon, and Linsdale (1930), "a considerable variety of larger plant species furnished situations favorable for some major activity of this bird species. The trees and shrubs that were definitely recorded as foraged through by the plain titmouse are the following: willow, cottonwood, sycamore, valley oak, live oak, black oak, blue oak, golden oak, several species of orchard trees, digger pine, and buckbrush. We were left with the impression that the blue oak is the tree within the Lassen section used for feeding place, nesting, and shelter by the largest number of these birds."

Courtship.—Dr. John B. Price (1936), who studied for six seasons the family relations of the plain titmouse at Stanford University, Calif., makes no mention of a courtship performance, nor can I find it mentioned elsewhere. But his studies reveal a tendency to remain mated for more than one year; he says:

"A titmouse usually keeps the same mate from year to year and there was only one known case of 'divorce'. Of a total of 14 pairs recaptured, 11 were mated together for at least two years and only 3 were not. No sex difference was found in the retention of territory from year to year. If a bird lost its mate the survivor, whether male or female, remained in the nesting territory and secured a new mate. In one case the new mate was known to be a juvenile of the year before. * * * An interesting fact is that there was only one case of 'divorce' where a bird took a new mate while its former mate was still known to be living. In all other cases where a titmouse took a new mate the former mate was never recaptured anywhere and quite probably was dead, especially as in several cases it was known to be several years old." One male "was banded as an adult in 1928 and was recaptured nesting in the same box in 1934 when it must have been at least seven years old." It was absent in 1935.

Nesting.—The birds that Dr. Price studied all nested in bird boxes; evidently they prefer to nest in boxes where these are available. Sixty-four adults were caught in the boxes and banded; there were 33 cases of adults renesting in the same box (a bird nesting in the same box for three years would be two cases of renesting) ; there were 17 cases of adults nesting in boxes from 43 to 90 yards away, which were practically in the same territory; there was only one case of nesting in a box 200 yards away, and none at a greater distance. "If the changing of nest-boxes were really a change of nesting territory one would expect that the former territory would be taken over by another pair of titmouses nesting in the first box. With the exception of the female that moved 200 yards, this never took place. The first box was always either empty or used by bluebirds or chickadees. Often a bird would alternate between two boxes from year to year."

The plain titmouse normally nests in holes in trees, either old woodpecker holes or natural cavities in the trunks or limbs of trees, often partially excavated by the birds in soft or rotten wood. Dawson (1923) says it is a mistake to think that this bird cannot excavate its own nest, and says:

"Two of the nests I have found (and *not* rifled) were excavated in the heart wood of live limbs of the blue oak *(Quercus douglasi),* not less than ten inches in diameter. * * * I once traced a Plain Titmouse to a hole about twenty feet up in one of those cliffs of mingled gravel and 'dobe' which line the banks of the San Jacinto River. * * * We found a neat, round aperture in the earth, which must have been barely large enough to admit the bird, being, in fact, so snug that it showed two separate 'scores' for the feet. This opened rapidly into an ample chamber with extensive inner recesses—a monument of toil. The nest proper, a great bed of rabbit-fur, was placed about one foot from the entrance."

Grinnell and Storer (1924), referring to the Yosemite region, say that "old woodpecker holes are used when available, but many, perhaps a majority, of nests are placed in naturally rotted-out cavities." The height from the ground varies according to the location of these cavities; one of their nests was only 33 inches and another 10½ feet from the ground; I have seen one that was 32 feet aloft, which is probably unusual. One of their nests was only 17 inches from a western bluebird's nest; it was "in a natural cavity of rather large size. The bottom held a mass of fine dry grasses, perhaps 4 inches in depth, and on top of this was a heavy felted lining of cow hair and rabbit fur. The top of this mat was 5½ inches * * * below the margin of the entrance." A nest in the A. D. DuBois collection was made of moss, grass, weed stems and fibers, and was lined with a few feathers and rabbit fur.

Eggs.—Six to eight eggs seem to be the commonest numbers laid by the plain titmouse, with seven the prevailing number. Among 22 sets in the Museum of Vertebrate Zoology, 14 were sets of seven. In 62 complete sets of eggs recorded by Dr. Price (1936), the numbers ranged from three to nine; there were six eggs in 12 nests, seven eggs in 17 nests, eight eggs in 14 nests, and nine eggs in 7 nests. Ernest Adams (1898) records a set of 12 eggs, which might have been the product of two females.

The eggs are mostly ovate, sometimes elongated to elliptical-ovate, and have practically no gloss. They are pure white and often entirely unmarked, but usually some of the eggs in a set, and sometimes all of them, are faintly marked with minute dots of very pale reddish brown. These pale markings are sometimes evenly distributed over the entire egg and sometimes very sparingly scattered. Whole sets are sometimes pure, unmarked white.

The measurements of 40 eggs average 17.4 by 13.4 millimeters; the eggs showing the four extremes measure **19.3** by 13.3, 18.4 by **14.2**, and **16.3** by **12.7** millimeters.

Young.—Mrs. Wheelock (1904) gives the period of incubation as 14 days, which matches the figures given for other titmice. Dr. Price (1936) was convinced, by his examination of "brood patches," that only the female incubates; "only females ever were captured incubating the eggs."

Mr. Adams (1898) says that the female is a very close sitter and has to be removed by hand, clinging tenaciously to the nest material and often bringing some of it out with her; even when thus forcibly removed, she returns to the nest immediately; he had to put one in his pocket to keep her out of the nest while he was removing the eggs.

Both parents assist in feeding the young, and the large broods keep them quite busy. Mrs. Wheelock (1904) says: "My theory that most young birds are fed by regurgitation *at first* was confirmed in this case by the fact that, although I was within twelve feet of the nest whenever either bird entered it during that first day, not once was any food visible in the beak of either. After the fourth day the worms and insects carried were frequently projecting on each side of the small beak, but up to that time there had been none seen, though a careful watch was kept with both opera glasses and naked eyes." Apparently, the young birds that she watched were about ready to leave the nest on the sixteenth day.

Evidently the young are driven away from the home territory as soon as they are able to care for themselves. Dr. Price (1936) banded 145 young birds, but only two "were recaptured nesting the following year, and both were more than a quarter of a mile distant from the box where hatched."

Plumages.—The juvenal plumage, even with a decided crest, is mainly assumed before the young bird leaves the nest. This is much like the adult plumage, but it is softer and less compact; the wing coverts are somewhat paler and indistinctly buffy at the tips. Most of the molts occur in August, but I have seen a bird in full juvenal plumage as late as August 29 and an adult molting as early as July 14. The postjuvenal molt includes the contour plumage and the wing coverts, but not the flight feathers. The postnuptial molt of adults is complete.

Food.—Prof. F. E. L. Beal (1907) examined 76 stomachs of the plain titmouse and says that "unlike most of the titmice, the plain tit eats less animal than vegetable food, the proportion being 43 percent of animal and 57 of vegetable." Bugs (Hemiptera) seem to be the favorite, 12 percent; the injurious black olive scale forms nearly 5 of this 12 percent; in the month of August, 34 percent of the contents of nine stomachs consisted of these scales, and one stomach was filled with them; other hemipterous food included leafhoppers, jumping plant-lice, and tree-hoppers. Caterpillars amounted to nearly 11 percent. Beetles formed nearly 7 percent, all harmful species, including the genus *Balaninus,* weevils with long snouts; these "insects, by means of this long snout, bore into nuts and acorns, wherein they deposit eggs, which hatch grubs that eat the nut. The tit finds these beetles while foraging upon the oaks. One stomach contained the remains of 13 of them, another 11, a third 8, and a fourth 7, while others contained fewer." Some of these were probably found while the bird was feeding upon the acorns. Hymenoptera, ants and wasps, made up about 6 percent of the food, and other insects, daddy-long-legs and grasshoppers, amounted to a little more than 5 percent: one stomach contained the remains of 13 grasshoppers. A few spiders were eaten, less than 1 percent.

In the vegetable food, fruit amounted to nearly 32 percent, three times as much as eaten by the linnet, and this appeared to be of the larger cultivated varieties: no seeds of wild berries were found. "Cherries were identified in a number of stomachs, and the pulp of the larger fruits was abundant. * * * Oats were found in a number of stomachs and constituted nearly 30 percent of the contents of two stomachs taken in January. * * *

"Leaf galls, seeds of poison oak, weed seeds, unidentifiable matter and rubbish make up the remainder, 24 percent, of the vegetable food."

Practically all the insects eaten by this titmouse are harmful, the scales exceedingly so; it is therefore very beneficial in protecting the trees of forest and orchard; it is not sufficiently abundant to do any very serious damage to cultivated fruits.

Behavior.—With all its somber colors the plain titmouse is a most attractive little bird, always cheery, active, and friendly as it forages among the oaks for its insect prey, pecking and prying into every crack and crevice, with its crest erected like a jaunty little jay and greeting us with its varied notes. Mr. Adams (1898) gives his first impression of it as follows:

After searching the tree to which my attention had been called for some time, my curious gaze rested upon a little gray bird which, with crest erected and with his whole frame seemingly alert, was pecking furiously at the bark of the oak, evidently in search of food. Now and then a single sharp note came to my ears, and occasionally one slightly prolonged and possessing a greater degree of authority. At times he seemed to be angry, and then his notes came faster and harsher, but when a fat insect fell to his lot, he at once became pacified, his notes were subdued, his crest lowered, and the once miniature Jay had become peaceful *Parus inornatus* once more. * * *

This Titmouse is not very sociable and never gathers into large flocks—in fact I have rarely seen more than three together at any time of the year. Like many others of the feathered tribe, he has an inherent hatred towards owls. I remember finding a nest of the California Screech Owl in a hollow trunk of an oak and on the outside a cavity containing the nest of a titmouse. The thin partition separating the two sitters was not such as to prevent the scratching of the owl being distinctly audible to the other. The female would often appear at the entrance of her home greatly agitated. Sometimes she would mount the rim of the trunk and peer down into the darkness as if to ascertain the cause of such a commotion. The male when he visited his mate, would perhaps at her request, fly repeatedly at the poor owl.

Mrs. Ruth Wheeler tells me that these titmice "are the most inquisitive of the smaller birds. Whenever any disturbance is caused in the woods, they are the first birds to arrive and raise an outcry. Whenever we set the camera up near a nest or a feeding station, a titmouse usually is soon on the scene carefully investigating."

Voice.—Ralph Hoffmann (1927) writes: "Spring comes to the brown hillsides of California as soon as the first rains break the long autumn drought; the cuckoo-flower and ferns push up through the mould, the gooseberries blossom and the Plain Tit begins his lively if monotonous refrain from the live oaks. Different birds have various forms of this spring song, *witt-y, witt-y, witt-y* or *ti-wee, ti-wee, ti-wee.* It is always a high clear whistle with a marked accent, and a persistence that shows the relationship of the bird to the Tufted Tit, with its *pée-to,* in the river bottoms of the Middle West. The rest of the year, when the

Plain Tit is hunting leisurely through the oaks, his commonest note is a scratchy *tsíck-a-dee-dee* or *tsíck-a-dear,* which has to make up to a California bird lover in the lowlands for the absence of the Black-capped Chickadee."

Mrs. Bailey (1902) says: "There is an indefinable charm about the slow, clearly enunciated *tu-whit, to-whit, tu-whit,* that echoes through the oaks, telling of the presence of the plain titmouse." Mrs. Wheelock (1904) says that "his common note of *tsee-day-day* is not unlike that of the mountain chickadee, and occasionally he indulges in a whistled *peto, peto* that reminds one of his pretty Eastern cousin."

W. L. Dawson (1923) adds a few more similar notes, and a *ssic-rap sssicrap,* and one that "sounded like *di di di tipoong, di di di tipoong,* the *di* notes very wooden and prosaic, the concluding member suddenly and richly musical."

Field marks.—A plump, chunky bird, plainly clad in somber grayish brown above and plain gray below, with a prominent crest, usually erected, could be no other than a plain titmouse. Its favorite haunts are among oaks, its behavior suggests the chickadees, and its notes though varied are characteristic of the family.

Enemies.—Titmice, like all other small birds, have to be constantly on the alert to avoid all the well-known predatory birds and mammals, but this species has an important enemy in the California jay. Dr. Price (1936) says: "Jays are often seen about nesting boxes containing young titmouses and sometimes perch on the box and peer inside. When the young birds leave the nest the jays often dive at them and kill them."

DISTRIBUTION

Range.—Western United States and northwestern Mexico; not migratory.

The range of the plain titmouse extends **north** to southern Oregon (Gold Hill and probably Blitzen Canyon); Utah (Boulder); and Colorado (Douglas Springs and Canyon City). **East** to central Colorado (Canyon City); extreme western Oklahoma (Kenton); New Mexico (Santa Fe, Corona, and Capitan Mountain); and western Texas (Guadalupe Mountain). **South** to Texas (Guadalupe Mountain); southern New Mexico (Silver City); and northern Baja California (Valladares). **West** to western Baja California (Valladares and Las Cruces); California (Twin Oaks, Pasadena, Watsonville, and Red Bluff); and western Oregon (Ashland, Medford, and Gold Hill).

At outlined the range is for the entire species, of which nine geographic races are recognized. The typical subspecies *(Parus inornatus*

inornatus) is found in California from Shasta and Mendocino Counties south to Kern and San Luis Obispo Counties; the Oregon titmouse *(P. i. sequestratus)* is found between the Coast and Cascade Ranges from southwestern Oregon south through Siskiyou County, Calif.; the San Diego titmouse *(P. i. transpositus)* is found in southwestern California from Santa Barbara County to San Diego County; the San Pedro titmouse *(P. i. murinus)* occupies the northern part of Baja California south to about latitude 30°; the ashy titmouse *(P. i. cineraceus)* is found in the Cape region of Baja California; while the gray titmouse *(P. i. ridgwayi)* occupies the Rocky Mountain and Great Basin portion of the range. The lead-colored plain titmouse *(P. i. plumbescens)* is found in southern Arizona and New Mexico; the Kern Basin plain titmouse *(P. i. kernensis)* in Kern County, Calif.; and the Warner Valley titmouse *(P. i. zaleptus)* in southern Oregon.

Egg dates.—California: 101 records, March 20 to July 16; 50 records, April 4 to 29, indicating the height of the season.

New Mexico: 19 records, May 3 to 28.

Mexico: 28 records, April 22 to May 31; 14 records, April 30 to May 14.

PARUS INORNATUS TRANSPOSITUS (Grinnell)

SAN DIEGO TITMOUSE

The San Diego titmouse occupies an area in southwestern California extending from Santa Barbara County to San Diego County.

The above scientific name was suggested by Dr. Grinnell (1928) to replace the name *murinus,* which was formerly applied to the plain tits of the above region; the latter name is now restricted to the birds of northwestern Lower California, the San Pedro titmouse. He gives as its characters, "as compared with *B. i. inornatus,* slightly larger and grayer, bill much heavier. As compared with *B. i. murinus,* browner, decidedly less leaden gray in cast of coloration; bill and feet less blackish, rectrices and remiges brownish rather than plumbeous."

The habits of this titmouse are apparently similar to those of the plain titmouse found farther north, which need not be repeated here.

The measuresments of 40 eggs average 17.4 by 13.3 millimeters; the eggs showing the four extremes measure **19.0** by **14.0,** and **13.0** by **9.5** millimeters; the latter egg might be considered a runt; the next smallest egg measures 16.0 by 12.0 millimeters.

PARUS INORNATUS MURINUS (Ridgway)
SAN PEDRO TITMOUSE

The San Pedro titmouse was originally described, as a new subspecies, by Dr. Joseph Grinnell (Grinnell and Swarth, 1926) under the subspecific name *affabilis,* as the race confined to the Sierra San Pedro Mártir. This region was included in the range of Mr. Ridgway's *murinus,* which he (1904) understood to extend from Los Angeles and San Bernardino Counties to the San Pedro Mártir Mountains.

Dr. Grinnell (1928), in a later paper, explains why Ridgway's name should apply to the San Pedro Mártir bird, why the name *affabilis* should be discarded, and why it was necessary for him to give a new name to the San Diego bird, which is now called *transpositus,* an appropriate name under the circumstances!

Dr. Grinnell (Grinnell and Swarth, 1926) says that the San Pedro titmouse "is the darkest, most leaden colored, of any of the subspecies of *Baeolophus inornatus,* showing no trace of the brown tinge that is apparent strongly in *inornatus* and somewhat less so in *murinus"* [=*transpositus*].

As its habitat seems to be in the live-oak association, we have no reason to think that its habits are any different from those of other races of the species.

The eggs are similar to those of the plain titmouse. The measurements of 40 eggs average 18.0 by 13.7 millimeters; the eggs showing the four extremes measure **19.8** by 14.5, 19.3 by **14.6, 16.2** by 13.1, and 16.5 by **12.2** millimeters.

PARUS INORNATUS CINERACEUS (Ridgway)
ASHY TITMOUSE

Far removed from its nearest allies, with none of the species in the wide intervening area, the ashy titmouse lives in a very restricted region in the mountains of the Cape region, near the southern tip of Lower California. William Brewster (1902) says that "it is a bird of the pine forests which cover portions of the summit and upper slopes of the high mountains near the southern extremity of the Peninsula. Here, according to Mr. Belding, it is 'common from 3,000 feet altitude upward.' On the Sierra de la Laguna Mr. Frazar found it quite as numerous in December as in May and June. None of the specimens killed at the latter season showed any indications of being about to breed, and the eggs, like those of many other birds which inhabit these mountains, are probably not laid much before midsummer."

Ridgway (1904) characterizes it as "similar in coloration of upper parts to *B. i. griseus* [= *ridgwayi*], but under parts much paler, and size slightly smaller."

Nothing seems to have been published on its habits.

PARUS INORNATUS RIDGWAYI Richmond

GRAY TITMOUSE

HABITS

This eastern race of the plain titmice has the widest range of the nine subspecies. The 1931 Check-list says that it "breeds in the Upper Austral Zone of the mountains from northeastern California, Nevada, southern Idaho, Utah, southwestern Wyoming, and Colorado to southeastern California, southern Arizona, southeastern New Mexico, and central western Texas."

Dr. Joseph Grinnell (1923), writing of the status of the gray titmouse in California, was "almost tempted to propose full specific status" for it, and says: "The Gray Titmouse is a very distinct form, separated sharply from the Plain Titmouse geographically as well as on the basis of phylogenetic characters. No intergradation between these two titmouses is known to take place. The Gray Titmouse in California is a rare bird. It has been found to exist only in small numbers and at a few widely scattered points. The general territory in which it occurs lies east of the Sierran divide, in the arid Great Basin faunal division. The life-zone occupied is the Upper Sonoran, and the association the piñon-juniper."

From the above and following quotations, it will be seen that the haunts of the gray titmouse are quite different from those of the plain titmouse, which seems to prefer mainly the various oak associations.

Ridgway (1877) says: "In the pine forests of the eastern slope of the Sierra Nevada, especially in their lower portion, and among the cedar and piñon groves on the desert ranges immediately adjacent to the eastward, the Gray Titmouse was a rather common species; but it did not seem to be abundant anywhere." According to Baird, Brewer, and Ridgway (1874), "Dr. Woodhouse met with this species in the San Francisco Mountains, near the Little Colorado River, New Mexico. He found it very abundant, feeding among the tall pines in company with the *Sitta pygmaea, S. aculeata,* and *Parus montanus.*" Mrs. Bailey (1928) writes of its haunts in New Mexico: "The attractive Gray Titmouse with its prettily crested head and soft Quaker-gray plumage is intimately associated with pleasant camps in the low, sun-filled junipers and nut pines of the mesas, the low desert ranges, and the foothills of the Rocky Mountains." She says that it ranges over the whole mountainous part of the State, and records it at various elevations from 4,600 to 8,000 feet. Although this titmouse is said to occur in the Chiricahua Mountains, in southern Arizona, we did not see it there, or anywhere else in that region; it is apparently a rare bird in Arizona.

Nesting.—The nesting habits of the gray titmouse seem to be similar to those of its California relatives. It nests in woodpecker holes and natural cavities in trees and stumps, or in bird boxes. W. E. Griffee writes to me: "My experience with this titmouse was limited to the spring of 1934 when, while living at Albuquerque, N. Mex., I put up a string of nesting boxes in the junipers and pinyon pines of the Sandia Mountain foothills, 20 miles east of Albuquerque. Evidently the birds were very common, because early in the season I procured four sets of eggs from the 25 or 30 (out of 50) boxes, which wood-chopping Spanish Americans had failed to find and knock down. Bottoms of the boxes were covered with a mixture of grass, bark strips, and dirt. A heavy lining of rabbit fur, rodent hair, etc., was well cupped to receive the eggs. Incubating birds sat tightly, almost like chickadees, and were difficult to flush, even after the tops of the boxes were removed."

Eggs.—What eggs of the gray titmouse I have seen are indistinguishable from those of the plain titmouse, as they might be expected to be. Mrs. Bailey (1928) calls them "plain white"; probably many eggs and even full sets of eggs are entirely unmarked. The measurements of 40 eggs average 17.5 by 13.7 millimeters; the eggs showing the four extremes measure **19.1** by 14.0, 18.4 by **14.2, 16.0** by 14.0, and 18.4 by **12.9** millimeters.

Behavior.—Henshaw (1875) writes: "Its habits much resemble those of its eastern congener *(L. bicolor).* It spends much of its time on the ground, searching for insects, and quite likely the piñon nuts and acorns may, during the fall and winter, form a part of its food, though I have never seen them pay any attention to these. It has much curiosity, and, though somewhat timid, will occasionally remain within easy distance of an intruding person; keeping a careful watch upon his motions, uttering its harsh, scolding notes, expressive alike of anger and fear. It has, in the early summer, a short, disconnected song, which, however, is often sweet and pleasing. I have never seen more than three or four together, even in the fall; but, in every company of the other Titmice, Warblers, or Bluebirds, a few of this species is always found."

Voice.—Although the notes of the gray titmouse, as well as all its habits, are similar to those of the species elsewhere, I am tempted to quote the following attractive account from the pen of Mrs. Florence Merriam Bailey (1928):

[In the] low sunny groves the wayfarer hears many of its small notes, delightfully homelike and conversational in tone, including its rapid *wheed-leah,* *wheed-leah, wheed-leah,* repeated three or four times in quick succession, and its chickadee-like *tsche-de-dee, tu-we-twee-twee,* sometimes used to preface its loud clear *pe-to* calls. But its most conversational notes are best heard at the nest, where you may perhaps listen to a variety of small talk, such as the infantile, lisping notes of the hungry, brooding bird coaxing her mate to feed her; the tender note of her mate calling her to come to the door for the food he has brought; pretty conjugal notes of greeting and farewell; the chattering scold and cries of anger, anxiety, and terror, heard when enemies threaten; sharp notes of warning to the young, and wails of grief when harm has come to the nestlings. Such notes, given emphasis by vivacious, eloquent movements and gestures, interpret the thoughts and feelings of these intense little feathered folk, almost as clearly as elaborate conversations do the emotions of less demonstrative human beings.

PARUS INORNATUS PLUMBESCENS (Grinnell)

LEAD-COLORED PLAIN TITMOUSE

In naming this subspecies, Dr. Joseph Grinnell (1934) says of it: "As compared with *Baeolophus inornatus griseus,* from the eastern part of the Great Basin region, north of the Colorado River: similar in general features, but bill smaller, especially shorter; tail shorter; coloration darker, more leaden hued, this tone most pronounced dorsally but pervading the lower parts also. Color of back, close to Deep Mouse Gray (of Ridgway, 1912, pl. LI)."

He gives as its range "New Mexico (at least southwestern) and parts of Arizona south of the Colorado and Little Colorado rivers."

PARUS INORNATUS KERNENSIS (Grinnell and Behle)

KERN BASIN PLAIN TITMOUSE

Dr. Joseph Grinnell and William H. Behle (1937) have named this local race of the plain titmouse, giving the following diagnosis: "Compared as to coloration with *B. i. inornatus,* dorsum grayer, less brownish, and flanks and underparts generally slightly less buffy, clearer whitish; compared with *B. i. transpositus,* less olivaceous dorsally, and paler gray below; less clearly gray dorsally, but paler below, than in *zaleptus.* In size characters, closest to *inornatus;* bill decidedly shorter, less massive, than in *zaleptus,* and less massive even than in *transpositus.*"

They give the range as "drainage basin of Kern River, within southeastern rim of San Joaquin Valley, in Kern County, and extreme southern Tulare County, California."

PARUS INORNATUS ZALEPTUS (Oberholser)

WARNER VALLEY TITMOUSE

The above name has been applied by Dr. H. C. Oberholser (1932) to the birds of this species, living in the Warner Valley region of southern Oregon. He describes them as "similar to *Baeolophus inornatus griseus,* but much more grayish above with practically none of the brownish tinge so evident in the latter race; also paler above; and somewhat lighter, more clearly grayish below, with little or no buffy wash." He says that this race is "very different from *Baeolophus inornatus sequestratus* Grinnell in its larger size and much paler, more grayish coloration." The habits, so far as known, are not distinctive.

PARUS WOLLWEBERI ANNEXUS Cassin

BRIDLED TITMOUSE

HABITS

The oddly marked bridled titmouse, with its sharply pointed crest, its black-and-white-striped head, and its vivacious and friendly manners, is, to my mind, the prettiest and the most attractive of all the crested tits. Only those of us who have traveled in Arizona or New Mexico, or farther south into the highlands of Mexico, have been privileged to see it, for it is a Mexican species that finds its northern limits in a rather restricted area in southwestern New Mexico and southern Arizona. We found it rather common in the oak-clad foothills of the Huachuca Mountains, where the striking color pattern of its pretty head gave it an air of distinction and always attracted our admiration. We found it most commonly from the base of the mountains, about 5,000 feet, up to about 6,000 feet. Harry S. Swarth (1904) writes: "This, one of the characteristic birds of the mountains of Southern Arizona, is found in the greatest abundance everywhere in the oak regions of the Huachucas, breeding occasionally up to 7,000 feet, but most abundant below 6,000 feet. On one occasion, late in the summer, I saw a Bridled Titmouse in a flock of Lead-colored Bush Tits on the divide of the mountains at about 8,500 feet, but it is very unusual to see the species at such an altitude."

Mrs. Bailey (1928) says of its haunts in New Mexico: "Small flocks of about half a dozen each, probably families, were eagerly met with among the blue oaks, junipers, and nut pines of San Francisco Canyon, where they were associated with Lead-colored Bush-Tits and Gray Titmice. Other small flocks of the prettily marked Bridled were later discovered in sycamores in the open valley, at the junction of White

Water Creek and San Francisco River; but they are more character-istically birds of the oak country."

Nesting.—We did not succeed in finding a nest of the bridled tit-mouse. The natural cavities in which they habitually nest are too numerous to be thoroughly explored, and it is almost impossible to make the sitting bird leave its nest by rapping on the tree. Once a bit of white in the bottom of a deep, dark cavity, which looked like a sitting bird, induced us to chop it out, but there was no nest in the hole, much less a bird!

My companion, Frank Willard, sent me his notes on two nests found in that locality in 1899. One, found on May 17, was in a natural cavity in an oak tree well up on the side of the mountain at about 6,800 feet; the entrance was through a small knot hole in live wood, 12 feet from the ground; the nest was made of grass and lichens. The other, found on May 20, was in a natural cavity, 15 feet up, in a dead oak by the roadside, well down the canyon, between 5,000 and 5,500 feet elevation.

W. E. D. Scott (1886) was, I believe, the first to publish an account of the nesting of this species, of which he writes: "On the two occasions that I have discovered the species breeding the nests were located in natural cavities in the live-oaks, close to my house. The first of these was found on May 9, 1884. I took the female as she was leaving the nest, which was in a cavity, formed by decay, in an oak stump. The opening of this hole was about three and a half feet from the ground; its diameter was about three inches inside, and it was some eighteen inches deep. The entrance was a small knot-hole where a branch had been broken off, and was only large enough to admit the parent birds. The hollow was lined with cottonwood down, the fronds of some small rock-ferns, and some bits of cotton-waste."

Of the other nest, found May 8, 1885, he says: "The small entrance was some six feet from the ground, and the cavity was a foot deep, and two and a half inches in diameter. It was lined on the bottom and well up on the sides with a mat composed of cottonwood down, shreds of decayed grasses, some hair from a rabbit, and many fragments of cotton-waste, gathered by the birds from refuse waste that had been used to clean the machinery of a mill hard by."

There are four nests in the Thayer collection, all taken in southern Arizona and all in natural cavities in oaks, at various heights from 4 to 28 feet above ground; all these nests are lined, more or less profusely, with soft, cottony substances that may have been the downy coverings of leaf buds, blossoms, or catkins, or possibly the cocoons of insects or spiders; one nest was made almost entirely of this material; the foundations of these nests consist of strips of coarse weed stems, fine grass stems and soft weed leaves, more or less mixed with the cottony substances. Herbert Brandt has sent me his notes on a nest that "was made entirely of silvery, curly leaves, an inch or two in length, fashioned into a shallow basket form, but so loosely held together that the nest was removed, intact, with difficulty."

Eggs.—Five to seven eggs make up the usual set for the bridled titmouse. The eggs are ovate and have little or no gloss. They are white and quite immaculate. The measurements of 50 eggs average 16.1 by 12.6 millimeters; the eggs showing the four extremes measure **18.0** by **14.0**, 13.7 by 12:3, and 14.0 by **11.5** millimeters.

Plumages.—I have seen no very young birds of this species. In the juvenal plumage the young bridled titmouse looks very much like the adult, but the "bridling" marks on the head are less sharply defined, the throat patch is mainly grayish, only the chin being clear black, and the whole plumage is softer and less compact. This plumage is worn until about the middle of July, when a molt of the contour feathers, but not the flight feathers, produces a first winter plumage, in which adults and young are alike.

Adults have a complete postnuptial molt beginning in July. In fresh fall plumage the back and rump are more olivaceous than in the more grayish worn plumage of the spring and summer. The sexes are alike in all plumages.

Food.—Nothing seems to have been recorded on the food of the bridled tit, but it probably does not differ materially from that of other titmice of this genus, all of which live in similar habitats and spend much of their time foraging in crevices in the bark, on the trunks and branches of the oaks, hunting for insects, their larvae and their eggs. Their food habits are probably mostly, if not wholly, beneficial.

Behavior.—After the young are strong on the wing, late in August, these active, sprightly little titmice may be seen flitting through the oak woods in family parties, the young learning to forage for themselves. Later in the fall they form larger groups. Henshaw (1875) considered that this species differs somewhat in its flocking habits from some of the other titmice. He writes:

Instead of being found in small companies or as stragglers on the skirts of the large flocks of other species, it habitually moves about in flocks, composed often of twenty-five, and even more, of its own species; its exclusiveness in this particular being quite noticeable, though once or twice I have seen a few on intimate terms of companionship with the other Chickadees. It pays especial attention to the oaks, in which trees they move about slowly from limb to limb, scrutinizing each crevice and fold of bark which is likely to serve as a hiding place for insects. They are thus very thorough in their search, but have less of the rapidity of movement and nervous energy which characterize other members of this group. They are less noisy, too; their notes, though Chickadee-like, being weaker and fainter, and not infrequently one may, when watching one or two of these birds, find himself surrounded by a large number, which have silently closed in around while he was wholly unconscious of their presence. They are strictly arboreal, sharing only to a slight degree the terrestrial habits which are common to the other Titmice, especially of this genus.

Mrs. Bailey (1928) says: "One that I watched hopped up the branches of a tree quite in the manner of a jay climbing his tree ladder."

Field marks.—The bridled titmouse is well marked and need not be mistaken from anything else. Its chickadeelike behavior and voice are obvious. Its pointed black crest distinguishes it from the white-cheeked black-capped chickadees; and the peculiar color pattern of its black and white face distinguishes it from the other crested titmice, and from most other birds as well.

DISTRIBUTION

Range.—Mexico, southern Arizona, and New Mexico; not migratory. The range of the bridled titmouse extends **north** to central Arizona (Prescott and probably Fort Verde); southern New Mexico (Alma and Pinos Altos); and Tamaulipas (Galindo). **East** to Tamaulipas (Galindo); Puebla (Chachapa); and Oaxaca (La Parada). **South** to Oaxaca (La Parada) and Morelos (Cuernavaca). **West** to Morelos (Cuernavaca); Durango (Arroya del Buey and Ciénaga de la Vacas); western Chihuahua (Mina Abundancia); Sonora (Oposura, La Chumata, and San Rafael); and central Arizona (Baboquivari Mountains, Santa Catalina Mountains, probably Sacaton, and Prescott).

This species has been separated into two subspecies, the typical form *(Parus wollweberi wollweberi)* being confined to southern Mexico. The race found in the United States and in Sonora and Chihuahua is known as *P. w. annexus.*

Egg dates.—Arizona: 21 records, April 19 to May 26; 11 records, April 25 to May 17, indicating the height of the season.

Texas: 6 records, March 13 to May 19.

AURIPARUS FLAVICEPS ORNATUS (Lawrence)

EASTERN VERDIN

PLATES 63, 64

HABITS

This little olive-gray bird, with a yellow head and chestnut shoulders, is one of the characteristic birds of the southwestern desert regions. I made its acquaintance in a dry wash in southeastern Arizona, where the hard stony soil supported a scanty growth of low mesquites, hack-berries, hawthorns, catclaws, and other little thorny shrubs, with a few scattering chollas. Here it was living in company with cactus wrens, crissal thrashers, and Palmer's thrashers. Elsewhere in that region we found it on the mesquite plains, on the greasewood and cholla flats, and on the low hillsides dotted with picturesque giant cactus. It and the other desert birds seem to make a living in the harsh and cruel desert, far from any water, where the soil is baked hard and dry and every living plant is armed with forbidding thorns; even the "horned toad," which is really a lizard, carries a crown of thorns on its head and lesser spikes on its body, to protect it. But the verdin is equal to the occasion and builds its own armored castles, protected by a mass of thorny twigs, in which to rear its young, and to which it can retire at night.

Dr. Joseph Grinnell (1914) says of the haunts of the verdin in the lower valley of the Colorado River: "The only essential condition for the presence of this species appeared to be stiff-twigged thorny bushes or trees of some sort. This requisite was met with in a variety of situa-tions, as in the screwbeans of the first bottom, mesquites of the second bottom, and catclaw, ironwood, palo verde and daleas of the desert washes. * * * While the birds were often seen in willows, arrowweed, and even low shrubs of *Atriplex* and sandburr, these were always within a limited radius of nests. As far as observation went, these birds do not need to visit water; some were met with as much as three miles away from the river up desert washes."

Near Brownsville, Tex., we found the verdin only in the high, dry, thorny chaparral, and not in the dense and heavy timber along the resacas. George Finlay Simmons (1925) says that, in the Austin region, "bushy mesquite valleys" are preferred to open deserts.

Nesting.—The remarkable nests of the verdin are much in evidence throughout its habitat, especially large for so tiny a bird, wonderfully well made, and surprisingly conspicuous, for they are usually placed at or near the end of a low limb, without a shred of leafage to hide them. The number of nests that one sees would seem to indicate that the bird is more abundant than it really is. But it is well known that the verdin builds roosting nests, or winter nests, as well as breeding nests. They are most industrious little nest builders. Furthermore, the nests are so firmly made that old nests probably persist for more than one year, perhaps several years. Most of the nests that we saw in Arizona were in mesquites, hackberries, or catclaws, but others have found them in palo verdes, stunted live oaks, *Zizyphus* bushes, chollas, and a variety of other thorny trees and shrubs.

Of the numerous descriptions of the marvelous nest of the verdin that have been published, I have selected Herbert Brandt's (1940) as best worth quoting:

This structure is a globular or oval interlacement of thorned twigs that may measure up to eight inches in outside diameter, although usually its axis is shorter in one direction than the other. The thorny sticks are so placed that on the bristling exterior their free ends project upward, quill-like, and protect the nest. Each twiglet measures from two to five inches, and the free end may protrude an inch or more, in orderly fashion, so at first glance the twig ends give the appearance of a strange little hedgehog sitting in a convenient crotch with quills ever ready.

The number of twigs employed in this abode depends largely on its size and varies from a few hundred to more than two thousand; in fact I have a nest, collected in Arizona, that by careful estimate has over two thousand twigs! Thus the amount of labor required to interweave and lodge each individual freshly broken twiglet is indeed prodigious and is perhaps unequalled in the nest-building of our small birds. * * *

One of the most interesting features of the Verdin's dwelling is its strength; so strongly is it built that it is really difficult to tear one apart, and even then it is necessary to wear heavy gloves because the multitude of thorns will effectively repel one's bare hands. The nest is so woven around the tough branching limbs that to remove it intact is impossible without cutting off the support; in consequence the winds of the sandstorms cannot harm it or its feathered tenants. In fact, this is the most perfectly defended and anchored fortress that any desert bird has devised, and the reason so many are seen is because they endure year after year in various disrepair despite the angry elements that sweep across the sandy plains, often for months on end.

These nests are found as low as two feet from the ground and up to a height of nearly twenty feet, yet they are usually placed in the lower half of the tree in which they are built, or in the upper part of bushes, but always well out toward the end of a branch. Here the structure is woven about a pronged fork, with its entrance almost invariably opening outward and downward. The stick quills usually bristle backward away from this threshold, pointing along the limb, and act as a barbed repellent to any crawling invader trying to reach it from behind. It is through this small hidden orifice, itself well thorned, that the bird enters, and when it does it must pass over a raised threshold that is built up so high that one can scarcely touch the contents of the interior without pressing down the elevated doorstep. The whole fortified little stronghold seems designed to keep safe its semi-concealed entrance.

After suggesting that the male probably builds several nests, among which his mate may select her choice, he continues:

Once she has decided on her apartment she proceeds to line it snugly. The first step is to cover the many rough, protruding rafter ends with a padding of leaves and grass fibers, and finally to line cozily the whole cavity with an abundance of feathers, large and small. This room, before the feather finish, measures up to four inches across and between two and three inches high, but after the lining is placed, loose feathers more or less fill the entire chamber. Then the walls are smooth and silky to the touch, and so carefully padded that seldom does a thorn jab through. In one instance I found the nest of a Verdin only four feet below that of a Pallid Horned Owl containing two large young. The Verdin's tiny stick-built suite was crammed full of fluffy reddish feathers seized from the tiger of the air that dwelt in the master apartment above.

Mr. Simmons (1925) describes the nest much as above and then adds that "woolly and sticky fibers and weeds bind the nest together, and the whole structure is well interwoven with cobwebs and spider webbing, with some plant down and thistle down used to block up crevices"; the inside is "first lined with spider webs, forming a very thin coat which covers the cup-bottom; then lined with a coat of small grass leaves and bits of dead leaves; then an inner coat of plant down, thistle down, spider webbing, bits of silk-like cocoons, and a number of tiny soft bird feathers, on which the eggs rest."

Mary Beal (1931), of Barstow, Calif., has seen a verdin's nest in an almond tree and in a tamarisk. The pair that built the nest in the almond tree had first built their usual nest in a mesquite in her back yard, but a pair of English sparrows took possession of it. The verdins started to build in a Chinese elm, but the sparrows tore the nest to pieces; and "every location the Verdin considered was made impossible by the annoying tactics of the sparrows. Finally, the harassed Verdin chose the branch of an almond tree in the midst of the adjoining orchard. The tree was blossoming when the nest was built, the lovely fragrant flowers almost concealing it. By the time the petals had fallen the leaves were out, keeping the nest securely hidden from casual sight. Here, in this unusual setting, the little family was reared in peace."

M. French Gilman (1902) says that, on the Colorado desert of southern California, "most frequently the nests are found in mesquite trees and the smoke tree or *Dalea spinosa,* Daley's thorn tree. But any spiny shrub will answer, as I have found nests in the screw-bean, cholla cactus, desert willow, tree-sage, catsclaw, Eriodictyon, and last month I found one in a grapevine growing up in a cottonwood tree. The nests will average about five feet from the ground though I have found them as low as 2½ feet and as high as ten or twelve feet."

Dr. Walter P. Taylor has sent me the following notes on nest-**building:**

The male seemed to be much busier than his mate; his yellow head and brilliant red epaulettes were prominent. With his mouth full of nesting material he took a look at me. Deciding I was quite safe he went to the nest, climbing into it from the bottom, and remaining for several moments, undoubtedly arranging his material. He reappeared, looked me over again, then resumed his search for nest material on the ground beneath a nearby catclaw. As he proceeded, he picked up many small twigs and dropped them again, being, apparently, very uncertain as to just what kind of a stick he wanted, and very wasteful of his energy. One twig in particular he handled for some time, then dropped it, apparently unintentionally, but seemed immediately to forget all about it, and went right on looking.

One that he watched on October 31, 1919, was apparently gathering material to line a winter nest: "One seen this morning picking cotton from a wad I had affixed to a hackberry to mark the site of a mouse trap. It pecked down on the cottony wad several times and until its bill held as much as possible. Then it flew to another branch of the hackberry and rearranged the cotton in its bill. Then it flew by 'flirty' flights to a mesquite not far away, then made off for a long flight over the mesa to a point where I could not follow it. This bird, or another, was back in a few moments for another load of cotton."

Mr. Sennett (1878) had several experiences indicating that the verdin will desert its nest, if the eggs are handled before the set is completed.

James B. Dixon tells me that the verdin apparently raises two broods in favorable seasons on the Colorado desert, as he has found nests with eggs in late February and early March and then found them with fresh eggs again during the first week in May of the same year.

Eggs.—The cozy nest of the verdin may contain anywhere from three to six eggs, but normally four; sets of five are not especially rare; Mr. Gilman (1902) states that sets of four and five are "about evenly divided as to frequency," though most others agree that four is by far the commonest number. The delicate little eggs are dainty and beautiful. The ground color is light bluish green, greenish blue, or bluish or greenish white. This is usually rather sparingly and irregularly marked with fine dots, small spots, or rarely with very small blotches of reddish brown. Usually the markings are much scattered, but sometimes they are concentrated in a ring around the large end. The measurements of 50 eggs average 15.3 by 11.0 millimeters; the eggs showing the four extremes measure **16.3** by 11.2, 15.2 by **12.2, 14.0** by 11.2, and 14.7 by **10.2** millimeters.

Young.—Whether both sexes incubate does not seem to be definitely known, but, as the male is known to build his own roosting nest, perhaps incubation is performed entirely by the female. The incubation period of most of the Paridae is about 14 days, but Mrs. Wheelock (1904) says:

In ten days after the last bluish white egg was laid, there were three infinitesimal bits of naked bird life, huddled tightly together in the middle of the feather-lined hollow. A slit carefully cut at this time and fastened shut after each observation enabled me to keep an exact record of the development of the brood. Although I could not watch the mother feeding the young, I am positive it was done by regurgitation, for she would eat as unconcernedly as if merely occupied with her own dinner, and fly at once with apparently empty mouth into the nest, emerging shortly to repeat the performance. During the first five days the male was not seen to go into the nest, but sang right merrily near by. After that time the young began to make themselves heard in hungry cries, and he began to carry food to them, which we could see in his bill. This food consisted almost exclusively of small green worms, and eggs and larvae of insects. The young Verdins remained in the nest quite three weeks, and long after their debut they returned to the nursery every night to sleep.

The young are fed by their parents for some time after they leave the nest and are well able to fly. They sit around in the bushes waiting to be fed, and uttering notes much like those of the adults but shorter and weaker, while their parents are foraging for food.

Plumages.—I have seen no very young verdins, but apparently they are hatched naked, and they probably acquire the juvenal contour plumage before they leave the nest. Young birds in juvenal plumage have no yellow on the head and no chestnut on the lesser wing coverts. The entire upper parts, crown, back, rump, and lesser wing coverts are uniform grayish brown, "hair brown"; the under parts are very pale brownish gray, nearly white posteriorly; the wings, except the lesser coverts, and the tail are as in the adult. The postnuptial molt of the adult begins before the end of July and may last well through September; I have seen molting adults as early as July 28 and as late as September 29. Probably the postjuvenal molt comes at about the same time.

Food.—Very little has been published on the food of the verdin, which seems to consist of insects and their larvae and eggs, and of wild fruits and berries. Dr. Taylor tells me that he has seen one eating the berries of the hackberry tree. Mrs. Bailey (1928) writes: "These little desert birds would seem almost independent of water, nests having been found at least ten miles from any known water. The question is whether by means of their insect food and berries they are made largely independent of other liquid."

Behavior.—In its movements and all its activities the verdin shows its relationship to the chickadees, as it flits about actively in the bushes searching for its food, clinging tenaciously to branches swayed by the wind, or hanging head downward from the tips of twigs, hunting every little crevice and the under sides of the foliage. During the nesting season it is shy and retiring; perhaps we should say sly, rather than shy, for it slips away unobserved from its nest and keeps out of sight in the nearest thicket; it is difficult to surprise one on its nest, and one is seldom seen near the nest unless it has young, when the little bird becomes quite bold, flitting about in the vicinity, chippering and scolding. But in winter its behavior is somewhat different, according to Mr. Brandt (1940), who says that "like the chickadee, the Verdin becomes more sociable, responding readily to my summons, and is one of the first birds to approach, showing little fear as it 'cheeps' in a thin voice and moves quickly about in anxious inquisitiveness."

Voice.—The verdin has a remarkable voice for so small a bird, one that would do credit to an oriole or a thrush. Dr. Taylor says in his notes: "The song of the verdin I put down as *tswee, tswee, tswee, tsweet!* All the calls are whistled. Another call is *tsee, tsoo, tsoor!* and *tsee, tsoo, tsooy!*" He writes the common short call note as *tsit, tsit, tsit, tsit;* the notes are run together more or less and are repeated very rapidly.

Mary Beal (1931) says: "The Verdin's song of three clear notes all on one key has rather a plaintive, resonant quality. One summer when I lay ill for all the weeks of June in a sleeping porch in the midst of many trees, those liquid bird-notes came to me across the orchard at intervals throughout the day. The vital quality compelled attention and puzzled me all that season, for I did not place the singer until the next spring when I saw a tiny Verdin in the act of sending forth those rich, full notes. The depth and carrying power of the tones are amazing in such a small bird—so different from its quick, sharp call-note."

Mrs. Wheelock (1904) writes: "The usual note of the adult Verdins is a chickadee-like 'tsee-tu-tu' uttered while hunting, chickadee fashion, among the terminal buds and under the leaves for their insect food, and this the nestlings mimic in two syllables as soon as they leave the nest,— 'tsee-tee, tsee-tee.' It is a cry of hunger, and never fails to bring the parent with food."

Enemies.—Dr. Herbert Friedmann (1929) records the verdin as "a poorly known victim of the Dwarf Cowbird." He found a cowbird's egg in one nest, near Brownsville, Tex., and Roy W. Quillen wrote to him that he has found "eggs of the Cowbird in a few nests of the Verdin." In all cases the entrances to the nests were much enlarged, and perhaps deserted.

Field marks.—The verdin is a tiny bird, about the size of a bushtit and much like it in general appearance and behavior, but it has a shorter tail and other distinctive markings; it is brownish gray above and paler below; in the male the head is largely quite bright yellow and in the female somewhat duller yellow; the lesser coverts on the bend of the wing are bright, reddish chestnut, but these do not show conspicuously unless the wings are partially open. Young birds in their first plumage in summer have no yellow on the head and no chestnut on the wings. The verdin's voice is quite distinctive.

Winter.—The verdin is a permanent resident in at least the warmer portions of our southwestern deserts; it does not have to migrate, for **it finds sufficient insect food in one form or another and lives well on** various wild fruits and berries. But it builds most interesting winter homes for its protection and warmth. Mrs. Bailey (1928) says that "in southern Arizona, out of fifteen Verdin nests that I found in one small tract, ten showed signs of winter occupation and nine were found to contain roosting birds, the small occupants being flushed at intervals from 4.28 p.m. until after sunset, at various dates from December 9, 1920, to March 13, 1921. Two of the little birds seen going to their nests went half an hour or more before sunset, when it was light enough to be seen by Sharp-shinned Hawks and any other too observant neighbor."

She noticed that these nests were usually under thick thorny trees or bushes, which gave the bird some additional protection as it went to its nest.

Mr. Gilman (1902) writes: "Last December I found two female winter nests and later saw several of both sexes. One of them in a mesquite tree was ten or twelve feet from the ground and measured more than eight inches long by seven wide and seven deep. Lining was about one and one-quarter inches thick and composed of feathers—quail, chicken and others. * * * The nests of male and female differ a little, the former being less elaborate, smaller, with not so much lining in it. The female *winter* nest differs but little from the *breeding* nest and I am inclined to believe in some cases is used as such."

W. L. Dawson (1923) says that "two male lodges in the M. C. O. are each only three inches in length over all, with openings at either end, and about two and a half inches of clear space inside—not room enough to turn around in, but just sufficient protection from the pounce of an Elf Owl. * * * Verdins are not gregarious, like Bush-tits; but also they are never solitary, for they roam the desert in pairs, or, in small family groups, or in loose association. It is here that the remarkable penetrative, or carrying power, of the *silp* note serves the Verdin in good stead, for it allows mated birds to hunt, say, a hundred yards apart, without actually losing each other."

DISTRIBUTION

Range.—Southwestern United States and northern Mexico; not regularly migratory.

The range of the verdin extends **north** to southern California (Victorville, Barstow, and Death Valley); southern Nevada (Corn Creek and Bunkerville); southwestern Utah (St. George); southern New Mexico (San Antonio, Tularosa Flats, and Carlsbad); and southwestern Texas (Monahars, Castle Mountains, Kerrville, and Sequin).

East to central Texas (Sequin, Corpus Christi, and Brownsville); and eastern Tamaulipas (Matamoros). **South** to northern Tamaulipas (Matamoros); southern Coahuila (Saltillo and Saral); probably Durango (Durango); and southern Baja California (San Jose del Cabo and Cape San Lucas). **West** to Baja California (Cape San Lucas, Magdalena Bay, San Ignacio, and San Felipe); and California (San Diego, Palm Springs, and Victorville).

Three subspecies of the verdin are now recognized by the American Ornithologists' Union (1944) committee on nomenclature. Modern research, for which the references are given in their nineteenth supplement to the Check-list, indicates that the Cape verdin *(Auriparus flaviceps flaviceps)* should stand as the type race of the species, as Sundevall's type apparently came from the southern half of Baja California. The eastern verdin *(A. f. ornatus)* occupies southern Texas, southern New Mexico, and southern Arizona; and Grinnell's verdin *(A. f. acaciarum)* ranges from southern Nevada and southwestern Utah to northern Baja California.

Egg dates.—Arizona: 40 records, March 4 to June 18; 20 records, April 17 to May 18, indicating the height of the season.

California: 56 records, March 6 to June 8; 28 records, March 28 to April 11.

Mexico: 26 records, March 22 to June 25; 14 records, April 7 to May 8.

Texas: 30 records, April 1 to June 5; 16 records, April 18 to May 6.

AURIPARUS FLAVICEPS ACACIARUM Grinnell

GRINNELL'S VERDIN

Dr. Joseph Grinnell (1931) made an exhaustive study of the nomenclature of this species and an extensive search for Sundevall's type, to which the reader is referred for the somewhat confusing details and a history of the nomenclatorial changes. In the course of his study he concluded that the verdins of southeastern California needed a new name, for which he proposed the subspecific name *acaciarum*. He describes this race as "similar to *Auriparus flaviceps flaviceps* (Sundevall), but with yellow of fore parts somewhat less intense and extensive; body color averaging a trifle browner, especially on dorsum; tail and wing, more notably the former, averaging a little longer; bill apparently averaging smaller. Similar to *A. f. ornatus* (Lawrence), but paler and a little smaller."

The new Check-list will give the range of this form as from southern Nevada and southwestern Utah to northern Lower California.

AURIPARUS FLAVICEPS FLAVICEPS (Sundevall)

CAPE VERDIN

HABITS

Many years ago Baird (1864) called attention to the principal characters distinguishing the verdins of the southern part of Lower California from those of Arizona and Texas, but he did not propose a new name for the race. The most concise description is given by Ridgway (1904), who says that it is similar to the northern race "but decidedly smaller (except bill), with yellow of head averaging brighter, and the forehead more frequently (?) tinged with orange-rufous; young, however, distinctly different in coloration from that of" the northern race, "the upper parts being olive, strongly tinged with olive-green, and the under tail-coverts (sometimes most of under parts) tinged with olive-yellow."

According to the 1931 Check-list, the Cape verdin occupies the "Lower Austral Zone in the southern part of Lower California, south of about lat. 30°, and in southwestern Sonora." William Brewster (1902) says that Frazar found it "abundant everywhere in the Cape Region except on the Sierra de la Laguna, where none were met with. It was breeding at La Paz in March, at Triunfo in April, and apparently at San José del Cabo in *November*, for on the third of that month Mr. Frazar found two nests about half completed on which the birds were busily at work." These November birds were probably building winter nests.

Griffing Bancroft (1930) writes of its haunts in central Lower California:

This is the most widely distributed and, I believe, the most abundant of the local birds. It occurs in every association of the region under discussion, excepting only the littoral sand dunes. On the lava-strewn mesas, where vegetation is barely able to maintain a foot-hold and where animal life seems almost impossible, isolated pairs of these fascinating little workers are to be found regularly and in surprising numbers. In the irrigated river beds they seek open spots where here and there a stray mesquite or a bit of cholla has been permitted to remain. Brush-covered mountain slopes, plains dotted with cholla, cardón, and tree yucca, dry river beds supporting dense mesquite and palo verde, and cañons where the palo blanco grows are equally their home sites.

Nesting.—The same observer writes: "Fifty percent of the nests are in cholla, forty percent in mesquite, and the other ten percent scattering. The latter include anything from elephant trees to matilija poppies." He continues:

When nest building begins both birds work industriously. They find an arrangement of cholla stems in which it is possible to construct a suitable circle about five inches in diameter. They build one of fine weed twigs or of grass stems which often have leaves still attached. These inch-long bits are fastened to the cactus with a layer of plant down, the bird standing within the rim and tucking in the material with a most business-like air. The next step carries the outside super-structure backward from the ring to supporting arms of cholla. The frame is of the same material as the original circle. The builders continue to work from the inside and soon the frame becomes a shell. That, in turn, is added to and padded until a thickness of perhaps half an inch is reached.

The result is a flexible nest. In marked contrast to those of Arizona and particularly the Vizcaíno Desert and Sonora it is hardly ever protected on the outside with reinforcement in the shape of thorns or larger twigs. * * *

The opening to the hollow globe is completed last. It is left just large enough to permit the entrance and egress of the parents and it is so placed as to face away from the plant on which the nest is built. It is almost level with the bottom (only once did I observe a hole squarely in the center), and it is often somewhat concealed with an overhang of building material. The interior design permits of the low entrance being safely used. The tunnel runs upward. At the interior end the wall of the nest drops abruptly or even outwardly. So the eggs lie directly below the entrance. It is interesting to note that this is not true of the nests of any other race of verdin.

The nests are lined with feathers and are located in the trees much as are those of the Arizona verdin. In fact, J. Stuart Rowley, who saw many nests in the same general region, tells me that the nesting habits are the same as in Arizona.

There are five nests of the Cape verdin in the Thayer collection in Cambridge. One of these, taken at Comondu on April 24, was 4 feet up in a mesquite and is quite unique, unlike any verdin's nest I have ever seen. It is made almost wholly of white woolly or cottony substances, reinforced with a few short pieces of fine twigs and weed stems, mixed with a few dry leaves and feathers; there are no long or thorny twigs even on the exterior, and the whole nest is conspicuously white.

The other four nests, collected at Purissima in May and June, are quite unlike the above and very different from any nests of the Arizona verdin in the almost complete absence of thorny or large twigs. They are all very much alike and are, or rather were, more or less globular structures, made up of great compact masses of short fine twigs, weed and grass stems, flower clusters, fine straws, insect cocoons, and various kinds of plant material; they contain considerable plant down in the lining, but very little of the white woolly material and only a few feathers; only one contains a few small thorny twigs on the outside. There is nothing in any of these nests that suggests the bristling, thorny fortresses of the Arizona birds.

Eggs.—Mr. Rowley tells me that his sets of the Cape verdin consist of three eggs, except for one set of five, taken April 27, 1933, near San Ignacio. Mr. Bancroft (1930) writes:

The number laid is definitely not more than three: I have seen but one set of four out of a hundred examined. Clutches of three outnumber two in a ratio of approximately four to three. Incubated singles comprise about ten per cent of the total.

Eggs of the Cape Verdin run through a wide range of sizes, shapes and colors. Many are half again as large as the average and many are fifty per cent smaller. There is the elongated type, one end almost a hemisphere and the other a cone-shaped point. On the other hand it is not rare to find them as perfectly elliptical as the typical humming bird egg. The ground color is green, the markings gray—facts established for us by an oculist with the proper instruments. The shade of green varies until almost blue is reached.

The great variation in size, as indicated above, is not shown in the series of measurements I have collected, and the 15 eggs of this race I have examined are practically indistinguishable from those of the Arizona verdin. The measurements of 40 eggs average 15.3 by 11.2 millimeters; the eggs showing the four extremes measure **16.7** by 11.0, 15.2 by **12.2**, 14.2 by 11.1, and 14.7 by **10.2** millimeters.

In all other respects, plumage changes, food, general behavior, and voice, the Cape verdin does not seem to differ from the Arizona bird.

PSALTRIPARUS MINIMUS MINIMUS (Townsend)

COAST BUSHTIT

PLATES 65-68

HABITS

Almost anywhere in California, except in the desert regions and in higher elevations in the mountains, and at almost any season of the year, except during the breeding season, one may observe jolly bands or loose flocks of these tiny, gray, long-tailed birds drifting through the live oaks and shrubby thickets, uttering high-pitched, twittering notes to keep in touch with each other as they feed. These charming little birds are so widely distributed and so universally abundant in southern California that they form one of the most interesting features in the landscape, a lively bit of bird life that one never tires of watching.

Authorities have differed somewhat as to the distribution of the California forms of the bushtit, but I believe it is now understood that this type race occupies a narrow coastal strip from extreme southwestern British Columbia southward to the Mexican border, and perhaps beyond, with a wider range in San Diego County, where it is especially abundant. Harry S. Swarth (1914), who has made an exhaustive study of the subject, seems to have shown that only one race, *P. m. minimus,* occurs in southern California, where formerly the inland race, *P. m. californicus,* was supposed to occupy a range in the interior.

"*P. minimus minimus* as compared with *P. m. californicus,* is darker colored throughout, birds seasonably comparable being contrasted, the under parts are heavily suffused with dusky, and the flanks are more distinctly vinaceous. These differences are quite as apparent in the juvenal plumage as in the adult, sometimes more so." (Swarth, 1914.)

Courtship.—Alice Baldwin Addicott (1938) has published a very full and detailed account of the behavior of the bushtit in the breeding season, from which I shall quote freely. As to the beginning of the mating season, she says:

As early as January and February flocks of bush-tits which have remained intact during the fall and winter start dividing into smaller and smaller groups. At the same time a few pairs may be found which have separated from the flocks and which have wandered off in search of nesting territory.
* * * At the beginning of the mating season, courtship may be observed in pairs which have separated from the flocks as well as within the small flocks which are existent during this part of the year. Courting consists chiefly of excited location notes, trills and sexual posturing. * * *
Territorial ownership appears to be poorly developed. When a stray bird enters the territory of a nesting pair, the latter may respond by chasing the intruder for a few seconds, giving utterance to excited alarm notes and trills, until the intruder leaves. However, in many instances a stray bird is ignored, and it may even be allowed to forage with the mated pair.

She goes on to show that toleration of stray birds in the nesting territory may often go so far as to permit a third bird to forage in the territory for an hour at a time and even to take part in the nesting activities, suggesting that the gregarious habits of the species may carry over into the breeding season.

Nesting.—The curious and beautiful nests of the bushtits are works of art and marvels of avian architecture. In marked contrast to the thorny castles of the verdins, the long, gourd-shaped, hanging pockets of the bushtits are made of the softest materials and are often prettily decorated or camouflaged. Some nests are more or less concealed among the foliage or among hanging bunches of beardlike lichens, but most of them are suspended in plain sight, where one might easily be overlooked as a stray wisp of lichens or an accumulation of plant debris.

The nests are hung in a variety of trees, saplings, or bushes at various heights, although a large majority are not over 15 feet above the ground.

Mrs. Addicott (1938) remarked that most of the nests she studied at Palo Alto, Calif., were in oaks, but this does not seem to be always true elsewhere. Grinnell, Dixon, and Linsdale (1936) have given the data for 38 nests on Point Lobos Reserve, Calif.; the kinds of trees occupied and the heights of the nests from the ground were as follows: 16

nests were in *Ceanothus* bushes, both living and dead, a 4½ to 11 feet; 12 were in pines at from 6 to 50 feet, only 4 of which were above 15 feet; 4 were in live oaks at from 7 to 20 feet; 3 were in sage bushes at from 4 to 4½ feet; 2 were in cypresses at from 7 to 10 feet; and 1 was in a *Baccharis* bush at 6 feet. In the northern portion of the range, many nests are found in conifers, spruces, firs, and hemlocks, often suspended from the ends of limbs 15 to 25 feet from the ground and in plain sight; but I found two nests near Seattle that were in "spirea" bushes 9 to 10 feet up. Nests have been found in eucalyptus and pepper trees, in willow and alder saplings, in *Kuntzia* and hazel bushes, and probably in a variety of other trees and shrubs.

Mrs. Addicott (1938) gives a full description of the bushtit's nest and how it is built by the busy pair of little architects; her paper is well illustrated with sketches and photographs. I quote from it in part:

The nest built by the Coast Bush-tit is an intricate, pendant structure, hung in a concealing clump of leaves of an overhanging branch, and it is built of materials which blend with its surroundings, such as mosses, lichens, oak leaves and spider web. The entrance consists of a hole, usually placed on one side near the top, either above or below the supporting twigs. Above the entrance is the hood which is carefully woven around several twigs and which covers the top of the nest. Below the entrance is the neck which is the passage to the bowl, where the eggs are laid. The nest is entered horizontally, but the passage bends immediately and is vertical in the neck. At the bottom the passage flares to make the bowl. The neck is the slenderest, and usually the thinnest, part. The widest portion is the bowl, and here the walls are much thicker and are heavily lined. These features combined with the thick floor of the bowl, make the latter a warm place for the development of eggs and young. * * *

The first step in the construction of any bush-tit nest is the building of the rim. This is a delicate circle of nest material bound together with spider web and supported between the forks of a twig or between two adjacent twigs to which it is firmly fastened. This circular rim is almost always horizontal, or nearly so, and in no case which has been observed does this hole ever remain as the final entrance of the nest. It is rather the rim of a preliminary open bag.

After the rim has been built, nest construction may proceed in either of two ways. In the first and most prevalent method, a small bag, perhaps an inch in depth, is hung from the rim, loosely woven and very thin and delicate. In building, the birds cling to the edge of the rim and hang head down into the bag, adding materials to strengthen and thicken it. After this first tiny sac has been made strong it is stretched and extended from within and then the thin places which result are filled in with more nest material. As the nest becomes longer, the birds enter it head first to carry on the work. After a bird disappears inside, the nest shakes violently and bulges out in place after place as the new material is added in the thin sections. The shaking apparently serves to stretch the structure. Most of the work is done from the inside, but some of the thick parts of the bowl are added to from the outside, the birds clinging to the sides as they work. The nest is now a long pendant bag, open at the top.

When the hood and final entrance of the nest are built, material is added to the back and sides of the original rim. Material is brought over the top until the original hole has been roofed over and the entrance thus shifted to one side of the top. Rarely one finds a nest with the entrance hole only partly roofed over. As the nest nears completion, a lining of spider web, down, or feathers is made for the passageway and the bowl. The bowl is thickened and filled in, and the walls above the floor of the nest for at least an inch are made quite thick. Material is added to the nest from time to time until the eggs have hatched, probably because the nest, being pendant, needs continual repairing.

In the second method, mentioned above, "a long extremely loose bag is constructed of strands of material hung from the rim"; this may be 5 to 8 inches long, instead of one an inch deep; otherwise the construction proceeds as above. Of the materials used in nest-building, she says: "Bush-tit nests are built of materials found commonly in the breeding territory. Lichens, mosses, grasses and the staminate flowers of the live oak, *Quercus agrifolia*, are constituents of almost all nests. These are woven together with hundreds of strands of spider web. Other materials found less commonly are filaree fruits, bark fibers, various plant downs, fir or spruce needles, oak leaves, acacia blossoms, blossoms of other plants such as broom and the pappi of composite flowers, feathers, bits of paper and string, and insect cocoons."

I have a series of six nests before me as I write, no two of which are alike; they vary greatly in size, shape, and bulk, as well as in the color of the material used. They vary in length from 7 to 10 inches and in the width of the bowl from barely 3 to over 4 inches, though these figures give only a faint idea of the variations in bulk. Nests 12 inches long are fairly common, some are as short as 6 inches, and Dr. B. W. Evermann (1881) measured one that was 21 inches in length. He also mentions nests hung in bunches of mistletoe, and says that others have been "found in sage and greasewood bushes, and one in a bunch of cactus."

The materials in the nests before me are quite varied and produce very different color effects, probably of concealing value. One, collected near Seattle, is constructed largely of very fine twigs and fine rootlets, firmly interwoven into a short bag, 7 inches long; it is decorated with bright green lichens or mosses and lined with soft down feathers or fur; it was in a "spirea" bush. Another similar nest is 10 inches long, and is interwoven with the twigs of a fir; it is made almost wholly of bright, yellowish-green mosses. Three California nests are still different; in one the dull dark-brown tone of the lichens and mosses is relieved by only a few bits of gray lichen; another is almost covered with soft, whitish, curly leaves or weed tops and cocoons or nests of spiders or insects, giving it a very pale tone; and in the third nest, the light, reddish brown blossoms, of which the nest is almost entirely made, produce that tone of color prettily offset by a circle of light buff plant down around the entrance.

According to Mrs. Addicott (1938) the time devoted to nest-building varies greatly and is subject to some interruption on account of bad weather or other disturbance. Nests started in February were actually worked on for 51 and 49 days in two cases, and for from 42 to 34 days in three other cases.

A nest started in April was completed in 13 days. "Second nests are built more quickly than first nests. Pairs disturbed during building, egg-laying or incubation frequently desert and build second nests, usually with new mates. * * * When one bird deserts a nest another mate is found to take its place. If both desert, they separate and seek new mates. * * * It might be suggested that the gregarious habits of the species during the rest of the year and the constant presence of unmated birds in small flocks during the nesting season are of significance here."

Leslie L. Haskin tells me that "after the nest is completed the birds seem to leave it for a time before actual occupancy begins. One nest that I observed closely was thus left unused for nearly thirty days, after which eggs were laid, and a thrifty brood brought forth. I am inclined to believe that during this time the parents use the nest for a nightly roost. I do know that, *after* the eggs are laid, both the male and female bird spend the night in the nest, a very cozy and comfortable bedroom. The same pair of birds appears to return to the same site, or one near by, year after year. When an occupied nest is found, it is not at all uncommon to find last year's nest close by. On one occasion I found a nest containing young, built upon a horizontal fir limb about 12 feet from the ground. At intervals of about 2 feet apart along the same limb, three other nests, or rather their remains, left from previous years, were hung, each one a little older and more bedraggled than the preceding one. It was evident that for at least four years this branch had been used by the same pair of birds."

W. E. Griffee writes to me of a nest that was used for three sets of eggs in one season: "The only occupied nest I have found in recent years was one which, on May 26, 1935, held young 4 or 5 days old. After this brood had flown, I took a set of 6 eggs, incubated 2 to 4 days, from the same nest on June 19th. As the nest was soiled with excrement from the first brood, I did not collect it, so the birds completed a third set of 6 eggs in it on about July 3rd or 4th." This was near Portland, Oreg., where he thinks bushtits are not so common as they were 30 years ago. From this and other reports, it seems that the bushtits often raise two broods in a season.

Carroll Dewilton Scott tells, in the notes sent to me, of the difficulties encountered by a pair of bushtits in their attempts to build a nest in a eucalyptus tree: "I could see the birds alight time after time in a cluster of limbs, about 12 feet from the ground, and often see bits of material fall to the ground. The bewildered birds would hop all about the spot, trying to find the stuff they had brought. But the eucalyptus limbs and leaves were so smooth that nothing would stick to them. All this day and the next they worked without making even the beginning of a nest. Twice they changed the nesting site without effect. Their ancestral experience had been with native plants, thick-leaved, usually prickly or rough. Finally, on March ninth, their persistence and patience were rewarded. They got a little circle of moss and fibres caught on the limbs and soon completed the nest."

S. F. Rathbun writes to me: "The bushtit [in western Washington] seems to favor localities that are more or less open, where the sunlight breaks among a growth that overruns old logged-off sections; this growth is in the nature of the hazel, small alders, young dogwoods, and more particularly the beautiful ocean-spray, or 'spirea' *(Holodiscus discolor)*. The little glades that will be found among such spots are especially liked by this bird, and the partiality shown by it for such as have a growth of *H. discolor* is very marked. In fact, it may be said that, wherever this occurs to any extent, one can expect to find the bushtit, and usually does. The ocean-spray is the hallmark of the bushtit.

"I have found the nests in many locations, but the birds have a fondness for building in the 'spirea'; and I think the reason for this is that, as the bush always has numbers of the dry flower clusters of the preceding year in evidence, the nest is better protected from view, as in a way it resembles a panicle of the dry blooms. I have several times found a nest attached to one of these dry flower clusters, becoming a part of it, as it were, and in this way the concealment became more effective." (See pl. 67.)

Eggs.—The commonest numbers of eggs in the nests of the bushtit run from 5 to 7, seldom fewer or more, but as many as 12, 13, and even 15 have been found; probably these large numbers are the products of two females, as 3 birds have been seen visiting a nest. W. C. Hanna has a set in his collection containing an egg of the dwarf cowbird; it would be interesting to know how it was deposited. The eggs are mostly ovate in shape and have little or no gloss. They are pure white and unmarked. The measurements of 50 eggs average 13.7 by 10.1 millimeters; the eggs showing the four extremes measure 14.7 by 10.2, 13.8 by 11.2, and 12.2 by 9.1 millimeters.

Young.—Authorities seem to agree that the incubation period for the bushtit is 12 days, the young hatching on the 13th. Based on her study of two nests, Mrs. Addicott (1938) makes the following statements:

Incubation apparently is started on the day the last egg is laid, or on the day before. The burden of incubation seems to be shared equally by the male and female. * * * On cold days the eggs are incubated almost constantly, the parents alternating about every ten minutes on the nest. On warm days much shorter periods are spent on the eggs, and the parents forage together to some extent. Both birds spend the nights in the nest.

The young are naked at hatching and down does not develop. The eyes are closed and remain closed at least through the seventh day.

The young are fed solid undigested food from the first day on, and lepidopterous larvae are carried into the nest a few hours after hatching.

During early stages the young are brooded and fed as much by one bird as the other. Toward the end of the period, one parent does about two-thirds of the foraging and feeding. The mate spends most of the time moving about in the nest tree. The young apparently leave the nest on the fourteenth or fifteenth day. They become independent of the parents within eight days after leaving the nest, but have been seen to feed themselves on the day of nest-leaving.

She says that while the young are being fed in the nest "feeding occurs from eight to twelve times an hour" and that the "fecal sacs were carried as far as fifteen feet from the nest." Of the behavior at the time of nest-leaving, she writes:

When the nestlings are ready to fly, the slightest disturbance sends them out of the nest. As one juvenile starts to leave, the impulse apparently spreads rapidly to the others. So quickly do they pop out of the nest, that one has the feeling that the nest has suddenly exploded. There is an incessant medley of juvenal trills.

The juveniles fly a little awkwardly and to a lower level when they leave the nest. They scatter in all directions, often alighting in the grass, uttering the trill all the while. The parents immediately become excited, uttering a rapid succession of alarm notes as they dash from one young bird to another in an evident effort to protect them and to get them together. This is quite a task, for the juveniles fly as far as twenty-five yards from the nest tree.

The parents spend from fifteen minutes to half an hour gathering the scattered family in low bushes or in a small tree. * * * Half an hour after nest-leaving the young start following the parents in their search for food, begging with trills as they go. * * *

As soon as the juveniles are able to fly well enough to follow the parents, the family moves about in typical flock formation, the parents doing all of the foraging for the young. This takes place at least the day after nest-leaving, and frequently only a few hours afterward on the same day.

* * * Feeding by the parents is continued from eight to fourteen days. One family was fed till the eighth day after leaving, when two of the juveniles were seen foraging for themselves, clumsily hanging upside down in search of food. It seems likely that the shortness of the juvenal tail makes this process difficult, since it has been observed that it is impossible for an adult without a tail to do this. * * *

Begging and feeding were observed in another family up to the fourteenth day after nest-leaving. Feeding of the entire brood lasted nine days, after which one or two individuals were fed at long intervals.

Plumages.—The young bushtit is hatched naked, with eyes closed; the eyes are not open until the eighth day or later, according to Mrs. Addicott (1938). Mrs. Wheelock (1904) says that on the sixth day the young were "covered with a hairlike grayish white down." This is very scanty and is worn for only a short time, as the juvenal plumage soon pushes it out, and the young bird is practically fully fledged when it leaves the nest and is able to fly for a short distance. The juvenal plumage is much like the faded and worn plumage of the spring and summer adult; Mr. Swarth (1914) says that this plumage, "with shorter and fluffier feathers, and with more extensively light-colored bases, gives a general effect that is rather mottled and uneven." This plumage is worn for about 2 months, or until toward the end of July, when the postjuvenal molt begins and continues through September. This is an incomplete molt, which does not involve the flight feathers; it produces a first winter plumage which is practically indistinguishable from that of the adult, dense and lustrous and dark colored. Adults have one complete postnuptial molt each year at about the same time, but beginning a little earlier in July and continuing a little later, or into October. Mr. Swarth (1914) says that the molt is "of quite long duration, about three months for adults, and a little less for the post-juvenal molt." Considerable wear and fading take place during the winter and spring, so that before the annual molt takes place the birds become quite dull in coloration, worn, and shabby.

Food.—Prof. F. E. L. Beal (1907) examined 353 stomachs of bushtits from California. He says:

The first analysis of the food of the year gives nearly 81 percent animal matter, composed entirely of insects and spiders, to 19 percent of vegetable. * * * The largest item in the insect portion of the bird's food consists of bugs (Hemiptera), which amount to over 44 percent of the whole. * * * Moreover, the particular families of Hemiptera so extensively eaten by the bush tit are the two that are most destructive to the interests of horticulture—namely, the plant-lice (Aphididae), and bark-lice, or scales (Coccidae). The last amounts to nearly 19 percent of the year's food, and are eaten in every month. * * * The large black olive scale *(Saissetia oleae)* was identified in 44 stomachs, but other species were also found. * * * While the San Jose scale was not positively determined [probably because its distinctive characters are too minute to be recognized in a mass of semi-digested food], another species of the same genus, the greedy scale *(Aspidiotus rapax),* was found in 4 stomachs, and scales not specifically identified were found in 113. Of a total of 353 stomachs, 158 held scales; several were entirely filled with them, and in quite a number upwards of 90 percent of their contents consisted of these insects. * * * The remaining portion of the hemipterous food of the bush tit, over 31 percent, is made up of plant-lice, tree-hoppers

(Membracidae), leaf-hoppers (Jassidae), some jumping plant-lice (Psyllidae), and a considerable number of false chinch bugs *(Nysius angustatus)*, with a few lace-bugs (Tingitidae).

Other insect food includes beetles, "somewhat over 10 percent," caterpillars, 16 percent, wasps and ants, 1½ percent, and the remainder of animal food, "about 8 percent," consists mainly of spiders. Of the vegetable food, less than 1 percent consists of fruit, pulp and skins, and the remainder is composed of a few seeds, granules of poison-oak, leaf galls, and rubbish, much of which is probably taken accidentally.

His analysis of the stomach contents of eight nestlings is of interest: "The animal matter comprised, approximately: Beetles 2, wasps 2, bugs 8, caterpillars and pupae 80, and spiders 7 percent. The point of greatest interest, however, lies in the fact that every one of these stomachs contained pupae of the coddling moth, distributed as follows: Two stomachs contained 2 each, two contained 3 each, one contained 4, one 7, one 9, and one 11, making 41 in all, or an average of over 5 to each."

From the above it will be seen that the bushtit is one of the most useful of the birds of California; it does practically no harm, except to eat a few beneficial ladybugs, in such small numbers as to be negligible, and it destroys immense numbers of the most harmful insects, most of which are so minute that only the microscopic eyes of these little birds could find them; and the larger birds would not bother to eat them. The great expansion of the fruit-growing industry in California has enabled these scale insects to increase enormously, and the scale-eating birds have not kept pace with them, so that artificial means must be employed to keep them under control.

Mr. Scott writes to me: "On January 20, 1917, I was surprised to find a flock of 24 bushtits feeding on ripe olives, both on the trees and on the ground. The birds were evidently hungry, as half a dozen flew to the ground within a few feet of me to peck the meat of the fallen olives, just as the house finches were doing."

Behavior.—Bushtits are sociable, friendly little birds, not only toward their human neighbors but among themselves, possessing many of the lovable and trustful traits of their relatives the chickadees. They show no fear of man and carry on their vocations with confident indifference to his near presence. But they are even fonder of their own society. Except during the short season when the pairs are occupied with their nesting activities, they travel about all through the rest of the year in loose flocks of varying sizes; small bunches of family parties join later into larger groups. I have often enjoyed watching a cloud of these little gray, long-tailed birds drifting through the trees and shrubbery on the edge of an arroyo in Pasadena.

The flock is somewhat scattered, and one cannot tell at first how many birds there are in the company, but they keep in touch with one another as they feed, with gentle twittering notes. They seem to be in constant motion as they travel along, hurriedly crossing the open spaces between the bushes, a few at a time, then more and more, all traveling in the same general direction; when 20 or 30 have crossed, and we think that all have gone, there are always a few stragglers hurrying along to catch up with the procession.

These flocks may consist of anywhere from half a dozen to 20 or 30 birds. Dawson (1923) has counted over 70, but usually there are less than 20. And, in winter, they may be accompanied by other small birds that forage with them, such as kinglets, wrens, and chickadees; these birds do not, I believe, follow along in the procession of bushtits.

Dr. Joseph Grinnell (1903) writes of the behavior of these flocks:

During such slowly moving excursions, each individual is rapidly gleaning through the foliage, assuming all possible attitudes in its search for tiny insects among leaves and twigs. * * * At times, especially towards evening, the flocks become more restless and move along from bush to bush and tree to tree much more rapidly than when feeding, the birds straggling hurriedly after each other in irregular succession. During these hurried cross-country excursions, the simple location-notes are pronounced louder and are interlarded at frequent intervals with a shrill quavering note. The faster the band travels, the louder and more oft-repeated becomes these all-important location-notes; for the greater becomes the danger of individuals becoming separated from the main flock. Bush-tits are usually hidden from each other in dense foliage. They have no directive color-marks; therefore, being gregarious birds, the great value of their location-notes becomes apparent.

Should a bush-tit lag far behind as to be beyond hearing of his fellows, he may suddenly come to a realization of his loneliness; he at once becomes greatly perturbed, flitting to the tallest available perch, and uttering the last mentioned note reinforced into a regular cry for his companions. This is usually heard by the distant band and several similar answering cries inform the laggard of the direction the flock has taken. Off he goes in zigzag precipitation and joins his fellows with evident relief.

He describes a peculiar behavior, also noted by others, that is evidently effective as a protective device:

A flock of bush-tits will be foraging as usual, with the ordinary uncertain medley of location-notes, when suddenly one or two birds utter several of the sharp alarm notes and then begin a shrill quavering piping. This is taken up by the whole flock, until there is a continuous monotonous chorus. At the same time every member of the scattered company strikes a stationary attitude in just the position it was when the alarm was first sounded, and this attitude is maintained until the danger is past. In nearly every case the danger is in the shape of a hawk, more especially of the smaller species such as the sharp-shinned or sparrow hawks. No matter how close the hawk approaches, the shrill chorus continues and even intensifies until the enemy has passed. The remarkable thing about this united cry, is that it is absolutely impossible to locate any single one of the birds by it. The chorus forms an indefinably confusing, all-pervading sound, which I know from personal experience to be most elusive. It may be compared in this respect to the sound of the cicada. * * * It seems reasonable to infer that this monotonous chorus of uncertain direction, at the same time as it sounds a general alarm, serves to conceal the individual birds, all of which at the same time maintain a statuesque, motionless attitude. * * * Scarcely any attention is ever paid by the bush-tits to large hawks, such as buteos, or to other large birds such as turkey vultures, pigeons, or jays. The bush-tits seem to be able to easily identify their real enemies at surprisingly long range.

Dr. Robert C. Miller (1921) has published an interesting paper on the flock behavior of the coast bushtit that is well worth reading; I quote from his summary as follows:

The flock moves from place to place by what may be termed the spread of impulse. An individual bird, moved no doubt by the hunger instinct, takes temporary leadership, and is followed to a new location by the others. There are no regularly assigned leaders, though probably the most venturesome birds assume the leadership most often. * * *
The method of flock movement makes evident the extreme improbability of there being any definite forage routes. The direction taken by the flock at any time is a matter of caprice, or the circumstances of the moment. Due to their dislike for crossing open spaces, however, the birds are likely to frequent areas where the vegetation is continuous and will generally avoid those where it is discontinuous, so that an impression of regularity in their forage movements may thus secondarily be given.

In all their movements the bushtits remind one strongly of the chickadees. Their flight is weak and apparently uncertain, though well adapted to their mode of life; they flit about rapidly and accurately in the foliage or bare twigs of trees and bushes; they seldom make long flights, and when they have to cross open spaces between covers they do so hurriedly and with a weak undulating flight. As gymnasts they are fully equal to the chickadees, and perhaps even more expert, for their longer tails give them even better control of movement and balance in foraging for their food about the tips of slender swaying twigs. Mrs. Bailey (1902) states it very well as follows: "Flitting from branch to branch they fly up to light upside down on the underside of a bough, and then without taking the trouble to turn right side up drop backwards to catch upside down on the tip of another twig, where they bend double over the terminal buds looking for food."

Carroll Dewilton Scott has sent me the following notes on rather unusual behavior of bushtits: "Only once in fifty years' association with brownie bushtits have I seen any show of belligerency. A flock of about 15 were hopping about in a small tree near the house and flying into a bed of flowers nearby. Suddenly two of the tiny birds were rolling about on the ground, fighting in dead earnest. Then they flew back to the tree, only to bounce around a few minutes later in a wheelbarrow that was standing under the tree. Now the most dramatic thing happened. The whole flock became excited and fluttered about the contestants, calling their shrill alarm notes and showing the greatest solicitation as long as the mites were fighting. In a few minutes all was as peaceful and merry as ever."

Of an unusual roosting habit, he says: "It seems strange to see these lowly midgets roosting in tall, open-branched eucalyptus trees, especially in winter. Several times in Balboa Park, San Diego, I had seen a flock fly into eucalyptus trees after sundown to roost. So, on December 27, we went to the locality about sunset. Between sunset and dark, a flock of 50 flew out of a brushy canyon to a dead acacia that stood between the canyon and a grove of eucalyptus, thence from one eucalyptus to another, some going a hundred feet or more before settling down for the night. Another instance of similar roosting in tall, swaying eucalyptus occurred on my place at Pacific Beach in 1935. All through November and December, even in gusty, rainy weather, a flock roosted every night in several tall eucalyptus near the house."

Illustrating the flocking habits of bushtits, Robert S. Woods writes to me: "No better demonstration of the intensely gregarious disposition of this species can be found than that which is afforded by a visit of the flock to a bird bath. Though there may be ample room around the rim of the basin, all will crowd together on one side, while newcomers and those from the outskirts of the group continually alight on the backs of the others, trying to force their way into the middle of the line. Even when only three are present, one of those on the outside may fly up and try to wedge itself between the other two. Apparently they feel safe or content only when flanked on both sides by others of their kind."

Mr. Rathbun, in his notes, tells of an incident that illustrates the sociability of bushtits; he found a nest toward dusk and says: "I lightly touched the branch to which the nest was attached, and, to my surprise, four tits flew from the nest; as this was too early in the season for any young of the year, I thought I would see what the nest contained and found six eggs that were well incubated." Apparently, two of the birds were the owners of the nest and the other two had taken up quarters in the nest for the night.

Voice.—Some of the notes of the bushtit are mentioned above in the quotations from Dr. Grinnell's (1903) excellent paper on this subject. He recognizes five distinct notes, or variations or combinations of notes, each of which seemed to him to signify some particular state of mind of the birds:

1. The simple location-note uttered while the birds are feeding and undisturbed, *"tsit, tsit; tsit; tsit."*

2. "From one to five of the simple notes uttered somewhat more loudly and followed by a rather shrill quavering note of longer duration," uttered when traveling more rapidly and not feeding, *"tsit, tsit, tsit, sre-e-e-e; tsit, sre-e-e-e."*

3. The same as the last "but pronounced with much more volume and emphasis," uttered by lone individuals when separated from the flock, *tsit, tsit, sre-e-e-e.*

4. Similar to the first note but greatly intensified, the alarm note, uttered when the nest is disturbed or an enemy discovered, *"tsit; tsit, tsit; tsit."*

5. "A shrill quavering trill, of the same quality as described under number 2 above, but without the preceding simple notes, and chanted continuously in a monotone by all members of a flock for as long as two minutes." This is the chorus, confusing note uttered in the presence or approach of an avian enemy, *sre-e-e-e-e,* etc.

Field marks.—There is no bird in California quite like the bushtit. It is a tiny, brownish-gray bird with a long tail and with no prominent recognition marks. The subspecies may be recognized by their coloration, as explained under each. A loose flock of feathered mites drifting through the tree tops or bushes could be safely recorded as bushtits about as far off as they could be seen.

Winter.—Bushtits are permanent residents throughout nearly all their range. Their behavior in winter has been referred to above.

DISTRIBUTION

Range.—Western United States, southern British Columbia, Mexico, and Guatemala; nonmigratory.

The range of the bushtit extends **north** to southwestern British Columbia (Point Grey and Chilliwack); northeastern Oregon (Canyon City Mountain); probably southwestern Wyoming (Green River); and central Colorado (Colorado Springs). **East** to central Colorado (Colorado Springs, Turkey Creek, Beulah, and Trinidad); western Oklahoma (Kenton); eastern New Mexico (Santa Rosa and Carlsbad); western Texas (Mount Ord and Castroville); Veracruz (Las Vigas and Mirador); and Guatemala (San Mateo and Tecpam). **South** to Guatemala (Tecpam and Huehuetenango); Chiapas (San Cristóbal); Oaxaca (Tehuantepec and La Parada); Michoacán (Patzcuaro); Jalisco (Haciendo el Molino and La Laguna); Tepic (Santa Teresa); and southern Baja California (Miraflores). **West** to Baja California (Miraflores, Victoria Mountains, San Fernando, and

El Rosario); California (San Diego, Santa Barbara, Palo Alto, East Park, and Yreka); western Oregon (Mosquito Ranger Station, Corvallis, and Portland); Washington (Olympia, Seattle, and Bellingham); and southwestern British Columbia (Boundary Bay and Point Grey).

The range as outlined is for the entire species, which has been separated into several geographic races, some of which are found only in Mexico and Guatemala. Those occurring in the United States, Canada, and northern Mexico are the coast bushtit *(Psaltriparus minimus minimus)*, which ranges along the Pacific coast from southwestern British Columbia south through California to the Mexican border; the California bushtit *(P. m. californicus)*, found in the interior from south-central Oregon, south to Kern County, Calif.; the black-tailed bushtit *(P. m. melanurus)* of northern Baja California; Grinda's bushtit *(P. m. grindae)*, which occurs in the mountains of the Cape district of Baja California; the lead-colored bushtit *(P. m. plumbeus)*, ranging in the Rocky Mountain region from eastern Oregon and western Wyoming south to Texas and northern Sonora; and Lloy'd bushtit *(P. m. lloydi[1])*. which is found from southern New Mexico and western Texas south into northern Mexico.

Egg dates.—Arizona: 33 records, April 8 to June 12; 17 records, April 17 to May 15, indicating the height of the season.

California: 124 records, February 26 to July 15; 62 records, April 1 to May 7.

Mexico: 7 records, April 9 to June 3.

New Mexico: 5 records, April 20 to June 3.

Texas: 3 records, April 11 to June 21.

Washington: 11 records, April 13 to July 3.

PSALTRIPARUS MINIMUS CALIFORNICUS Ridgway

CALIFORNIA BUSHTIT

This interior race of the bushtits is described by Ridgway (1904) as "similar to *P. m. minimus* but decidedly paler, the pileum light broccoli brown in spring and summer, the back, etc., olive-gray instead of deep smoke gray. (The autumnal and winter plumage very similar to the spring and summer plumage of *P. m. minimus.)*" Swarth (1914) says of the distinguishing characters of *californicus:* "As compared with *P. minimus minimus,* of clear gray and white tones of color, rather than of the brownish hue of that subspecies. Typical *californicus* is often almost pure white beneath, noticeably so in the juvenal plumage. Sides and flanks slightly or not at all tinged with vinaceous."

---

[1] Recognized as a subspecies of *Psaltriparus melanotis* after this account was written.

452 BULLETIN 191, UNITED STATES NATIONAL MUSEUM

The range of the California bushtit, as now understood, includes the interior valley regions, chiefly in the Lower and Upper Sonoran Zones, exclusive of desert regions, from Jackson County, Oreg., to Kern County, Calif. Mountain ranges and intervening deserts both seem to serve as effective barriers at certain places between the two subspecies.

I cannot find anything in the literature and have received no contributed notes to indicate that any of the habits of this inland race differ materially from those of the coast form. As it lives in a somewhat less humid environment, it probably selects some different species of trees and shrubs for its nesting sites, such as madrones, junipers, and sage on occasions, though it evidently shows a preference for oaks. It apparently builds its nests of similar materials and eats similar kinds of food. In short, practically all that has been written about the coast bushtit would apply equally well to the present form. Their eggs are indistinguishable. The measurements of 40 eggs of *californicus* average 14.1 by 10.5 millimeters; the eggs showing the four extremes measure 15.3 by 10.0, 13.0 by 11.1, 12.8 by 10.1, and 14.0 by 9.9 millimeters.

Enemies.—Dr. Herbert Friedmann (1929) reports the finding of an egg of the dwarf cowbird in a nest of the California bushtit, but, as it was found in Riverside County, it probably refers to the coast bushtit. This seems to be the only known time that the species has been imposed upon. It is a mystery how the cowbird can enter such nests as those of the bushtit and the verdin without so enlarging the entrance as to cause the owners to desert.

In this connection, the reader is referred to what E. C. Stuart Baker has to say about similar difficulties encountered by the Himalayan cuckoo, in his contribution to my Bulletin 176, page 87.

PSALTRIPARUS MINIMUS MELANURUS Grinnell and Swarth

BLACK-TAILED BUSHTIT

In describing and naming this Baja California subspecies, Grinnell and Swarth (1926) say that it is "as compared with *Psaltriparus minimus minimus,* of southern California, of darker, more plumbeous general coloration. In *minimus* there is a brownish tinge to the plumage, above and below, that is lacking in *melanurus.* This difference is most outstandingly apparent on wings and tail; *melanurus* is, comparatively speaking, a 'black-tailed' bushtit. * * * The color differences distinguishing *melanurus* and *minimus* are readily apparent in fresh plumaged birds. Bush-tits change rapidly in appearance with wear and fading of the feathers, and worn-plumaged individuals of these two subspecies no longer exhibit the differences that are so easily seen in early fall.

Melanurus in its dark slaty color is readily distinguished at any season from the paler subspecies, *P. m. californicus;* and it is, of course, as readily told from the still paler species, *P. plumbeus."*

This is one of several new subspecies that have been described from the Sierra San Pedro Mártir region. Its known range seems to extend from the United States boundary southward to about latitude 30°, and from the crest of the above mountains to the sea. It occupies chiefly the Upper Sonoran Life Zone but extends locally into the Transition and Lower Sonoran Zones.

It probably does not differ materially in its habits from other adjacent races of the species. J. Stuart Rowley writes to me: "Near Socorro, Lower California, a nest of this bird was found on April 18, 1933. The nest was placed in a low bush near our camp and contained five fresh eggs. The nest and habits of these birds were similar to those of the California races."

The measurements of 40 eggs average 13.7 by 10.3 millimeters; the eggs showing the four extremes measure **14.8** by 10.7, 14.0 by **11.1,** **12.8** by 10.1, and 13.4 by **9.7** millimeters.

PSALTRIPARUS MINIMUS GRINDAE Ridgway
GRINDA'S BUSHTIT
HABITS

Grinda's bushtit was long regarded as a distinct species, and Mr. Ridgway (1904) treated it as such in his Birds of North and Middle America. It was named by Lyman Belding, in his manuscript sent to Mr. Ridgway, in honor of his friend Don Francisco C. Grinda, of La Paz. Ridgway's (1883) original description of it is as follows:

Entire pileum uniform light brown, or isabella-color (exactly as in some specimens of *P. minimus*); side of head similar, but paler, and gradually fading into white on chin and throat; remaining lower parts very pale smoky-gray, with a faint lilac tinge (exactly as in *P. minimus*). Upper parts light plumbeous-gray, in very marked and abrupt contrast with the brown of the nape. * * *

This pretty new species, while combining, to a certain degree, the characters of *P. minimum* and *P. plumbeus,* is yet apparently quite distinct from both. In the brown head and color of the under parts it agrees exactly with the forr er. but the resemblance ends there. From the latter it differs in much whiter throat and decidedly clearer, more bluish, shade of the upper parts, in both of which respects there is a close resemblance to *P. melanotis.* The bill is very slender, like that of *P. plumbeus.*

The range of Grinda's bushtit seems to be limited to the Cape region of Lower California, chiefly in the Upper Sonoran Zone and in the mountains. William Brewster (1902) says that Mr. Frazar found it "occurring almost as numerously about San José del Rancho as on the

Sierra de la Laguna. It is a sedentary species, of which each individual bird probably spends its entire life within a very limited area, for Mr. Frazar noticed no marked seasonal variations in the number of its representatives at any of the localities which he visited."

Nesting.—Mr. Brewster (1902) writes: "A nest found on May 24 in the top of a small pine about eight feet above the ground, on the Sierra de la Laguna, is similar in shape to the nests of *P. m. californicus* and *P. plumbeus.* It is nine inches long, with a diameter varying from two to two and one half inches. The entrance hole is in one side near the top. The walls are composed of small, dry leaves, fern-down, catkins, spiders' cocoons, yellowish usnea and grayish lichens, all these materials being felted into a thick, tenacious fabric of a generally mixed brown and grayish color. There were no eggs, the nest being not quite finished when taken."

There is a set of three eggs in the Doe collection, University of Florida, that was collected by J. Stuart Rowley near Miraflores on May 3, 1933. The nest was in an "oak-like tree," about 6 feet from the ground, and was made of mosses, fine downy fibers, and feathers.

Eggs.—The eggs of Grinda's bush-tit are indistinguishable from those of other bushtits. The measurements of eight eggs average 13.5 by 10.1 millimeters; the eggs showing the four extremes measure **14.2** by **9.9**, **11.5** by 10.1, and 12.2 by **10.4** millimeters.

Plumages.—Mr. Brewster (1902) describes the juvenal plumage as "differing from the adult in being ashier beneath, with a decided purplish tinge on the sides; the back paler bluish, the crown light purplish brown; the outer tail feathers with their outer webs ashy white to the shaft; the secondaries and wing coverts edged and tipped with grayish or rusty white."

He says that a bird in "first winter plumage," taken November 28, is "similar to the young just described, but with the crown deep purplish brown; the back darker or more slaty than in the adult; the wings and tail more bluish; the outer tail feathers with exceedingly narrow light margins on their outer webs." It seems to me that this bird, which I have seen, is an adult in fresh autumn plumage, as it does not have the juvenal tail, described above; the postjuvenal molt does not involve the flight feathers, and, if this were a first winter bird, it should still have the juvenal tail.

I have also examined the molting specimen he refers to, taken July 28, which is also evidently an adult. Adults apparently have a complete post nuptial molt, beginning in July, and they are darker and more richly colored after this molt.

In all its other habits, food, behavior, and voice, it probably does not differ from other races of the species, if due allowance be made for the difference in environment.

PSALTRIPARUS MINIMUS PLUMBEUS (Baird)

LEAD-COLORED BUSHTIT

HABITS

This bushtit, which was long considered to be a distinct species, is now regarded as the easternmost representative of a western species. It has a wide distribution in the general region of the Rocky Mountains, according to the 1931 Check-list, "from eastern Oregon and western Wyoming south to northern Sonora and western Texas, and from eastern California to central Colorado." Its range in California seems to be a very narrow one, which Swarth (1914) defines as limited to the "desert region of the southeastern portion of the State, in Mono, Inyo, and northern San Bernardino counties. A discontinuous range, being confined to the Upper Sonoran zone of the various desert mountain chains and the east slope of the Sierra Nevada, these tracts being separated by vast expanses of Lower Sonoran, uninhabited by the species."

The lead-colored bushtit evidently intergrades with the California bushtit at the western border of its range in eastern California and with Lloyd's bushtit at the southeastern border of its range in western Texas. Mr. Swarth (1914) treated the lead-colored bushtit as a full species and seemed loath to regard it as a subspecies, though he discussed the subject quite fully and evidently felt that the three forms are very closely related. Grinnell, Dixon, and Linsdale (1930) discuss in considerable detail the status of certain specimens collected in the Lassen Peak region, and seem to favor the subspecies theory.

Referring to the Tobaye region of Nevada, Dr. Jean M. Linsdale (1938b) reports this bushtit as "a common bird of the lower part of the mountains, between 6000 and 8000 feet; noted once as high as 8700 feet. * * *

"Prominent among the kinds of plants frequented by bushtits were the following: tall sage brush, piñon, mountain mahogany, birch, willow, dogwood, limber pine, and aspen. The species occurred over the ridges and along the streams; the greatest number being found on the floor of cañons near their mouths at the base of the mountains."

We found the lead-colored bushtit common and well distributed in all the mountain ranges of southern Arizona but entirely absent from the low, arid regions of the southwestern part of the State. In the Huachucas, it ranged well up toward the summits but was most abundant between 4,000 and 7,000 feet in the mouths of canyons, in the foothills, and on the lower mountain slopes, especially where the large trees were scattered, leaving large, open, sunny areas, overgrown with scrub oaks, small madrones, scattered junipers, and a variety of other shrubbery.

The lead-colored bushtit is intermediate in its characters between the California bushtit on the west and Lloyd's on the southeast, being a plainly colored bird without the distinctive head markings of either of the other two forms.

Nesting.—The nesting habits of the lead-colored bushtit are similar to those of the species elsewhere, though some different species of trees and shrubs are utilized as nesting sites and the nests are made of such material as is locally available. Of the six nests recorded in our Arizona notes, one was at the end of a pendant limb of a live oak, three were in oak scrub, one was in a small juniper, and one in a madrona bush; the juniper nest was only 6 feet from the ground and the nest in the live oak was 9 feet up, the others being at intermediate heights. They were all at altitudes ranging from 4,000 to 7,000 feet. The madrona nest, now before me, is a beautiful structure; it was made largely of green mosses, whitish lichens, and buff plant down, mixed with a few small dry leaves, fine plant fibers, etc., all firmly matted together; it was profusely lined with small, gray, downy feathers, and what looks like mouse fur.

Bendire (1887) says that the nests are not always "strictly pensile, but are woven into and supported by small twigs and branches of the oak bushes (*Quercus undulata?*) in which they are built. Several nests were placed in bunches of a species of mistletoe (probably *Phoredendron flavescens*), and in these cases the nests are supported and placed directly in the forks of this plant. * * * The nests are outwardly composed of the dried, curled-up leaves of the white sage, plant-down of a pinkish tint, spider webs, small bits of mosses and lichens, and are thickly lined inside with soft, small feathers. * * * The nests are placed in about equal proportions in low oak bushes, from 5 to 7 feet from the ground, generally well concealed by the foliage, or in bunches of mistletoe in oak or mesquite trees, from 15 to 20 feet high."

Swarth (1904) says that the earlier nests are all in the lower foothill regions, "but later in the season [in the Huachucas] they nest abundantly in the higher altitudes, sometimes high up in the pine trees. I saw one nest at the very top of a tall pine, but the tree was growing on a steep hill side, and the nest was about on a level with the trail from which I saw it."

Mrs. Bailey (1928) says that in the Chisos Mountains, Tex., the nests are made in nut pines, 12 to 15 feet from the ground. And, in New Mexico, nests were built in junipers and cottonwoods; one nest that she saw was made mostly of sheep wool with small woolly leaves and oak tassels interwoven. Mrs. Wheelock (1904) reports blackberry vines as favorite nesting sites in eastern California.

Eggs.—The lead-colored bushtit usually lays five or six eggs, which are just like other bushtits' eggs, ovate in shape and pure white in color. The measurements of 48 eggs average 13.4 by 10.2 millimeters; the eggs showing the four extremes measure **14.5** by 10.2, 14.2 by **10.7**, **12.5** by 10.2, and 13.0 by **9.9** millimeters.

Young.—Two broods are often, perhaps usually, raised in a season and often at very short intervals. A. J. van Rossem (1936) flushed from a nest what he estimated was a brood of seven or eight young just before dusk. The next morning, four young, just able to fly, left the nest as he approached; and, much to his surprise, he found in the nest five perfectly fresh eggs. The birds that flew from the nest the previous evening may have been adult birds that had gone into the nest to roost, but the interesting point is that the eggs were laid before the young left the nest; thus the first brood had helped to start incubation on the second brood!

Plumages.—The sequence of plumages and molts in the lead-colored bushtit is the same as in the other races of the species, but the juvenal plumage exhibits some very interesting variations. Mr. Swarth (1914) writes of this plumage:

Practically like adult. The gray of the upper parts is duller, less of a blue-gray, the brown cheeks are not so sharply contrasted against the rest of the head, and there is a faintly indicated black line over the auriculars and on the nape. Unlike the adults, the young of *plumbeus* exhibit considerable diversity in markings, and while the above described specimen represents the plumage perhaps most frequently encountered, there is a large proportion of birds with more or less extensive black markings on the head. In a few specimens there is no trace of head markings, a number have them faintly indicated, as in the specimen described above, and in others the patterns vary from a narrow line extending backward from the eye, to nearly as extensive a black marking as in the adult male of *P. m. lloydi* (See Swarth, 1913, pp. 399-401).

It was these black markings on the heads of young *plumbeus* that led to the erroneous extension of the range of *lloydi* into southern Arizona and New Mexico.

The postjuvenal molt of *plumbeus* begins during the last week of July, or earlier. I have seen molting adults from August 8 to September 13.

I can find nothing reported on the food, behavior, or voice of this bushtit that differs in any respect from what has been written about the California races, but shall quote the following passage from the facile pen of Dr. Elliott Coues (1878), which so aptly describes the flocking habit of the species: "They are extremely sociable—the gregarious instinct common to the Titmice reaches its highest development in their case, and flocks of forty or fifty—some say even of a hundred—may be seen after the breeding season has passed, made up of numerous families, which, soon after leaving the nest, meet kindred spirits, and enter into intimate friendly relations. Often, in rambling through the shrubbery, I have been suddenly surrounded by a troop of the busy birds, perhaps unnoticed till the curious chirping they keep up attracted my attention; they seemed to *pervade* the bushes. If I stood still, they came close around me, as fearless as if I were a stump, ignoring me altogether."

PSALTRIPARUS MELANOTIS LLOYDI Sennett

LLOYD'S BUSHTIT

HABITS

Lloyd's bushtit was originally described by George B. Sennett (1888) as a full species; Ridgway (1904) treated it as a subspecies of *Psaltriparus melanotis,* the black-eared bushtit of Mexico. In his original description Sennett stated that in the adult male the sides of the head are "glossy black, which extends backward on each side, meeting and forming a collar on lower back of neck." The adult female has the "ear-patches clear glossy brown instead of black. * * * This species is distinct from *P. melanotis,* Black-eared Bush-Tit, by reason of total absence of both brown on back and rufous on underparts. It is easily distinguished from *P. plumbeus* by the collar, and by the black instead of ashy brown on sides of head. Aside from the head markings it is more like *P. plumbeus* in color than *P. melanotis,* but it has a much whiter throat and a larger bill."

The range of Lloyd's bushtit, as given in the 1931 Check-list, includes the "mountains of the southeastern desert region, mainly in the Upper Austral Zone, from southern New Mexico and central western Texas (mountains between Pecos River and Rio Grande) south into Sonora and Chihuahua."

Ridgway (1904) extended the range into southern Arizona, but Swarth (1913) has shown that this was an error. The Arizona specimens of the supposed *lloydi* race, originally named *P. santaritae,* are all birds in juvenal plumage. Mr. Swarth (1913) has demonstrated that the young of *plumbeus,* in juvenal plumage, have more or less black markings on the head of the male, even in specimens taken as far away from the supposed range of *lloydi* as Nevada. This matter is fully discussed in his paper, to which the reader is referred.

The status of Lloyd's bushtit, as at least of casual occurrence, in southern New Mexico, seems to be established, for Mrs. Bailey (1928) says that "a full plumaged adult male was taken in the San Luis Mountains, July 19, 1892 (Mearns), and is now in the collection of the United States National Museum." There may be other specimens of females and young, which are not so readily distinguished from *plumbeus*.

Van Tyne and Sutton (1937) do not agree with the concept that *lloydi* is a subspecies of *minimus;* they treat it as subspecies of *melanotis*, and evidently regard *minimus* and *melanotis* as specifically distinct. They say:

All of the forty-three Brewster County [Texas] specimens we have examined are without exception clearly *melanotis* or *minimus*. In this region *melanotis* is confined to higher altitudes more definitely than is *minimus* but the breeding ranges of the two forms overlap widely and their relations seem to be those of two distinct species. The only bit of contrary evidence we noted was the fact that on May 5, 1932, Dr. Peet collected at Boot Spring an adult male *melanotis* in company with a breeding female *minimus*. The two birds seemed to be traveling together, and no other Bush-tits were seen about at the time. The whole problem of the relation between these two forms is a fascinating one which calls for more study in this critical region.

Nesting.—Mr. Sennett (1888) reports a nest taken in Presidio County, Tex., on June 21, 1887, by William Lloyd, for whom he named the species. It was found in Limpia Canyon, at an altitude of 6,200 feet, and was fastened to twigs of a cedar seven feet from the ground. "The cedar tree was twenty-five feet high, situated on a divide between two ravines."

There is a set of five eggs in the Doe collection in Florida, said to be of this subspecies; it was taken by Capt. R. W. Barrell on April 20, 1890, in Grant County, N. Mex., which is in the southwestern corner of the State and within the *possible* breeding range of this race; the nest was placed 5 feet up in a live oak. There is a set of seven eggs in my collection, taken by E. F. Pope in the Comanche Mountains, Tex., on April 11, 1912; the nest "was suspended on the end of a drooping branch of a small pine, 12 feet from the ground."

Eggs.—The eggs of Lloyd's bushtit are apparently just like those of other bushtits. The measurements of 23 eggs average 13.8 by 10.5 millimeters; the eggs showing the four extremes measure 14.5 by 10.6, 14.0 by 11.4, 13.2 by 10.0 millimeters.

Plumages.—The following remarks by Van Tyne and Sutton (1937), based on specimens from Brewster County, Tex., are interesting as showing some of the characters of *lloydi* and some of its variations in plumage:

The best characters for distinguishing this species from *Psaltriparus minimus* are: black on the sides of the nape and on the auricular region, gray crown contrasting strongly with the more olivaceous back, throat usually much whiter than the rest of the under parts, strong vinaceous wash on sides and flanks. In addition the "face" is not Drab or Light Drab as in *plumbeus*, but is Hair Brown (in males this brown is usually suffused or mottled with black in varying degrees). A dozen of our Brewster County males can be arranged in a series to show perfect gradation from a face that is nearly pure Hair Brown to one that is practically black. Many of the intermediates show a curious mottling of black on a brown background. We were at first inclined to consider that the more brown-faced specimens were immature, but three juvenal-plumaged males collected by A. C. Lloyd on May 25, 1933, are among the most black-faced of the whole series. In these juvenile birds the vinaceous wash on the flanks is almost imperceptible. The black-faced juveniles make it obvious that the description by Ridgway, which characterizes the young males of *lloydi* as having only black ear coverts, is inadequate. Apparently Sennett was correct in stating that the young are 'similar to adults.' Of the three adult females examined, one (June 5) has a Hair Brown face, well-marked auricular region, and a strong vinaceous wash below; the other two, more worn females (July 21), are separable from *plumbeus* only by grayer faces and by blackish auricular feathers.

In all other respects, food, behavior, and voice, this bushtit does not differ materially from the other bushtits.

LITERATURE CITED

ABBOTT, CLINTON GILBERT.
   1929. Watching long-crested jays. Condor, vol. 31, pp. 124-125.
ADAMS, ERNEST.
   1898. Notes on the plain titmouse. Osprey, vol. 2, pp. 81-82.
ADDICOTT, ALICE BALDWIN.
   1938. Behavior of the bush-tit in the breeding season. Condor, vol. 40, pp. 49-63.
AIKEN, CHARLES EDWARD HOWARD, and WARREN, EDWARD ROYAL.
   1914. Birds of El Paso County, Colorado. Colorado College Publ., gen. ser., No. 74 (sci. ser., vol. 12, No. 13, pt. 2), pp. 497-603.
ALDOUS, CLARENCE MORONI.
   1937. Eastern crows nesting on or near the ground. Auk, vol. 54, pp. 393-394.
ALDOUS, SHALER EUGENE.
   1942. The white-necked raven in relation to agriculture. U. S. Fish and Wildlife Res. Rep. 5, 56 pp.
ALDRICH, JOHN WARREN, and NUTT, DAVID C.
   1939. Birds of eastern Newfoundland. Sci. Publ. Cleveland Mus. Nat. Hist., vol. 4, pp. 13-42.
ALEXANDER, FRANK McDANIEL.
   1930. Notes on the birds of south central Kansas. Wilson Bull., vol. 42, pp 241-244.
ALEXANDER, HORACE GUNDRY.
   1927. A list of the birds of Latium, Italy, between June 1911 and February 1916. Compiled from the notes and letters of the late C. J. Alexander. Ibis, ser. 12, vol. 3, pp. 659-691.
ALLEN, FRANCIS HENRY.
   1910. Warbling song of the Hudsonian chickadee. Auk, vol. 27, pp. 86-87.
   1919. The aesthetic sense in birds as illustrated by the crow. Auk, vol. 36, pp. 112-113.
AMERICAN ORNITHOLOGISTS' UNION.
   1931. Check-list of North American birds, ed. 4.
   1944. Nineteenth supplement to the American Ornithologists' Union check-list of North American birds. Auk, vol. 61, pp. 441-464.
   1945. Twentieth supplement to the American Ornithologists' Union check-list of North American birds. Auk, vol. 62, pp. 436-449.
ANDERSON, RUDOLPH MARTIN.
   1907. The birds of Iowa. Proc. Davenport Acad. Sci., vol. 40, pp. 125-417.
ANTHONY, ALFRED WEBSTER.
   1889. New birds from Lower California, Mexico. Proc. California Acad. Sci., ser. 2, vol. 2, pp. 73-82.
   1893. Birds of San Pedro Martir, Lower California. Zoe, vol. 4, pp. 228-247.
ATTWATER, HENRY PHILEMON.
   1892. List of birds observed in the vicinity of San Antonio, Baxter County, Texas. Auk, vol. 9, pp. 337-345.
AUDUBON, JOHN JAMES.
   1842. The birds of America, vol. 4.

AUSTIN, OLIVER LUTHER, JR.
  1932. The birds of Newfoundland Labrador. Mem. Nuttall Orn. Club, No. 7.
AVERILL, A. B.
  1895. Nest of the magpie. Oregon Nat., vol. 2, p. 136.
BAGG, AARON CLARK.
  1939. Nesting of the Acadian chickadee in Maine. Auk, vol. 56, p. 190.
BAILEY, ALFRED MARSHALL.
  1927. Notes on the birds of southeastern Alaska. Auk, vol. 44, pp. 351-367.
BAILEY, FLORENCE MERRIAM.
  1902. Handbook of birds of the Western United States.
  1904. Additional notes on the birds of Upper Pecos. Auk, vol. 21, pp. 349-363.
  1928. Birds of New Mexico.
BAILEY, HAROLD HARRIS.
  1913. The birds of Virginia.
  1925. The birds of Florida.
BAILEY, VERNON.
  1903. The white-necked raven. Condor, vol. 5, pp. 87-89.
BAIRD, SPENCER FULLERTON.
  1864. Review of American birds, in the museum of the Smithsonian Institution,
        pt. 1: North and Middle America. Smithsonian Misc. Coll., No. 181.
BAIRD, S. F.; BREWER, THOMAS MAYO; and RIDGWAY, ROBERT.
  1874. A history of North American birds: Land birds, vols. 1 and 2.
BAKER, ROLLIN HAROLD.
  1940. Crow depredation on heron nesting colonies. Wilson Bull., vol. 52, pp.
        124-125.
BALDWIN, DOROTHY A.
  1935. Black-capped chickadee age-records. Bird-Banding, vol. 6, p. 69.
BALL, STANLEY CRITTENDEN.
  1938. Summer birds of the Forillon, Gaspé County, Quebec. Can. Field Nat.,
        vol. 52, pp. 95-103.
BANCROFT, GRIFFING.
  1930. The breeding birds of central Lower California. Condor, vol. 32, pp.
        20-49.
BARLOW, CHESTER.
  1901. Some characteristics of the mountain chickadee. Condor, vol. 3, pp.
        111-114.
BARROWS, WALTER BRADFORD.
  1912. Michigan bird life. Spec. Bull. Dept. Zool. and Physiol. Michigan Agr.
        College, 822 pp.
BATCHELDER, CHARLES FOSTER.
  1884. Description of the first plumage of Clark's crow. Auk, vol. 1, pp. 16-17.
BEAL, FOSTER ELLENBOROUGH LASCELLES.
  1897. The blue jay and its food. U. S. Dept. Agr. Yearbook for 1896, pp.
        197-206.
  1907. Birds of California in relation to the fruit industry, pt. 1. Biol. Surv.
        Bull. 30.
  1910. Birds of California in relation to the fruit industry, pt. 2. Biol Surv.
        Bull. 34.

BEAL, F. E. L.; MCATEE, WALDO LEE; and KALMBACH, EDWIN RICHARD.
    1916. Common birds of southeastern United States in relation to agriculture.
        Farmers' Bull. 755.
BEAL, MARY.
    1931. Verdin ways. Bird-Lore, vol. 33, pp. 399-400.
BECK, ROLLO HOWARD.
    1895. Notes on the blue-fronted jay. Nidologist, vol. 2, p. 158.
BEEBE, CHARLES WILLIAM.
    1905. Two bird-lovers in Mexico.
BENDIRE, CHARLES EMIL.
    1887. Notes on a collection of birds' nests and eggs from southern Arizona
        Territory. Proc. U. S. Nat. Mus., vol. 10, pp. 551-558.
    1895. Life histories of North American birds. U. S. Nat. Mus. Spec. Bull. 3.
BERGTOLD, WILLIAM HENRY.
    1917. A study of the incubation periods of birds.
BERRY, SAMUEL STILLMAN.
    1922. Magpies versus livestock: An unfortunate new chapter in avian de-
        predations. Condor, vol. 24, pp. 13-17.
BLINCOE, BENEDICT JOSEPH.
    1923. Random notes on the feeding habits of some Kentucky birds. Wilson
        Bull., vol. 35, pp. 63-71.
BOLLES, FRANK.
    1896. At the north of Bearcamp water.
BOWLES, JOHN HOOPER.
    1900. The Northwest crow. Condor, vol. 2, pp. 84-85.
    1908. A few summer birds of Lake Chelan, Washington. Condor, vol. 10,
        pp. 191-193.
    1909. Notes on *Parus rufescens* in western Washington. Condor, vol. 12, pp.
        65-70.
BOWLES, J. H., and DECKER, FRANK RUSSELL.
    1930. The ravens of the State of Washington. Condor, vol. 32, pp. 192-201.
    1931. The ferruginous rough-leg in Washington. Murrelet, vol. 12, pp. 65-70.
BRADBURY, WILLIAM CHASE.
    1917a. Notes on the black-crowned night heron near Denver. Condor, vol.
        19, pp. 142-143.
    1917b. Notes on the nesting habits of the Clarke nutcracker in Colorado.
        Condor, vol. 19, pp. 149-155.
    1918. Nesting of the Rocky Mountain jay. Condor, vol. 20, pp. 197-208.
BRADSHAW, FRED.
    1930. Unusual nesting sites. Can. Field Nat., vol. 44, pp. 149-150.
BRALY, JOHN CLAUDE.
    1931. Nesting of the piñon jay in Oregon. Condor, vol. 33, p. 29.
BRANDT, HERBERT WILLIAM.
    1940. Texas bird adventures.
BRAUND, FRANK WILLIAM, and MCCULLAGH, ERNEST PERRY.
    1940. The birds of Anticosti Island, Quebec. Wilson Bull., vol. 52, pp. 96-123.
BREWSTER, WILLIAM.
    1883. Crows fishing. Bull. Nuttall Orn. Club, vol. 8, p. 59.

1886. An ornithological reconnaissance in western North Carolina. Auk, vol. 3, pp. 173-179.

1902. Birds of the Cape region of Lower California. Bull. Mus. Comp. Zool., vol. 41, No. 1, pp. 1-241.

1906. The birds of the Cambridge region of Massachusetts. Mem. Nutall Orn. Club, No. 4.

1937. The birds of the Lake Umbagog region of Maine, pt. 3. Bull. Mus. Comp. Zool., vol. 66, pt. 3, pp. 408-521.

1938. The birds of the Lake Umbagog region of Maine, pt. 4. Bull. Mus. Comp. Zool., vol. 66, pt. 4, pp. 525-620.

BRIMLEY, CLEMENT SAMUEL.
1888. Nesting of the tufted tit in 1888. Ornithologist and Oologist, vol. 13, p. 142.

BROCK, SYDNEY E.
1910. Incubation and fledging periods in birds. Zoologist, vol. 14, pp. 117-118.

BROOKS, ALLAN.
1931. The relationships of the American magpie. Auk, vol. 48, pp. 271-272.

BROOKS, WINTHROP SPRAGUE.
1920. A new jay from Anticosti Island. Proc. New England Zool. Club, vol. 7, pp. 49-50.

BROUN, MAURICE.
1941. Migration of blue jays. Auk, vol. 58, pp. 262-263.

BROWN, D. E.
1930. Nesting habits of the Steller jay *(Cyanocitta stelleri stelleri)* in western Washington. Murrelet, vol. 11, pp. 68-69.

BROWN, NATHAN CLIFFORD.
1879. A list of birds observed at Coosada, central Alabama. Bull. Nuttall Orn. Club, vol. 4, pp. 7-13.

BRYANT, WALTER (PIERC)E.
1888. Unusual nesting sites, 2. Proc. California Acad. Sci., ser. 2, vol. 1, pp. 7-10.

1889. Descriptions of the nests and eggs of some Lower California birds, with a description of the young plumage of *Geothlypis beldingi*. Proc. California Acad. Sci., ser. 2, vol. 2, pp. 20-24.

BURKITT, J. P.
1936. Young rooks, their survival and habits. British Birds, vol. 29, pp. 334-338.

BURLEIGH, THOMAS DEARBORN.
1918. The Hudsonian chickadee *(Penthestes hudsonicus* subsp. ?) in northeastern Pennsylvania in June. Auk, vol. 35, p. 230.

1930. Notes on the bird life of northeastern Washington. Auk, vol. 47, pp. 48-63.

BUTTS, WILBUR KINGSLEY.
1931. A study of the chickadee and white-breasted nuthatch by means of marked individuals. Bird-Banding, vol. 2, pp. 1-26.

CAHALANE, VICTOR HARRISON.
1944. A nutcracker's search for buried food. Auk, vol. 61, p. 643.

CAMERON, EWEN SOMERLED.
1907. The birds of Custer and Dawson Counties, Montana. Auk, vol. 24, pp. 389-406.
1908. The birds of Custer and Dawson Counties, Montana. Auk, vol. 25, pp. 39-56.
CASSIN, JOHN.
1852. Illustrations of the birds of California, Texas, Oregon, British and Russian America.
CHADBOURNE, ARTHUR PATTERSON.
1896. The Hudsonian chickadee *(Parus hudsonicus)*, red-breasted nuthatch *(Sitta canadensis)*, and golden-crowned kinglet *(Regulus satraps)* in Plymouth County, Mass., in summer. Auk, vol. 13, p. 346.
CHAMBERLAIN, MONTAGUE.
1884. Prehensile feet of the crow *(Corvus frugivorus)*. Auk, vol. 1, p. 92.
CHAPMAN, FRANK MICHLER.
1898. Notes on birds observed at Jalapa and Las Vigas, Vera Cruz, Mexico Bull. Amer. Mus. Nat. Hist., vol. 10, pp. 15-43.
COBURN, CHARLES ARTHUR.
1914. The behavior of the crow, *Corvus americanus*, Aud. Journ. Anim. Behavior, vol. 4, pp. 185-201.
COLLINGE, WALTER EDWARD.
1924. The food of some British wild birds.
COTTAM, CLARENCE, and KNAPPEN, PHOEBE.
1939. Food of some uncommon North American birds. Auk, vol. 56, pp. 138-169.
COUES, ELLIOTT.
1871. The long-crested jay. Amer. Nat., vol. 5, pp. 770-775.
1874. Birds of the Northwest.
1878. Birds of the Colorado Valley, pt. 1. U. S. Geol. Surv. Terr. Misc. Publ. 11.
CRAM, ELOISE BLAINE.
1927. Bird parasites of the nematode suborders Strongylata, Ascaridata, and Spirurata. U. S. Nat. Mus. Bull. 140.
CRIDDLE, NORMAN.
1923. The American magpie in Manitoba. Can. Field Nat., vol. 37, pp. 25-26.
1927. A tale of four crows. Can. Field Nat., vol. 41, pp. 179-183.
CROOK, COMPTON.
1936. A winter food supply for the crow. Auk, vol. 53, pp. 337-338.
CRUICKSHANK, ALLAN DUDLEY.
1939. The behavior of some Corvidae. Bird-Lore, vol. 41, pp. 78-81.
CURRIER, EDMONDE SAMUEL.
1904. Summer birds of the Leech Lake region, Minnesota. Auk, vol. 21, pp. 29-44.
CUSHING, JOHN ELDREDGE, JR.
1941. Winter behavior of ravens at Tomales Bay, California. Condor, vol. 43, pp. 103-107.
DALES, MARIE.
1925. A marauding blue jay. Wilson Bull., vol. 37, p. 224.

DARCUS, S. J.
   1930. Notes on birds of the northern part of the Queen Charlotte Islands
         in 1927. Can. Field Nat., vol. 44, pp. 45-49.
DAWSON, WILLIAM LEON.
   1923. The birds of California, vol. 1.
DAWSON, W. L., and BOWLES, JOHN HOOPER.
   1909. The birds of Washington, vol. 1.
DECKER, FRANK RUSSELL, and BOWLES, JOHN HOOPER.
   1931. Summer birds of the Blue Mountains, Washington. Murrelet, vol. 12,
         pp. 12-14.
DICE, LEE RAYMOND.
   1917. Habits of the magpie in southeastern Washington. Condor, vol. 19,
         pp. 121-124.
   1918. The birds of Walla Walla and Columbia Counties, southeastern Wash-
         ington. Auk, vol. 35, pp. 40-51, 148-161.
   1920. Notes on some birds of interior Alaska. Condor, vol. 22, pp. 176-185.
DICKEY, DONALD RYDER, and VAN ROSSEM, ADRIAAN JOSEPH.
   1938. The birds of El Salvador. Publ. Field Mus. Nat. Hist., zool. ser., vol.
         23, pp. 1-635.
DICKS, FORD.
   1938. Activities of Steller's jays in a filbert orchard. Murrelet, vol. 19, p. 17.
DILLE, FREDERICK MONROE.
   1888. Nesting of the black-billed magpie. Ornithologist and Oologist, vol. 13,
         p. 23.
DINGLE, EDWARD VON SIEBOLD.
   1922. Peculiar note of Carolina chickadee. Auk, vol. 39, pp. 572-573.
DIXON, JAMES BENJAMIN.
   1934. Nesting of the Clark nutcracker in California. Condor, vol. 36, pp.
         229-234.
DIXON, JOSEPH SCATTERGOOD.
   1938. Birds and mammals of Mount McKinley National Park, Alaska. Nat.
         Park Serv. Faunal Ser., No. 3.
DOOLITTLE, EDWARD ARTHUR.
   1919. A strange blue jay flight. Auk, vol. 36, p. 572.
DUBOIS, ALEXANDER DAWES.
   1918. An albino magpie. Condor, vol. 20, p. 189.
DWIGHT, JONATHAN, JR.
   1897. The whistled call of *Parus atricapillus* common to both sexes. Auk,
         vol. 14, p. 99.
   1900. The sequence of plumages and moults of the passerine birds of New
         York. Ann. New York Acad. Sci., vol. 13, pp. 73-360.
EATON, ELON HOWARD.
   1903. An epidemic of roup in the Canandaigua crow roost. Auk, vol. 20,
         pp. 57-59.
EIFRIG, CHARLES WILLIAM GUSTAVE.
   1905. A one-legged crow. Auk, vol. 22, pp. 312-313.
ELLICOTT, GRACE.
   1906. Note on food of blue jay. Guide to Nature, vol. 1, p. 168.
ELTON, CHARLES, and BUCKLAND, FRANK.
   1928. The gape-worm (*Syngamus trachea* Montagu) in rooks (*Corvus frugi-
         legus* L.). Parasitology, vol. 20, pp. 448-450.

ERICHSEN, WALTER JEFFERSON.
   1919. Some summer birds of Liberty County, Georgia.
ERICKSON, MARY MARILLA.
   1937. A jay shoot in California. Condor, vol. 39, pp. 111-115.
ERRINGTON, PAUL LESTER.
   1935. Food habits of mid-west foxes. Journ. Mamm., vol. 16, pp. 192-200.
EVERMANN, BARTON WARREN.
   1881. Least titmouse. Ornithologist and Oologist, vol. 6, p. 19.
FARGO, WILLIAM GILBERT.
   1927. Feeding station habit of fish crow. Auk, vol. 44, pp. 566-567.
FARLEY, FRANK LEGRANGE.
   1925. Changes in the status of certain animals and birds during the past
      fifty years in central Alberta. Can. Field Nat., vol. 20, pp. 200-202.
   1932. Birds of the Battle River region.
FERRY, JOHN FARWELL.
   1910. Birds observed in Saskatchewan during the summer of 1909. Auk,
      vol. 27, pp. 185-204.
FINLEY, WILLIAM LOVELL.
   1907. Two studies in blue. Condor, vol. 9, pp. 121-127.
FISHER, WALTER KENRICK.
   1902. A trip to Mono Lake, ornithological and otherwise. Condor, vol. 4,
      pp. 1-11.
FLEMING, JAMES HENRY, and LLOYD, HOYES.
   1920. Ontario bird notes. Auk, vol. 37, pp. 429-439.
FORBUSH, EDWARD HOWE.
   1907. Useful birds and their protection.
   1912. The chickadee. Bird-Lore, vol. 14, pp. 372-375.
   1927. Birds of Massachusetts and other New England States, vol. 2.
FOX, HERBERT.
   1923. Disease in captive wild mammals and birds.
FRAZAR, MARSTON ABBOTT.
   1887. An ornithologist's summer in Labrador. Ornithologist and Oologist,
      vol. 12, pp. 33-35.
FRIEDMANN, HERBERT.
   1925. Notes on the birds observed in the lower Rio Grande Valley of Texas
      during May, 1924. Auk, vol. 42, pp. 537-554.
   1929. The cowbirds: A study in the biology of social parasitism.
   1938. Additional hosts of the parasitic cowbirds. Auk, vol. 55, pp. 41-50.
GARDNER, LEON LLOYD.
   1926. Experiments in the economic control of the western crow (Corvus
      brachyrhynchos hesperis). Auk, vol. 43, pp. 447-461.
GEIST, OTTO WILLIAM.
   1936. Notes on a fight between Alaska jays and a weasel. Condor, vol. 38,
      pp. 174-175.
GIBSON, LANGDON.
   1922. Bird notes from north Greenland. Auk, vol. 39, pp. 350-363.
GILL, GEOFFREY.
   1920. Blue jay vs. mouse. Bird-Lore, vol. 22, p. 161.
GILLESPIE, MABEL.
   1930. Behavior and local distribution of tufted titmice in winter and spring.
      Bird-Banding, vol. 1, pp. 113-127.

GILMAN, MARSHALL FRENCH.
  1902. Notes on the verdin. Condor, vol. 4, pp. 88-89.
  1907. Magpies on the La Plata. Condor, vol. 9, pp. 9-12.
  1908. Birds on the Navajo Reservation in New Mexico. Condor, vol. 10,
         pp. 146-152.
GOODHUE, ISABEL.
  1919. The song of the blue jay. Auk, vol. 36, pp. 111-112.
GOSS, NATHANIEL STICKNEY.
  1885. *Cyanocitta stelleri frontalis* nesting in holes in trees. Auk, vol. 2, p. 217.
  1891. History of the birds of Kansas.
GREEN, MORRIS MILLER.
  1889. Biological Survey field notes, Canaveral, Fla., April 1889.
GRINNELL, JOSEPH.
  1900a. Birds of the Kotzebue Sound region, Alaska. Pacific Coast Avifauna,
         No. 1.
  1900b. New races of birds from the Pacific coast. Condor, vol. 2, pp. 127-128.
  1901. The long-tailed jay. Auk, vol. 18, p. 188.
  1903. Call notes of the bush-tit. Condor, vol. 5, pp. 85-87.
  1904. The origin and distribution of the chestnut-backed chickadee. Auk, vol.
         21, pp. 364-382.
  1908. The biota of the San Bernardino Mountains. Univ. California Publ.
         Zool., vol. 5, pp. 1-170.
  1914. An account of the mammals and birds of the lower Colorado Valley.
         Univ. California Publ. Zool., vol. 12, pp. 51-294.
  1918. The subspecies of the mountain chickadee. Univ. California Publ. Zool.,
         vol. 17, pp. 505-515.
  1923. The present state of our knowledge of the gray titmouse in California.
         Condor, vol. 25, pp. 135-137.
  1928. Notes on the systematics of west American birds, 2. Condor, vol. 30,
         pp. 153-156.
  1931. The type locality of the verdin. Condor, vol. 33, pp. 163-168.
  1934. The New Mexico race of plain titmouse. Condor, vol. 36, pp. 251-252.
GRINNELL, JOSEPH, and BEHLE, WILLIAM HARROUN.
  1937. A new race of titmouse, from the Kern Basin of California. Condor,
         vol. 39, pp. 225-226.
GRINNELL, JOSEPH; DIXON, JOSEPH; and LINSDALE, JEAN MYRON.
  1930. Vertebrate natural history of a section of northern California through
         the Lassen Peak region. Univ. California Publ. Zool., vol. 35.
  1936. Vertebrate animals of Point Lobos Reserve, 1934-35.
GRINNELL, JOSEPH, and STORER, TRACY IRWIN.
  1924. Animal life in the Yosemite.
GRINNELL, JOSEPH, and SWARTH, HARRY SCHELWALD.
  1926. New species of birds *(Penthestes, Baeolophus, Psaltriparus, Chamaea)*
         from the Pacific coast of North America. Univ. California Publ.
         Zool., vol. 30, pp. 163-175.
GUTHRIE, JOSEPH EDWARD.
  1932. Snakes versus birds; birds versus snakes. Wilson Bull., vol. 44,
         pp. 88-113.
HAGERUP, ANDREAS THOMSEN.
  1891. The birds of Greenland.

HARDING, KATHERINE CLARK.
   1932. Age record of black-capped chickadee 93789. Bird-Banding, vol. 3,
      p. 118.
HARLOW, RICHARD CRESSON.
   1922. The breeding habits of the northern raven in Pennsylvania. Auk,
      vol. 39, pp. 399-410.
HENSHAW, HENRY WETHERBEE.
   1875. Report upon ornithological collections made in portions of Nevada, Utah,
      California, Colorado, New Mexico and Arizona during the years
      1872, 1873, and 1874. (Wheeler Survey.)
HICKS, LAWRENCE EMERSON, and DAMBACH, CHARLES A.
   1935. Sex ratios and weights in wintering crows. Bird-Banding, vol. 6,
      pp. 65-66.
   1936. A statistical survey of the winter bird life of southeastern Ohio—
      Muskingum County. Wilson Bull., vol. 48, pp. 273-275.
HOFFMANN, RALPH.
   1904. A guide to the birds of New England and eastern New York.
   1927. Birds of the Pacific States.
HOOD, FREDA L.
   1916. Nesting habits of the tufted titmouse. Bird-Lore, vol. 18, p. 178.
HORNING, JAMES E.
   1923. Crows building in low willows—Alberta. Auk, vol. 40, pp. 327-328.
HOWELL, ALFRED BRAZIER.
   1917. Birds of the Islands off the coast of southern California. Pacific Coast
      Avifauna, No. 12.
HOWELL, ARTHUR HOLMES.
   1913. Descriptions of two new birds from Alabama. Proc. Biol. Soc. Wash-
      ington, vol. 26, pp. 199-202.
   1932. Florida bird life.
HUEY, LAURENCE MARKHAM.
   1942. Two new wrens and a new jay from Lower California, Mexico. Trans.
      San Diego Soc. Nat. Hist., vol. 9, pp. 427-434.
IMLER, RALPH H.
   1939. Comparison of the food of the white-necked ravens and crows in
      Oklahoma. Wilson Bull., vol. 51, pp. 121-122.
ISELY, DWIGHT.
   1912. A list of the birds of Sedgwick County, Kansas. Auk, vol. 29, pp. 25-44.
JACOBS, JOSEPH WARREN.
   1935. Red type of crow eggs. Auk, vol. 52, pp. 189-190.
JELLISON, WILLIAM LIVINGSTON, and PHILIP, CORNELIUS BECKER.
   1933. Faunae of nests of the magpie and crow in western Montana. Can. Ent.,
      vol. 65, pp. 26-31.
JENSEN, JENS KNUDSEN.
   1923. Notes on the nesting birds of northern Santa Fe County, New Mexico.
      Auk, vol. 40, pp. 452-469.
   1925. Mountain chicadee with an adopted family. Auk, vol. 42, p. 593.
JONES, LYNDS.
   1910. The birds of Cedar Point and vicinity. Wilson Bull., vol. 22, pp. 172-182.
JOURDAIN, FRANCIS CHARLES ROBERT.
   1929. Protective mimicry of the chickadee. Auk, vol. 46, p. 123.

1938. The handbook of British birds, vol. 1. (By H. F. Witherby, F. C. R. Jourdain, Norman F. Ticehurst, and Bernard W. Tucker.)

JUDD, SYLVESTER DWIGHT.
   1902. Birds of a Maryland farm. Biol. Surv. Bull. 17.

JUNG, CLARENCE SCHRAM.
   1930. Notes on birds of the delta region of the Peace and Athabasca Rivers. Auk, vol. 47, pp. 533-541.

KAEDING, HENRY BARROILHET.
   1897. Notes on the yellow-billed magpie. Oologist, vol. 14, pp. 15-17.

KALMBACH, EDWIN RICHARD.
   1920. The crow in its relation to agriculture. Farmers' Bull. 1102.
   1927. The magpie in relation to agriculture. U. S. Dept. Agr. Techn. Bull. 24.
   1939. The crow in its relation to agriculture. Farmers' Bull. 1102, rev. ed.

KALMBACH, E. R., and ALDOUS, SHALER EUGENE.
   1940. Winter banding of Oklahoma crows. Wilson Bull., vol. 52, pp. 198-206.

KALTER, LOUIS BIESER.
   1932. Birds attracted to small-flowered leaf cup. Auk, vol. 49, p. 365.

KELSO, JOHN EDWARD HENRY.
   1926. Birds of the Arrow Lakes, West Kootenay District, British Columbia. Ibis, ser. 12, vol. 2, pp. 689-723.

KENNARD, FREDERIC HEDGE.
   1898. Habits of the blue jay. Auk, vol. 15, p. 269.

KITE, VITAE.
   1925. A tufted titmouse goes wool-gathering. Bird-Lore, vol. 27, pp. 180-181.

KNEELAND, SAMUEL.
   1883. Prehensile feet of the crow. Science, vol. 2, pp. 265-266.

KNIGHT, ORA WILLIS.
   1908. The birds of Maine.

KNIGHT, WILBUR CLINTON.
   1902. The birds of Wyoming.

KRAMER, GUSTAV.
   1930. Stimme von Raben- und Nebelkrähe. Orn. Monatsb., Jahrg. 38, p. 146.

KUMLIEN, LUDWIG.
   1879. Contributions to the natural history of Arctic America. U. S. Nat. Mus. Bull. 15.

KUMLIEN, LUDWIG, and HOLLISTER, NED.
   1903. The birds of Wisconsin. Bull. Wisconsin Nat. Hist. Soc., new ser., vol. 3, Nos. 1-3.

LACEY, HOWARD.
   1903. Notes on the Texan jay. Condor, vol. 5, pp. 151-153.

LANGILLE, JAMES HIBBERT.
   1884. Our birds in their haunts.

LEMMON, ISABELLA McC.
   1904. A blue jay household. Bird-Lore, vol. 6, pp. 89, 90.

LEWIS, HARRISON FLINT.
   1931. Unsuspecting chickadees. Can. Field Nat., vol. 45, pp. 30-31.

LILFORD, Lord.
   1860. See Powys, Hon. Thomas Lyttleton.

LINCOLN, FREDERICK CHARLES.
1927. Returns from banded birds, 1923 to 1926. U. S. Dept. Agr. Techn. Bull. 26.
1939. The migration of American birds.
LINSDALE, JEAN MYRON.
1937. The natural history of magpies. Pacific Coast Avifauna, No. 25.
1938a. Environmental responses of the vertebrates in the Great Basin. Amer. Midl. Nat., vol. 19, pp. 1-206.
1938b. Geographic variation in some birds in Nevada. Condor, vol. 40, pp. 36-38.
LORENZ, KONRAD Z.
1937. The companion in the bird's world. Auk, vol. 54, pp. 245-273.
LOW, SETH.
1934. Notes on Cape Cod crow movements. Bird-Banding, vol. 5, pp. 192-193.
MACFARLANE, RODERICK ROSS.
1891. Notes on and list of birds and eggs collected in Arctic America, 1861-1866. Proc. U. S. Nat. Mus., vol. 14, pp. 413-446.
MACMILLAN, DONALD BAXTER.
1918. Four years in the White North.
MACOUN, JOHN, and MACOUN, JAMES MELVILLE.
1909. Catalogue of Canadian birds, ed. 2.
MACPHERSON, ARTHUR HOLTE.
1929. A list of the birds of inner London. British Birds, vol. 22, pp. 222-244
MAILLIARD, JOHN WARD.
1912. Concerning nesting sites of the California jay. Condor, vol. 14, p. 42.
MAILLIARD, JOSEPH.
1900. California jay again. Condor, vol. 2, pp. 58-59.
1904. California jays and cats. Condor, vol. 6, pp. 94-95.
1908. Cooper hawks attacking crows. Condor, vol. 10, p. 129.
1920. Notes on nutcrackers in Monterey County, California. Condor, vol. 22, pp. 160-161.
1927. The birds and mammals of Modoc County, California. Proc. California Acad. Sci., ser. 4, vol. 16, pp. 261-359.
1931. Unique nesting site of Santa Cruz chickadees. Condor, vol. 33, pp. 220-221.
MAYAUD, NOEL.
1933. Notes et remarques sur quelques corvides. La pie Pica pica (L.). Alauda, ser. 3, vol. 5, pp. 362-382
MAYNARD, CHARLES JOHNSON.
1896. The birds of eastern North America.
MCATEE, WALDO LEE.
1914. Birds transporting food supplies. Auk, vol. 31, pp. 404-405.
1926. The relation of birds to woodlots in New York State. Roosevelt Wildlife Bull., vol. 4, pp. 7-152.
MCLAUGHLIN, RICHARD BURTON.
1888. Nesting of the tufted titmouse. Ornithologist and Oologist, vol. 13, pp. 61-63.
MCMANUS, REID.
1935. Feedings habits of the raven in winter. Auk, vol. 52, p. 89.
MEISE, WILHELM.
1928. Der Verbreitung der Aaskrähe (Formenkreis Corvus corvus L.). Journ. für Orn., 1928, pp. 1-203.

MERRIAM, CLINTON HART.
1885. A remarkable migration of Canada jays. Auk, vol. 2, p. 107.
MERRILL, JAMES CUSHING.
1876. Notes on Texan birds. Bull. Nuttall Orn. Club, vol. 1, pp. 88-89.
1878. Notes on the ornithology of southern Texas, being a list of birds observed in the vicinity of Fort Brown, Texas, from February, 1876, to June, 1878. Proc. U. S. Nat. Mus., vol. 1, pp. 118-173.
MILLER, ALDEN HOLMES.
1933. The Canada jays of northern Idaho. Trans. San Diego Soc. Nat. Hist., vol. 7, pp. 289-297.
1943a. A new race of Canada jay from coastal British Columbia. Condor, vol. 45, pp. 117-118.
1943b. A new race of brown-headed chickadee from northern Washington. Occ. Pap. Mus. Zool. Louisiana State Univ., no. 14, pp. 261-263.
MILLER, ROBERT CUNNINGHAM.
1921. The flock behavior of the coast bush-tit. Condor, vol. 23, pp. 121-127.
MINOT, HENRY DAVIS.
1895. The land and game-birds of New England, ed. 2.
MITCHELL, CHARLES A., and DUTHIE, R. C.
1929. Tuberculosis in crows. Amer. Rev. Tuberculosis, vol. 19, No. 2.
MITCHELL, HORACE HEDLEY.
1915. Crows nesting on the ground. Auk, vol. 32, p. 229.
MOORE, WILLIAM HENRY.
1904. The Canada jay. Ottawa Nat., vol. 18, pp. 142-144.
MORTIMER, D. [=B. (BENJAMIN)].
1890. Notes on habits of a few birds of Orange County, Florida. Auk, vol. 7, pp. 337-343.
MOUSLEY, HENRY.
1916. Five years personal notes and observations on the birds of Hatley, Stanstead County, Quebec—1911-1915. Auk, vol. 33, pp. 57-73.
1924. Further notes and observations on the birds of Hatley, Stanstead County, Quebec. Auk, vol. 41, pp. 572-589.
MUNRO, JAMES ALEXANDER.
1919. Notes on some birds of the Okanagan Valley, British Columbia. Auk, vol. 36, pp. 64-74.
1929. Notes on the food habits of certain Raptores in British Columbia and Alberta. Condor, vol. 31, pp. 112-116.
1935. Black-headed jay mimicking loon. Condor, vol. 37, p. 170.
MURIE, OLAUS JOHAN.
1928. Notes on the Alaska chickadee. Auk, vol. 45, pp. 441-444.
NEHRLING, HENRY.
1893. Our native birds of song and beauty, vol. 1.
NELSON, ARNOLD LARS.
1934. Some early summer food preferences of the American raven in southeastern Oregon. Condor, vol. 36, pp. 10-15.
NELSON, EDWARD WILLIAM.
1887. Report upon natural history collections made in Alaska between the years 1877 and 1881. U. S. Signal Service Arctic Ser., No. 3.
NETHERSOLE-THOMPSON, CAROLINE and DESMOND.
1940. Display of the hooded crow. British Birds, vol. 34, p. 135.

NETHERSOLE-THOMPSON, DESMOND, and MUSSELWHITE, DONALD WOODWARD.
1940. Male rook incubating. British Birds, vol. 34, p. 44.
NICE, MARGARET MORSE.
1931. The birds of Oklahoma, rev. ed.
1933. Robins and Carolina chickadees remating. Bird-Banding, vol. 4, p. 157.
NICHOLSON, DONALD JOHN.
1936. Observations on the Florida blue jay. Wilson Bull., vol. 48, pp. 26-33.
NICHOLSON, EDWARD MAX, and KOCH, LUDWIG.
1936. Songs of wild birds.
NIETHAMMER, GÜNTHER.
1937. Handbuch der deutschen Vogelkunde, vol. 1.
NUTTALL, THOMAS.
1832. A manual of ornithology of the United States and of Canada. Land birds.
OBERHOLSER, HARRY CHURCH.
1896. A preliminary list of the birds of Wayne County, Ohio. Bull. Ohio Agr. Exp. Stat., vol. 1, No. 4, pp. 243-353.
1897. Critical notes on the genus *Auriparus*. Auk, vol. 14, pp. 390-394.
1914. Four new birds from Newfoundland. Proc. Biol. Soc. Washington, vol. 27, pp. 43-54.
1917. The status of *Aphelocoma cyanotis* and its allies. Condor, vol. 19, pp. 94-95.
1918. The common ravens of North America. Ohio Journ. Sci., vol. 18, pp. 213-225.
1920. Washington region. Bird-Lore, vol. 22, p. 106.
1921. The geographic races of *Cyanocitta cristata*. Auk, vol. 38, pp. 83-89.
1932. Descriptions of new birds from Oregon, chiefly from the Warner Valley region. Sci. Publ. Cleveland Mus. Nat. Hist., vol. 4, no. 1, 12 pp.
1937. Description of a new chickadee from the Eastern United States. Proc. Biol. Soc. Washington, vol. 50, pp. 219-220.
OLDHAM, CHARLES.
1930. The shell-smashing habit of gulls. Ibis, ser. 12, vol. 6, pp. 239-243.
OSGOOD, WILFRED HUDSON.
1901. Natural history of the Queen Charlotte Islands, British Columbia. North Amer. Fauna, No. 21, pp. 7-38.
PACKARD, FRED MALLERY.
1936. A black-capped chickadee victimized by the eastern cowbird. Bird-Banding, vol. 7, pp. 129-130.
PALMER, WILLIAM.
1885. Abundance of *Parus atricapillus* near Washington. Auk, vol. 2, p. 304.
1890. Notes on the birds observed during the cruise of the United States Fish Commission schooner *Grampus* in the summer of 1887. Proc. U. S. Nat. Mus., vol. 13, pp. 249-265.
PATCH, CLYDE LOUIS.
1922. A biological reconnaissance on Graham Island of the Queen Charlotte group. Can. Field Nat., vol. 36, pp. 133-136.
PEARSE, THEED.
1938. A remarkable influx of ravens into the Comox district, Vancouver Island, B. C. Murrelet, vol. 19, pp. 11-13.

PETERS, HAROLD SEYMORE.
    1936. A list of external parasites from birds of the eastern part of the United
        States. Bird-Banding, vol. 7, pp. 9-27.
PETERS, JAMES LEE.
    1920. A new jay from Alberta. Proc. New England Zool. Club, vol. 7,
        pp. 51-52.
    1927. Descriptions of new birds. Proc. New England Zool. Club, vol. 9,
        pp. 111-113.
PETTINGILL, ELEANOR RICE.
    1937. Grand Manan's Acadian chickadees. Bird-Lore, vol. 39, pp. 277-282.
PHILIPP, PHILIP BERNARD, and BOWDISH, BEECHER SCOVILLE.
    1919. Further notes on New Brunswick birds. Auk, vol. 36, pp. 36-45.
PHILIPSON, W. RAYMOND.
    1933. The rook roosts of South Northumberland and the boundaries between
        their feeding territories. British Birds, vol. 27, pp. 66-71.
PICKENS, ANDREW LEE.
    1928. Auditory protective mimicry of the chickadee. Auk, vol. 45, pp. 302-304.
PIERCE, FRED JOHN.
    1922. A crow that nearly "looped the loop." Wilson Bull., vol. 34, p. 115.
PIERS, HARRY.
    1898. Remarkable ornithological occurrence in Nova Scotia. Auk, vol. 15,
        pp. 195-196.
POTTER, LAURENCE BEDFORD.
    1927. Freak nesting site of a magpie. Condor, vol. 29, p. 249.
    1932. Unusual nesting sites. Can. Field Nat., vol. 46, p. 49.
POWYS, THOMAS LYTTLETON (afterward Lord LILFORD).
    1860. Notes on birds observed in the Ionian Islands, and the Provinces of
        Albania proper, Epirus, Acarnania, and Montenegro. Ibis, vol. 2,
        pp. 1-10, 133-140, 228-239.
PRICE, JOHN BASYL.
    1936. The family relations of the plain titmouse. Condor, vol. 38, pp. 23-28.
PYCRAFT, WILLIAM PLANE.
    1918. Some neglected aspects in the study of young birds. Trans. Norfolk
        and Norwich Nat. Soc., vol. 10, pp. 408-416.
RATHBUN, SAMUEL FREDERICK.
    1911. Notes on birds of Seattle, Washington. Auk, vol. 28, pp. 492-494.
    1916. The Lake Crescent region, Olympic Mountains, Washington, with notes
        regarding its avifauna. Auk, vol. 33, pp. 357-370.
RAY, MILTON SMITH.
    1916. More summer birds of San Francisco County. Condor, vol. 18, pp.
        222-227.
REED, JAMES HARRIS.
    1897. A novel idea of a tufted titmouse. Auk, vol. 14, p. 325.
REED, WARD.
    1927. A note on a habit of the tufted titmouse. Wilson Bull., vol. 39, p. 107.
RHOADS, SAMUEL NICHOLSON.
    1894. A reprint of the North American Zoology, by George Ord, pp. 290-361.

RIDGWAY, ROBERT.
  1877. United States geological exploration of the fortieth parallel, pt. 3:
    Ornithology.
  1882. Descriptions of several new races of American birds. Proc. U. S. Nat.
    Mus., vol. 5, pp. 9-15.
  1883. Descriptions of some new birds from Lower California, collected by
    Mr. L. Belding. Proc. U. S. Nat. Mus., vol. 6, pp. 154-156.
  1904. The birds of North and Middle America. U. S. Nat. Mus. Bull. 50,
    pt. 3.
  1912. Color standards and color nomenclature.
ROBERTS, THOMAS SADLER.
  1936. The birds of Minnesota, ed. 2, vol. 2.
ROCKWELL, ROBERT BLANCHARD.
  1907. The Woodhouse jay in western Colorado. Condor, vol. 9, pp. 81-84.
  1909. The use of magpies' nests by other birds. Condor, vol. 11, pp. 90-92.
  1910. An albino magpie. Condor, vol. 12, p. 45.
ROCKWELL, R. B., and WETMORE, ALEXANDER.
  1914. A list of birds from the vicinity of Golden, Colorado. Auk, vol. 31,
    pp. 309-333.
ROWLEY, JOHN STUART.
  1935. Notes on some birds of Lower California, Mexico. Condor, vol. 37,
    pp. 163-168.
  1939. Breeding birds of Mono County, California. Condor, vol. 41, pp. 247-254.
RUBEY, WILLIAM WALDEN.
  1933. Flight maneuvers of the raven. Bird-Lore, vol. 35, pp. 143-145.
RUSSELL, RICHARD JOEL.
  1931. Dry climates of the United States. Univ. California Publ. Geol., vol. 4,
    pp. 1-41.
SAGE, JOHN HALL; BISHOP, LOUIS BENNETT; and BLISS, WALTER PARKS.
  1913. The birds of Connecticut.
SAUNDERS, ARETAS ANDREWS.
  1914. The birds of Teton and northern Lewis and Clark Counties, Montana.
    Condor, vol. 16, pp. 124-144.
  1921. A distributional list of the birds of Montana. Pacific Coast Avifauna,
    No. 14.
SCHALOW, HERMAN.
  1904. Die Vogel der Arktis. Fauna Arctica (Römer and Schaudinn), pp.
    82-288.
SCOTT, WILLIAM EARL DODGE.
  1886. On the breeding habits of some Arizona birds. Auk, vol. 3, pp. 81-86.
SCOTT, WILLIAM LOUIS.
  1884. The winter Passeres and Picariae of Ottawa. Auk, vol. 1, pp. 156-161.
SELOUS, EDMUND.
  1901. Bird-watching.
  1927. Realities of bird life.
SENNETT, GEORGE BURRITT.
  1878. Notes on the ornithology of the lower Rio Grande of Texas, from ob-
    servations made during the season of 1877. Bull. U. S. Geol. and
    Geogr. Surv. Terr., vol. 4, pp. 1-66.

1879. Further notes on the ornithology of the lower Rio Grande of Texas, from observations made during the spring of 1878. Bull. U. S. Geol. and Geogr. Surv. Terr., vol. 5, pp. 371-440.

1888. Descriptions of a new species and two new subspecies of birds from Texas. Auk. vol. 5, pp. 43-46.

SETON, ERNEST THOMPSON.

1890. The birds of Manitoba. Proc. U. S. Nat. Mus., vol. 13, pp. 457-643.

SHELLEY, LEWIS ORMAN.

1926. Chickadees eating bees. Bird-Lore, vol. 28, pp. 337-338.

SILLOWAY, PERLEY MILTON.

1903. Birds of Fergus County, Montana. Fergus County Free High School Bull. 1.

SIMMONS, GEORGE FINLAY.

1925. Birds of the Austin region.

SIMPSON, ALAN H.

1926. Hooded crows killing a lamb. British Birds, vol. 19, p. 283.

SIMPSON, GEORGE BUCHANAN.

1925. Oregon jays. Can. Field Nat., vol. 39, pp. 29-30.

SKINNER, MILTON PHILO.

1916. The nutcrackers of Yellowstone Park. Condor, vol. 18, pp. 62-64.

1921. Notes on the Rocky Mountain jay in the Yellowstone National Park. Condor, vol. 23, pp. 147-151.

1928. A guide to the winter birds of the North Carolina sandhills.

SMITH, AUSTIN PAUL.

1910. Miscellaneous notes from the lower Rio Grande. Condor, vol. 12, pp. 93-103.

1916. Additions to the avifauna of Kerr Co., Texas. Auk, vol. 33, pp. 187-193.

SMITH, E. IRWIN.

1924. As a bird saw it. Bird-Lore, vol. 26, p. 177.

SMITH, WILBUR FRANKLIN.

1905. Blue jays at home. Bird-Lore, vol. 7, pp. 268-271.

SOPER, JOSEPH DEWEY.

1928. A faunal investigation of southern Baffin Island. Nat. Mus. Canada Bull. 53.

STOCKARD, CHARLES RUPERT.

1905. Nesting habits of birds in Mississippi. Auk, vol. 22, pp. 146-158.

STONE, WITMER.

1899. A search for the Reedy Island crow roost. Bird-Lore, vol. 1, pp. 177-180.

1926. Changed habits of blue jay at Philadelphia. Auk, vol. 43, p. 239.

1937. Bird studies at Old Cape May.

STREET, JOHN FLETCHER.

1918. Hudsonian chickadee on the Pocono Mountain, Pa. Auk, vol. 35, pp. 230-231.

SUTTON, GEORGE MIKSCH.

1929. Can the Cooper's hawk kill a crow? Auk, vol. 46, p. 235.

1932. The birds of Southampton Island. Exploration of Southampton Island, Hudson Bay, pt. 2: Zoology, sect. 2.

1934. Notes on the birds of the western panhandle of Oklahoma. Ann. Carnegie Mus., vol. 24, pp. 1-50.

1935. A new blue jay from the western border of the Great Basin. Auk, vol. 52, pp. 176-177.

SVIHLA, ARTHUR.

1933. An abnormally colored black-billed magpie. Murrelet, vol. 14, pp. 44-45.

SWAINSON, WILLIAM, and RICHARDSON, JOHN.

1831. Fauna Boreali-Americana, vol. 2: Birds.

SWANN, HARRY KIRKE.

1913. A dictionary of English and folk-names of British birds.

SWARTH, HARRY SCHELWALD.

1904. Birds of the Huachuca Mountains, Arizona. Pacific Coast Avifauna, No. 4.

1911. Birds and mammals of the 1909 Alexander Alaska Expedition. Univ. California Publ. Zool., vol. 7, pp. 9-172.

1912. Report on a collection of birds and mammals from Vancouver Island. Univ. California Publ. Zool., vol. 10, pp. 1-124.

1913. The status of Lloyd's bush-tit as a bird in Arizona. Auk, vol. 30, pp. 399-401.

1914. The California forms of the genus *Psaltriparus*. Auk, vol. 31, pp. 499-526.

1918. The Pacific coast jays of the genus *Aphelocoma*. Univ. California Publ. Zool., vol. 17, pp. 405-422.

1922. Birds and mammals of the Stikine River region of northern British Columbia and southeastern Alaska. Univ. California Publ. Zool., vol. 24, pp. 125-314.

1926. Report on a collection of birds and mammals from the Atlin region, northern British Columbia. Univ. California Publ. Zool., vol. 30, pp. 51-162.

TAVERNER, PERCY ALGERNON.

1919. The birds of the Red Deer River, Alberta. Auk, vol. 36, pp. 248-265.

1926. Birds of western Canada. Victoria Mem. Mus. Bull. 41.

1940. Canadian status of the long-tailed chickadee. Auk, vol. 57, pp. 536-541.

TAVERNER, P. A., and SWALES, BRADSHAW HALL.

1907. The birds of Point Pelee. Wilson Bull., vol. 19, pp. 133-153.

1908. The birds of Point Pelee. Wilson Bull., vol. 20, pp. 107-129.

TAYLOR, WALTER PENN.

1912. Field notes on amphibians, reptiles and birds of northern Humboldt County, Nevada, with a discussion of some of the faunal features of the region. Univ. California Publ. Zool., vol. 7, pp. 319-436.

TAYLOR, W. P., and SHAW, WILLIAM THOMAS.

1927. Mammals and birds of Mount Rainier National Park.

TERRES, JOHN KENNETH.

1940. Birds eating tent caterpillars. Auk, vol. 57, p. 422.

THAYER, HARRIET CARPENTER.

1901. Our blue jay neighbors. Bird-Lore, vol. 3, pp. 50-53.

THOMS, CRAIG SHARPE.

1927. Winning the chickadee. Bird-Lore, vol. 29, pp. 191-192.

TODD, WALTER EDMOND CLYDE.
   1928. A new blue jay from southern Florida. Auk, vol. 45, pp. 364-365.
   1940. Birds of western Pennsylvania.
TODD, W. E. C., and SUTTON, G. M.
   1936. Taxonomic remarks on the Carolina chickadee, *Penthestes carolinensis.*
         Proc. Biol. Soc. Washington, vol. 49, pp. 69-70.
TORREY, BRADFORD.
   1885. Birds in the bush.
   1889. A rambler's lease.
   1904. Nature's invitation.
TOWNSEND, CHARLES WENDELL.
   1905. The birds of Essex County, Massachusetts. Mem. Nuttall Orn. Club,
         No. 3.
   1918. A winter crow roost. Auk, vol. 35, pp. 405-416.
   1923. The voice and courtship of the crow. Bull. Essex County Orn. Club,
         vol. 5, pp. 4-8.
   1927. Notes on the courtship of the lesser scaup, everglade kite, crow, and
         boat-tailed and great-tailed grackles. Auk, vol. 44, pp. 549-554.
TOWNSEND, C. W., and ALLEN, GLOVER MORRILL.
   1907. Birds of Labrador. Proc. Boston Soc. Nat. Hist., vol. 33, pp. 277-428.
TUCKER, BERNARD WILLIAM.
   1938. The handbook of British birds, vol. 1. (By H. F. Witherby, F. C. R.
         Jourdain, Norman F. Ticehurst, and B. W. Tucker.)
TYLER, JOHN GRIPPER.
   1913. Some birds of the Fresno district, California. Pacific Coast Avifauna,
         No. 9.
TYLER, WINSOR MARRETT.
   1912. The shrike in action. Bird-Lore, vol. 14, pp. 351-352.
   1920. An odd note of the blue jay. Bird-Lore, vol. 22, pp. 160-161.
TYRRELL, WILLIAM BRYANT.
   1934. Bird notes from Whitefish Point, Michigan. Auk, vol. 51, pp. 21-26.
UPTON, LUCY H.
   1916. Interesting performance of a tufted titmouse. Bird-Lore, vol. 18, pp.
         125-126.
USSHER, RICHARD JOHN, and WARREN, ROBERT.
   1900. The birds of Ireland.
VAN DYKE, TERTIUS.
   1913. A narrow escape. Bird-Lore, vol. 15, pp. 112-113.
VAN ROSSEM, ADRIAAN JOSEPH.
   1927. Eye shine in birds, with notes on the feeding habits of some goatsuckers.
         Condor, vol. 29, pp. 25-28.
   1928. A northern race of the mountain chickadee. Auk, vol. 45, pp. 104-105.
   1931. Descriptions of new birds from the mountains of southern Nevada.
         Trans. San Diego Soc. Nat. Hist., vol. 6, pp. 325-332.
   1936. A note on the nesting of the bush-tit. Condor, vol. 38, p. 170.
VAN TYNE, JOSSELYN.
   1928. A diurnal local migration of the black-capped chickadee. Wilson Bull.,
         vol. 40, p. 252.
   1929. Notes on some birds of the Chisos Mountains of Texas. Auk, vol. 46,
         pp. 204-206.

Van Tyne, Josselyn, and Sutton, George Miksch.
1937. The birds of Brewster County, Texas. Mus. Zool. Univ. Michigan Misc. Publ. 37.
Wallace, George John.
1941. Winter studies of color-banded chickadees. Bird-Banding, vol. 12, pp. 49-67.
Warne, Frank L.
1926. "Crows is crows." Bird-Lore, vol. 28, pp. 110-116.
Warren, Edward Royal.
1912. The magpies of Culebra Creek. Bird-Lore, vol. 14, pp. 329-333.
1916. Notes on the birds of the Elk Mountain region, Gunnison County, Colorado. Auk, vol. 33, pp. 292-317.
Warren, Oscar Bird.
1899. A chapter in the life of the Canada jay. Auk, vol. 16, pp. 12-19.
Wayne, Arthur Trezevant.
1910. Birds of South Carolina. Contr. Charleston Mus., No. 1.
Weed, Clarence Moores.
1898. The winter food of chickadees. New Hampshire Coll. Agr. Exp. Stat. Bull. 54.
Wheaton, John Maynard.
1882. Report on the birds of Ohio. Geol. Surv. Ohio, vol. 4: Zoology and Botany, pp. 187-628.
Wheeler, Harry Edgar.
1922. The fish crow in Arkansas. Wilson Bull., vol. 34, pp. 239-240.
Wheelock, Irene Grosvenor.
1904. Birds of California.
White, Stewart Edward.
1893. Birds observed on Mackinac Island, Michigan, during the summers of 1889, 1890, and 1891. Auk, vol. 10, pp. 221-230.
Widmann, Otto.
1880. Notes on birds of St. Louis, Mo. Bull. Nuttall Orn. Club, vol. 5, pp. 191-192.
1907. A preliminary catalog of the birds of Missouri.
Willard, Francis Cottle.
1912. Migration of the white-necked raven. Condor, vol. 14, pp. 107-108.
Willett, George.
1941. Variation in North American ravens. Auk, vol. 58, pp. 246-249.
Wilson, Alexander, and Bonaparte, Charles Lucien.
1832. American ornithology, vols. 1, 3.
Wilson, Ralph R.
1923. An unusual experience. Bird-Lore, vol. 25, p. 124.
Witherby, Harry Forbes.
1938. The handbook of British birds, vol. 1. (By H. F. Witherby, F. C. R. Jourdain, Norman F. Ticehurst, and Bernard W. Tucker.)
Wolfe, Lloyd Raymond.
1931. Ground nesting of crows in Wyoming. Condor, vol. 33, pp. 124-125.
Woodcock, John.
1913. A friendly chickadee. Bird-Lore, vol. 15, pp. 373-375.

480   BULLETIN 191, UNITED STATES NATIONAL MUSEUM

Wright, Horace Winslow.
1909. Birds of the Boston Public Garden.
1912. Morning awakening and even-song. Auk, vol. 29, pp. 307-327.
1914. Acadian chickadees (Penthestes hudsonicus littoralis) in Boston and vicinity in the fall of 1913. Auk, vol. 31, pp. 236-242.
1917. Labrador chickadee (Penthestes hudsonicus nigricans) in Boston and vicinity in the fall of 1916. Auk, vol. 34, pp. 164-170.
1918. Labrador chickadee (Penthestes hudsonicus nigricans) in its return flight from the fall migration of 1916. Auk, vol. 35, pp. 37-40.
Yarrell, William.
1882. A history of British birds, ed. 4, vol. 2. Revised and enlarged by Alfred Newton.
Yeates, George Kirkby.
1934. The life of the rook.
Zimmer, John Todd.
1911. Some notes on the winter birds of Dawes County. Proc. Nebraska Orn. Union, vol. 5, pp. 19-30.
Zimmermann, Rudolf.
1931. Einiges über das Brutgeschäft deutscher Rabenvögel. Orn. Monatsb. Jahrg. 39, pp. 99-102.

INDEX

cristata, Cyanocitta, 35, 56, 79, 84.
Cyanocitta cristata, 33, 51, 53, 55.
Crook, Compton, on eastern crow, 240.
Crow, eastern, 226.
fish, 275.
Florida, 260.
hooded, 295.
northwestern, 269.
southern, 259.
western, 262.
Crowell, John, 377.
Crows, 1.
Cruickshank, A. D., x.
on eastern crow, 245.
Cruttenden, J. R., on northern blue jay,
35.
cryptoleucus, Corvus, 215.
Currier, E. S., on eastern crow, 250.
Cushing, J. E., Jr., on American raven,
212.
Cyanocephalus cyanocephalus, 302.
Cyanocitta, 87.
cristata, 35, 56, 79, 84.
cristata bromia, 32, 51, 53, 55.
cristata cristata, 33, 51, 53, 55.
cristata cyanotephra, 51, 56.
cristata florincola, 53.
cristata semplei, 51, 53, 55, 56.
stelleri, 64, 65, 72, 74, 100.
stelleri annectens, 63, 64, 65, 71, 72,
77.
stelleri azteca, 63.
stelleri carbonacea, 57, 63, 65.
stelleri carlottae, 63, 64.
stelleri coronata, 63.
stelleri diademata, 63, 64, 65, 71, 72,
76.
stelleri frontalis, 63, 65.
stelleri macrolopha, 65.
stelleri percontatrix, 63, 76.
stelleri stelleri, 56, 65, 71.
cyanotephra, Cyanocitta cristata, 51, 56.
cyanotis, Aphelocoma coerulescens, 102,
113.

Dales, Marie, on northern blue jay, 44.
Dambach, C. A. (See under Hicks, L. E.)
Darcus, S. J., on northwestern crow, 270.
Davis, D. E., x.
Davis, Frank S., 256.
Davis, W. B., on yellow-billed magpie,
163, 166.
Dawson, W. L., on American magpie,
138, 152.
on American raven, 203, 204, 206.
on California jay, 93, 94.
on chestnut-backed chickadee, 386,
387, 389, 390.
on Clark's nutcracker, 319.
on coast bushtit, 447.
on eastern verdin, 434.
on plain titmouse, 414, 418.

Dawson, W. L., on Santa Cruz jay, 115,
116, 117, 118.
on yellow-billed magpie, 163, 166.
on western crow, 263.
Dawson, W. L., and Bowles, J. H., on
black-capped chickadee, 329
on chestnut-backed chickadee, 387.
on gray jay, 30, 31.
on Grinnell's chickadee, 357.
on Steller's jay, 61.
Decker, F. R., and Bowles, J. H., on
Clark's nutcracker, 317, 320.
(See also under Bowles, J. H.)
De Groot, Dudley S., on Barlow's chickadee, 393.
Denslow, Henry C., 45.
on northern blue jay, 48.
Desert California jay, 104.
Devitt, O. E., x.
on Hudsonian chickadee, 373.
diademata, Cyanocitta stelleri, 63, 64, 65,
71, 72, 76.
Dice, L. R., on Alaska jay, 21, 23.
on Hudsonian chickadee, 372.
on long-tailed chickadee, 340.
Dickey, D. R., and van Rossem, A. J., on
American raven, 202.
Dickey, S. S., on black-capped chickadee,
325, 326, 327.
on Canada jay, 2.
on Carolina chickadee, 346, 347, 349,
350.
on chestnut-backed chickadee, 385,
388, 389.
on eastern crow, 231, 232.
on fish crow, 275, 276.
on Hudsonian chickadee, 372.
on northern blue jay, 37.
on northern raven, 184, 187, 188, 189,
190, 191, 195, 198.
on Steller's jay, 62.
on tufted titmouse, 394, 395, 398, 400,
401, 402, 403, 404.
Dicks, Ford, on Steller's jay, 60.
Dille, F. M., on American magpie, 145.
Dingle, Edward von S., x.
on Carolina chickadee, 344-352.
Dixon, J. B., on American raven, 204.
on California jay, 94, 99.
on Clark's nutcracker, 312, 315.
on eastern verdin, 431.
on pinyon jay, 303.
Dixon, J. S., on Alaska chickadee, 369.
on Alaska jay, 24.
(See also under Grinnell, Joseph.)
Doe, C. E., x.
on Oregon jay, 27.
on Xantus's jay, 106.
Dryobates pubescens, 128.
DuBois, A. D., on American magpie, 142.
on Canada jay, 11.
on American raven, 205.

PLATE 37

Cochise County, Ariz., May 29, 1922.   A. C. Bent.

Cochise County, Ariz., May 31, 1922.   A. C. Bent.

NESTING OF THE WHITE-NECKED RAVEN.

PLATE 38

Cochise County, Ariz.   F. C. Willard.

NESTING OF THE WHITE-NECKED RAVEN.

PLATE 39

Rehoboth, Mass., May 5, 1906.

A. C. Bent.

NESTING OF THE EASTERN CROW.

PLATE 40

C. L. Broley.

Manitoba

A. C. Bent

Chatham, Mass., May 28, 1904.

LOW NESTING OF THE EASTERN CROW.

PLATE 41

W. E. Shore.

YOUNG EASTERN CROWS

Near Toronto, Ontario, May 29, 1941.

PLATE 42

Less than a week old.

Cordelia J. Stanwood.

Erie County, N. Y.

S. A. Grimes.

YOUNG EASTERN CROWS.

PLATE 43

J. G. Suthard.

Orange County, Calif., April 14, 1940.

UNUSUALLY LARGE SET OF EGGS OF THE WESTERN CROW.

PLATE 44

J. E. Patterson.

NESTING OF THE WESTERN CROW.

Near Ashland, Oreg., April 26, 1924.

PLATE 45

Southern California.
W. L. and Irene Finle

Packed in.

Salinas River, Calif., May 1934.
E. C. Aldrich.

Nest-leaving age.

YOUNG WESTERN CROWS.

PLATE 46

Duval County, Fla.   S. A. Grimes.

Nesting site.

Bulls Island, S. C.   A. D. Cruickshank.

Adult

FISH CROW.

PLATE 47

Yosemite National Park. E. C. Aldrich.

Altitude 12,000 feet, Mount Clark.

HABITAT OF CLARK'S NUTCRACKER.

PLATE 48

Adult on nest.

Mono County, Calif.　　　　　　　　　　　　　　　　　　　E. N. Harrison.

NEST OF CLARK'S NUTCRACKER.

PLATE 49

H. D. and Ruth Wheeler.

CLARK'S NUTCRACKER.

PLATE 50

Ithaca, N. Y., May 26, 1918.   A. A. Allen.

Nest in a bird box.

Harwich, Mass., July 13, 1923.   A. C. Bent.

Adult feeding young.

BLACK-CAPPED CHICKADEE.

PLATE 51

Near Toronto, Ontario.

BLACK-CAPPED CHICKADEES.

H. M. Halliday.

PLATE 52

Ashland, Oreg., June 5, 1913.   J. E. Patterson.

NEST OF OREGON CHICKADEE.

PLATE 53

ADULT AND YOUNG OF OREGON CHICKADEE.

PLATE 54

Duval County, Fla., April 1933. S. A. Grimes.

Nesting site.

Greene County, Pa., May 9, 1919. S. S. Dickey.

CAROLINA CHICKADEE.

PLATE 55

J. E. Patterson.

Klamath County, Oreg., May 27, 1925.

J. E. Patterson.

Jackson County, Oreg., May 25, 1928

NESTING OF SHORT-TAILED CHICKADEES.

PLATE 56

Near Gilroy, Calif., April 25, 1926.   J. E. Patterson

NEST OF BARLOW'S CHICKADEE.

PLATE 57

Yellowstone National Park July 1935.   A. A. Allen.

Adult at nest in a bird box.

California   H. D. and Ruth Wheeler.

MOUNTAIN CHICKADEES, TWO SUBSPECIES

PLATE 58

Maine, June 20, 1940.

ACADIAN CHICKADEE.

Eliot Porter.

PLATE 59

June 10, 1928.

Matane County, Quebec, June 1927.   W. J. Brown.

NESTING STUB AND YOUNG OF ACADIAN CHICKADEE.

PLATE 60

S. S. Dickey.

Greene County, Pa.

S. S. Dickey.

Waynesburg, Pa.

NESTING SITES OF TUFTED TITMOUSE.

PLATE 61

Nest in a syrup can in a pear tree.

Duval County, Fla., April 24, 1931.   S. A. Grimes.

NESTING OF THE TUFTED TITMOUSE.

PLATE 62

PLAIN TITMICE, ADULTS.

H. D. and Ruth Wheeler.

PLATE 63

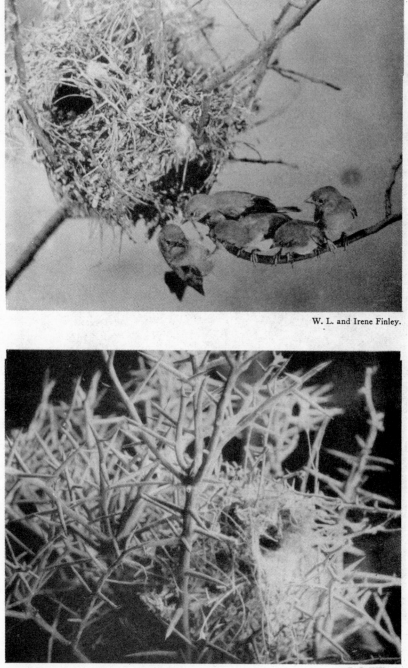

W. L. and Irene Finley.

F C. Willard

NESTS OF THE EASTERN VERDIN.

PLATE 64

S. A. Grimes.

EASTERN VERDIN AND NEST.

Cameron County, Tex., June 1940.

PLATE 65

COAST BUSHTIT AND NEST

PLATE 66

Portland Oreg.　　　　　　　　　　　　　　W. L. and Irene Finley.

COAST BUSHTIT AND NEST

PLATE 67

L. L. Haskin.

NEST OF COAST BUSHTIT IN BUSH OF HOLIDISCUS DISCOLOR.

PLATE 68

Portland, Oreg.   W. L. and Irene Finley.

Portland, Oreg.   W. L. Finley and H. T. Bohlman.

COAST BUSHTITS.

A CATALOGUE OF SELECTED DOVER BOOKS
IN ALL FIELDS OF INTEREST

A CATALOGUE OF SELECTED DOVER BOOKS
IN ALL FIELDS OF INTEREST

THE DEVIL'S DICTIONARY, Ambrose Bierce. Barbed, bitter, brilliant witticisms in the form of a dictionary. Best, most ferocious satire America has produced. 145pp. 20487-1 Pa. $1.75

ABSOLUTELY MAD INVENTIONS, A.E. Brown, H.A. Jeffcott. Hilarious, useless, or merely absurd inventions all granted patents by the U.S. Patent Office. Edible tie pin, mechanical hat tipper, etc. 57 illustrations. 125pp. 22596-8 Pa. $1.50

AMERICAN WILD FLOWERS COLORING BOOK, Paul Kennedy. Planned coverage of 48 most important wildflowers, from Rickett's collection; instructive as well as entertaining. Color versions on covers. 48pp. 8¼ x 11. 20095-7 Pa. $1.50

BIRDS OF AMERICA COLORING BOOK, John James Audubon. Rendered for coloring by Paul Kennedy. 46 of Audubon's noted illustrations: red-winged blackbird, cardinal, purple finch, towhee, etc. Original plates reproduced in full color on the covers. 48pp. 8¼ x 11. 23049-X Pa. $1.50

NORTH AMERICAN INDIAN DESIGN COLORING BOOK, Paul Kennedy. The finest examples from Indian masks, beadwork, pottery, etc. — selected and redrawn for coloring (with identifications) by well-known illustrator Paul Kennedy. 48pp. 8¼ x 11. 21125-8 Pa. $1.50

UNIFORMS OF THE AMERICAN REVOLUTION COLORING BOOK, Peter Copeland. 31 lively drawings reproduce whole panorama of military attire; each uniform has complete instructions for accurate coloring. (Not in the Pictorial Archives Series). 64pp. 8¼ x 11. 21850-3 Pa. $1.50

THE WONDERFUL WIZARD OF OZ COLORING BOOK, L. Frank Baum. Color the Yellow Brick Road and much more in 61 drawings adapted from W.W. Denslow's originals, accompanied by abridged version of text. Dorothy, Toto, Oz and the Emerald City. 61 illustrations. 64pp. 8¼ x 11. 20452-9 Pa. $1.50

CUT AND COLOR PAPER MASKS, Michael Grater. Clowns, animals, funny faces ... simply color them in, cut them out, and put them together, and you have 9 paper masks to play with and enjoy. Complete instructions. Assembled masks shown in full color on the covers. 32pp. 8¼ x 11. 23171-2 Pa. $1.50

STAINED GLASS CHRISTMAS ORNAMENT COLORING BOOK, Carol Belanger Grafton. Brighten your Christmas season with over 100 Christmas ornaments done in a stained glass effect on translucent paper. Color them in and then hang at windows, from lights, anywhere. 32pp. 8¼ x 11. 20707-2 Pa. $1.75

CREATIVE LITHOGRAPHY AND HOW TO DO IT, Grant Arnold. Lithography as art form: working directly on stone, transfer of drawings, lithotint, mezzotint, color printing; also metal plates. Detailed, thorough. 27 illustrations. 214pp.
21208-4 Pa. $3.00

DESIGN MOTIFS OF ANCIENT MEXICO, Jorge Enciso. Vigorous, powerful ceramic stamp impressions — Maya, Aztec, Toltec, Olmec. Serpents, gods, priests, dancers, etc. 153pp. 6⅛ x 9¼. 20084-1 Pa. $2.50

AMERICAN INDIAN DESIGN AND DECORATION, Leroy Appleton. Full text, plus more than 700 precise drawings of Inca, Maya, Aztec, Pueblo, Plains, NW Coast basketry, sculpture, painting, pottery, sand paintings, metal, etc. 4 plates in color. 279pp. 8⅜ x 11¼. 22704-9 Pa. $4.50

CHINESE LATTICE DESIGNS, Daniel S. Dye. Incredibly beautiful geometric designs: circles, voluted, simple dissections, etc. Inexhaustible source of ideas, motifs. 1239 illustrations. 469pp. 6⅛ x 9¼. 23096-1 Pa. $5.00

JAPANESE DESIGN MOTIFS, Matsuya Co. Mon, or heraldic designs. Over 4000 typical, beautiful designs: birds, animals, flowers, swords, fans, geometric; all beautifully stylized. 213pp. 11⅜ x 8¼. 22874-6 Pa. $5.00

PERSPECTIVE, Jan Vredeman de Vries. 73 perspective plates from 1604 edition; buildings, townscapes, stairways, fantastic scenes. Remarkable for beauty, surrealistic atmosphere; real eye-catchers. Introduction by Adolf Placzek. 74pp. 11⅜ x 8¼. 20186-4 Pa. $2.75

EARLY AMERICAN DESIGN MOTIFS, Suzanne E. Chapman. 497 motifs, designs, from painting on wood, ceramics, appliqué, glassware, samplers, metal work, etc. Florals, landscapes, birds and animals, geometrics, letters, etc. Inexhaustible. Enlarged edition. 138pp. 8⅜ x 11¼. 22985-8 Pa. $3.50
23084-8 Clothbd. $7.95

VICTORIAN STENCILS FOR DESIGN AND DECORATION, edited by E.V. Gillon, Jr. 113 wonderful ornate Victorian pieces from German sources; florals, geometrics; borders, corner pieces; bird motifs, etc. 64pp. 9⅜ x 12¼. 21995-X Pa. $2.75

ART NOUVEAU: AN ANTHOLOGY OF DESIGN AND ILLUSTRATION FROM THE STUDIO, edited by E.V. Gillon, Jr. Graphic arts: book jackets, posters, engravings, illustrations, decorations; Crane, Beardsley, Bradley and many others. Inexhaustible. 92pp. 8⅛ x 11. 22388-4 Pa. $2.50

ORIGINAL ART DECO DESIGNS, William Rowe. First-rate, highly imaginative modern Art Deco frames, borders, compositions, alphabets, florals, insectals, Wurlitzer-types, etc. Much finest modern Art Deco. 80 plates, 8 in color. 8⅜ x 11¼. 22567-4 Pa. $3.50

HANDBOOK OF DESIGNS AND DEVICES, Clarence P. Hornung. Over 1800 basic geometric designs based on circle, triangle, square, scroll, cross, etc. Largest such collection in existence. 261pp. 20125-2 Pa. $2.75

VICTORIAN HOUSES: A TREASURY OF LESSER-KNOWN EXAMPLES, Edmund Gillon and Clay Lancaster. 116 photographs, excellent commentary illustrate distinct characteristics, many borrowings of local Victorian architecture. Octagonal houses, Americanized chalets, grand country estates, small cottages, etc. Rich heritage often overlooked. 116 plates. 11⅜ x 10. 22966-1 Pa. $4.00

STICKS AND STONES, Lewis Mumford. Great classic of American cultural history; architecture from medieval-inspired earliest forms to 20th century; evolution of structure and style, influence of environment. 21 illustrations. 113pp. 20202-X Pa. $2.50

ON THE LAWS OF JAPANESE PAINTING, Henry P. Bowie. Best substitute for training with genius Oriental master, based on years of study in Kano school. Philosophy, brushes, inks, style, etc. 66 illustrations. 117pp. 6⅛ x 9¼. 20030-2 Pa. $4.50

A HANDBOOK OF ANATOMY FOR ART STUDENTS, Arthur Thomson. Virtually exhaustive. Skeletal structure, muscles, heads, special features. Full text, anatomical figures, undraped photos. Male and female. 337 illustrations. 459pp. 21163-0 Pa. $5.00

AN ATLAS OF ANATOMY FOR ARTISTS, Fritz Schider. Finest text, working book. Full text, plus anatomical illustrations; plates by great artists showing anatomy. 593 illustrations. 192pp. 7⅞ x 10¾. 20241-0 Clothbd. $6.95

THE HUMAN FIGURE IN MOTION, Eadweard Muybridge. More than 4500 stopped-action photos, in action series, showing undraped men, women, children jumping, lying down, throwing, sitting, wrestling, carrying, etc. "Unparalleled dictionary for artists," American Artist. Taken by great 19th century photographer. 390pp. 7⅞ x 10⅝. 20204-6 Clothbd. $12.50

AN ATLAS OF ANIMAL ANATOMY FOR ARTISTS, W. Ellenberger et al. Horses, dogs, cats, lions, cattle, deer, etc. Muscles, skeleton, surface features. The basic work. Enlarged edition. 288 illustrations. 151pp. 9⅜ x 12¼. 20082-5 Pa. $4.50

LETTER FORMS: 110 COMPLETE ALPHABETS, Frederick Lambert. 110 sets of capital letters; 16 lower case alphabets; 70 sets of numbers and other symbols. Edited and expanded by Theodore Menten. 110pp. 8⅛ x 11. 22872-X Pa. $3.00

THE METHODS OF CONSTRUCTION OF CELTIC ART, George Bain. Simple geometric techniques for making wonderful Celtic interlacements, spirals, Kells-type initials, animals, humans, etc. Unique for artists, craftsmen. Over 500 illustrations. 160pp. 9 x 12. USO 22923-8 Pa. $4.00

SCULPTURE, PRINCIPLES AND PRACTICE, Louis Slobodkin. Step by step approach to clay, plaster, metals, stone; classical and modern. 253 drawings, photos. 255pp. 8⅛ x 11. 22960-2 Pa. $5.00

THE ART OF ETCHING, E.S. Lumsden. Clear, detailed instructions for etching, drypoint, softground, aquatint; from 1st sketch to print. Very detailed, thorough. 200 illustrations. 376pp. 20049-3 Pa. $3.75

CONSTRUCTION OF AMERICAN FURNITURE TREASURES, Lester Margon. 344 detail drawings, complete text on constructing exact reproductions of 38 early American masterpieces: Hepplewhite sideboard, Duncan Phyfe drop-leaf table, mantel clock, gate-leg dining table, Pa. German cupboard, more. 38 plates. 54 photographs. 168pp. 8⅜ x 11¼. 23056-2 Pa. $4.00

JEWELRY MAKING AND DESIGN, Augustus F. Rose, Antonio Cirino. Professional secrets revealed in thorough, practical guide: tools, materials, processes; rings, brooches, chains, cast pieces, enamelling, setting stones, etc. Do not confuse with skimpy introductions: beginner can use, professional can learn from it. Over 200 illustrations. 306pp. 21750-7 Pa. $3.00

METALWORK AND ENAMELLING, Herbert Maryon. Generally conceded best all-around book. Countless trade secrets: materials, tools, soldering, filigree, setting, inlay, niello, repoussé, casting, polishing, etc. For beginner or expert. Author was foremost British expert. 330 illustrations. 335pp. 22702-2 Pa. $3.50

WEAVING WITH FOOT-POWER LOOMS, Edward F. Worst. Setting up a loom, beginning to weave, constructing equipment, using dyes, more, plus over 285 drafts of traditional patterns including Colonial and Swedish weaves. More than 200 other figures. For beginning and advanced. 275pp. 8¾ x 6⅜. 23064-3 Pa. $4.50

WEAVING A NAVAJO BLANKET, Gladys A. Reichard. Foremost anthropologist studied under Navajo women, reveals every step in process from wool, dyeing, spinning, setting up loom, designing, weaving. Much history, symbolism. With this book you could make one yourself. 97 illustrations. 222pp. 22992-0 Pa. $3.00

NATURAL DYES AND HOME DYEING, Rita J. Adrosko. Use natural ingredients: bark, flowers, leaves, lichens, insects etc. Over 135 specific recipes from historical sources for cotton, wool, other fabrics. Genuine premodern handicrafts. 12 illustrations. 160pp. 22688-3 Pa. $2.00

THE HAND DECORATION OF FABRICS, Francis J. Kafka. Outstanding, profusely illustrated guide to stenciling, batik, block printing, tie dyeing, freehand painting, silk screen printing, and novelty decoration. 356 illustrations. 198pp. 6 x 9. 21401-X Pa. $3.00

THOMAS NAST: CARTOONS AND ILLUSTRATIONS, with text by Thomas Nast St. Hill. Father of American political cartooning. Cartoons that destroyed Tweed Ring; inflation, free love, church and state; original Republican elephant and Democratic donkey; Santa Claus; more. 117 illustrations. 146pp. 9 x 12. 22983-1 Pa. $4.00
23067-8 Clothbd. $8.50

FREDERIC REMINGTON: 173 DRAWINGS AND ILLUSTRATIONS. Most famous of the Western artists, most responsible for our myths about the American West in its untamed days. Complete reprinting of *Drawings of Frederic Remington* (1897), plus other selections. 4 additional drawings in color on covers. 140pp. 9 x 12. 20714-5 Pa. $3.95

EARLY NEW ENGLAND GRAVESTONE RUBBINGS, Edmund V. Gillon, Jr. 43 photographs, 226 rubbings show heavily symbolic, macabre, sometimes humorous primitive American art. Up to early 19th century. 207pp. 8⅜ x 11¼.
21380-3 Pa. $4.00

L.J.M. DAGUERRE: THE HISTORY OF THE DIORAMA AND THE DAGUERREOTYPE, Helmut and Alison Gernsheim. Definitive account. Early history, life and work of Daguerre; discovery of daguerreotype process; diffusion abroad; other early photography. 124 illustrations. 226pp. 6⅙ x 9¼. 22290-X Pa. $4.00

PHOTOGRAPHY AND THE AMERICAN SCENE, Robert Taft. The basic book on American photography as art, recording form, 1839-1889. Development, influence on society, great photographers, types (portraits, war, frontier, etc.), whatever else needed. Inexhaustible. Illustrated with 322 early photos, daguerreotypes, tintypes, stereo slides, etc. 546pp. 6⅛ x 9¼. 21201-7 Pa. $5.95

PHOTOGRAPHIC SKETCHBOOK OF THE CIVIL WAR, Alexander Gardner. Reproduction of 1866 volume with 100 on-the-field photographs: Manassas, Lincoln on battlefield, slave pens, etc. Introduction by E.F. Bleiler. 224pp. 10¾ x 9.
22731-6 Pa. $5.00

THE MOVIES: A PICTURE QUIZ BOOK, Stanley Appelbaum & Hayward Cirker. Match stars with their movies, name actors and actresses, test your movie skill with 241 stills from 236 great movies, 1902-1959. Indexes of performers and films. 128pp. 8⅜ x 9¼. 20222-4 Pa. $2.50

THE TALKIES, Richard Griffith. Anthology of features, articles from Photoplay, 1928-1940, reproduced complete. Stars, famous movies, technical features, fabulous ads, etc.; Garbo, Chaplin, King Kong, Lubitsch, etc. 4 color plates, scores of illustrations. 327pp. 8⅜ x 11¼. 22762-6 Pa. $6.95

THE MOVIE MUSICAL FROM VITAPHONE TO "42ND STREET," edited by Miles Kreuger. Relive the rise of the movie musical as reported in the pages of Photoplay magazine (1926-1933): every movie review, cast list, ad, and record review; every significant feature article, production still, biography, forecast, and gossip story. Profusely illustrated. 367pp. 8⅜ x 11¼. 23154-2 Pa. $7.95

JOHANN SEBASTIAN BACH, Philipp Spitta. Great classic of biography, musical commentary, with hundreds of pieces analyzed. Also good for Bach's contemporaries. 450 musical examples. Total of 1799pp.
EUK 22278-0, 22279-9 Clothbd., Two vol. set $25.00

BEETHOVEN AND HIS NINE SYMPHONIES, Sir George Grove. Thorough history, analysis, commentary on symphonies and some related pieces. For either beginner or advanced student. 436 musical passages. 407pp. 20334-4 Pa. $4.00

MOZART AND HIS PIANO CONCERTOS, Cuthbert Girdlestone. The only full-length study. Detailed analyses of all 21 concertos, sources; 417 musical examples. 509pp. 21271-8 Pa. $6.00

THE FITZWILLIAM VIRGINAL BOOK, edited by J. Fuller Maitland, W.B. Squire. Famous early 17th century collection of keyboard music, 300 works by Morley, Byrd, Bull, Gibbons, etc. Modern notation. Total of 938pp. 8⅜ x 11.
ECE 21068-5, 21069-3 Pa., Two vol. set $15.00

COMPLETE STRING QUARTETS, Wolfgang A. Mozart. Breitkopf and Härtel edition. All 23 string quartets plus alternate slow movement to K156. Study score. 277pp. 9⅜ x 12¼. 22372-8 Pa. $6.00

COMPLETE SONG CYCLES, Franz Schubert. Complete piano, vocal music of Die Schöne Müllerin, Die Winterreise, Schwanengesang. Also Drinker English singing translations. Breitkopf and Härtel edition. 217pp. 9⅜ x 12¼.
22649-2 Pa. $4.50

THE COMPLETE PRELUDES AND ETUDES FOR PIANOFORTE SOLO, Alexander Scriabin. All the preludes and etudes including many perfectly spun miniatures. Edited by K.N. Igumnov and Y.I. Mil'shteyn. 250pp. 9 x 12. 22919-X Pa. $5.00

TRISTAN UND ISOLDE, Richard Wagner. Full orchestral score with complete instrumentation. Do not confuse with piano reduction. Commentary by Felix Mottl, great Wagnerian conductor and scholar. Study score. 655pp. 8⅛ x 11.
22915-7 Pa. $11.95

FAVORITE SONGS OF THE NINETIES, ed. Robert Fremont. Full reproduction, including covers, of 88 favorites: Ta-Ra-Ra-Boom-De-Aye, The Band Played On, Bird in a Gilded Cage, Under the Bamboo Tree, After the Ball, etc. 401pp. 9 x 12.
EBE 21536-9 Pa. $6.95

SOUSA'S GREAT MARCHES IN PIANO TRANSCRIPTION: ORIGINAL SHEET MUSIC OF 23 WORKS, John Philip Sousa. Selected by Lester S. Levy. Playing edition includes: The Stars and Stripes Forever, The Thunderer, The Gladiator, King Cotton, Washington Post, much more. 24 illustrations. 111pp. 9 x 12.
USO 23132-1 Pa. $3.50

CLASSIC PIANO RAGS, selected with an introduction by Rudi Blesh. Best ragtime music (1897-1922) by Scott Joplin, James Scott, Joseph F. Lamb, Tom Turpin, 9 others. Printed from best original sheet music, plus covers. 364pp. 9 x 12.
EBE 20469-3 Pa. $6.95

ANALYSIS OF CHINESE CHARACTERS, C.D. Wilder, J.H. Ingram. 1000 most important characters analyzed according to primitives, phonetics, historical development. Traditional method offers mnemonic aid to beginner, intermediate student of Chinese, Japanese. 365pp. 23045-7 Pa. $4.00

MODERN CHINESE: A BASIC COURSE, Faculty of Peking University. Self study, classroom course in modern Mandarin. Records contain phonetics, vocabulary, sentences, lessons. 249 page book contains all recorded text, translations, grammar, vocabulary, exercises. Best course on market. 3 12" 33⅓ monaural records, book, album. 98832-5 Set $12.50

THE BEST DR. THORNDYKE DETECTIVE STORIES, R. Austin Freeman. The Case of Oscar Brodski, The Moabite Cipher, and 5 other favorites featuring the great scientific detective, plus his long-believed-lost first adventure — 31 New Inn — reprinted here for the first time. Edited by E.F. Bleiler. USO 20388-3 Pa. $3.00

BEST "THINKING MACHINE" DETECTIVE STORIES, Jacques Futrelle. The Problem of Cell 13 and 11 other stories about Prof. Augustus S.F.X. Van Dusen, including two "lost" stories. First reprinting of several. Edited by E.F. Bleiler. 241pp. 20537-1 Pa. $3.00

UNCLE SILAS, J. Sheridan LeFanu. Victorian Gothic mystery novel, considered by many best of period, even better than Collins or Dickens. Wonderful psychological terror. Introduction by Frederick Shroyer. 436pp. 21715-9 Pa. $4.00

BEST DR. POGGIOLI DETECTIVE STORIES, T.S. Stribling. 15 best stories from EQMM and The Saint offer new adventures in Mexico, Florida, Tennessee hills as Poggioli unravels mysteries and combats Count Jalacki. 217pp. 23227-1 Pa. $3.00

EIGHT DIME NOVELS, selected with an introduction by E.F. Bleiler. Adventures of Old King Brady, Frank James, Nick Carter, Deadwood Dick, Buffalo Bill, The Steam Man, Frank Merriwell, and Horatio Alger — 1877 to 1905. Important, entertaining popular literature in facsimile reprint, with original covers. 190pp. 9 x 12. 22975-0 Pa. $3.50

ALICE'S ADVENTURES UNDER GROUND, Lewis Carroll. Facsimile of ms. Carroll gave Alice Liddell in 1864. Different in many ways from final Alice. Handlettered, illustrated by Carroll. Introduction by Martin Gardner. 128pp. 21482-6 Pa. $1.50

ALICE IN WONDERLAND COLORING BOOK, Lewis Carroll. Pictures by John Tenniel. Large-size versions of the famous illustrations of Alice, Cheshire Cat, Mad Hatter and all the others, waiting for your crayons. Abridged text. 36 illustrations. 64pp. 8¼ x 11. 22853-3 Pa. $1.50

AVENTURES D'ALICE AU PAYS DES MERVEILLES, Lewis Carroll. Bué's translation of "Alice" into French, supervised by Carroll himself. Novel way to learn language. (No English text.) 42 Tenniel illustrations. 196pp. 22836-3 Pa. $2.50

MYTHS AND FOLK TALES OF IRELAND, Jeremiah Curtin. 11 stories that are Irish versions of European fairy tales and 9 stories from the Fenian cycle — 20 tales of legend and magic that comprise an essential work in the history of folklore. 256pp. 22430-9 Pa. $3.00

EAST O' THE SUN AND WEST O' THE MOON, George W. Dasent. Only full edition of favorite, wonderful Norwegian fairytales — Why the Sea is Salt, Boots and the Troll, etc. — with 77 illustrations by Kittelsen & Werenskiöld. 418pp. 22521-6 Pa. $4.00

PERRAULT'S FAIRY TALES, Charles Perrault and Gustave Doré. Original versions of Cinderella, Sleeping Beauty, Little Red Riding Hood, etc. in best translation, with 34 wonderful illustrations by Gustave Doré. 117pp. 8⅛ x 11. 22311-6 Pa. $2.50

MOTHER GOOSE'S MELODIES. Facsimile of fabulously rare Munroe and Francis "copyright 1833" Boston edition. Familiar and unusual rhymes, wonderful old woodcut illustrations. Edited by E.F. Bleiler. 128pp. 4½ x 6⅜. 22577-1 Pa. $1.50

MOTHER GOOSE IN HIEROGLYPHICS. Favorite nursery rhymes presented in rebus form for children. Fascinating 1849 edition reproduced in toto, with key. Introduction by E.F. Bleiler. About 400 woodcuts. 64pp. 6⅞ x 5¼. 20745-5 Pa. $1.00

PETER PIPER'S PRACTICAL PRINCIPLES OF PLAIN & PERFECT PRONUNCIATION. Alliterative jingles and tongue-twisters. Reproduction in full of 1830 first American edition. 25 spirited woodcuts. 32pp. 4½ x 6⅜. 22560-7 Pa. $1.00

MARMADUKE MULTIPLY'S MERRY METHOD OF MAKING MINOR MATHEMATICIANS. Fellow to Peter Piper, it teaches multiplication table by catchy rhymes and woodcuts. 1841 Munroe & Francis edition. Edited by E.F. Bleiler. 103pp. 4⅝ x 6.
22773-1 Pa. $1.25
20171-6 Clothbd. $3.00

THE NIGHT BEFORE CHRISTMAS, Clement Moore. Full text, and woodcuts from original 1848 book. Also critical, historical material. 19 illustrations. 40pp. 4⅝ x 6. 22797-9 Pa. $1.25

THE KING OF THE GOLDEN RIVER, John Ruskin. Victorian children's classic of three brothers, their attempts to reach the Golden River, what becomes of them. Facsimile of original 1889 edition. 22 illustrations. 56pp. 4⅝ x 6⅜.
20066-3 Pa. $1.50

DREAMS OF THE RAREBIT FIEND, Winsor McCay. Pioneer cartoon strip, unexcelled for beauty, imagination, in 60 full sequences. Incredible technical virtuosity, wonderful visual wit. Historical introduction. 62pp. 8⅜ x 11¼. 21347-1 Pa. $2.50

THE KATZENJAMMER KIDS, Rudolf Dirks. In full color, 14 strips from 1906-7; full of imagination, characteristic humor. Classic of great historical importance. Introduction by August Derleth. 32pp. 9¼ x 12¼. 23005-8 Pa. $2.00

LITTLE ORPHAN ANNIE AND LITTLE ORPHAN ANNIE IN COSMIC CITY, Harold Gray. Two great sequences from the early strips: our curly-haired heroine defends the Warbucks' financial empire and, then, takes on meanie Phineas P. Pinchpenny. Leapin' lizards! 178pp. 6⅛ x 8⅜. 23107-0 Pa. $2.00

THE BEST OF GLUYAS WILLIAMS. 100 drawings by one of America's finest cartoonists: The Day a Cake of Ivory Soap Sank at Proctor & Gamble's, At the Life Insurance Agents' Banquet, and many other gems from the 20's and 30's. 118pp. 8⅜ x 11¼. 22737-5 Pa. $2.50

THE MAGIC MOVING PICTURE BOOK, Bliss, Sands & Co. The pictures in this book move! Volcanoes erupt, a house burns, a serpentine dancer wiggles her way through a number. By using a specially ruled acetate screen provided, you can obtain these and 15 other startling effects. Originally "The Motograph Moving Picture Book." 32pp. 8¼ x 11. 23224-7 Pa. $1.75

STRING FIGURES AND HOW TO MAKE THEM, Caroline F. Jayne. Fullest, clearest instructions on string figures from around world: Eskimo, Navajo, Lapp, Europe, more. Cats cradle, moving spear, lightning, stars. Introduction by A.C. Haddon. 950 illustrations. 407pp. 20152-X Pa. $3.50

PAPER FOLDING FOR BEGINNERS, William D. Murray and Francis J. Rigney. Clearest book on market for making origami sail boats, roosters, frogs that move legs, cups, bonbon boxes. 40 projects. More than 275 illustrations. Photographs. 94pp. 20713-7 Pa. $1.25

INDIAN SIGN LANGUAGE, William Tomkins. Over 525 signs developed by Sioux, Blackfoot, Cheyenne, Arapahoe and other tribes. Written instructions and diagrams: how to make words, construct sentences. Also 290 pictographs of Sioux and Ojibway tribes. 111pp. 6⅛ x 9¼. 22029-X Pa. $1.50

BOOMERANGS: HOW TO MAKE AND THROW THEM, Bernard S. Mason. Easy to make and throw, dozens of designs: cross-stick, pinwheel, boomabird, tumblestick, Australian curved stick boomerang. Complete throwing instructions. All safe. 99pp. 23028-7 Pa. $1.75

25 KITES THAT FLY, Leslie Hunt. Full, easy to follow instructions for kites made from inexpensive materials. Many novelties. Reeling, raising, designing your own. 70 illustrations. 110pp. 22550-X Pa. $1.25

TRICKS AND GAMES ON THE POOL TABLE, Fred Herrmann. 79 tricks and games, some solitaires, some for 2 or more players, some competitive; mystifying shots and throws, unusual carom, tricks involving cork, coins, a hat, more. 77 figures. 95pp. 21814-7 Pa. $1.25

WOODCRAFT AND CAMPING, Bernard S. Mason. How to make a quick emergency shelter, select woods that will burn immediately, make do with limited supplies, etc. Also making many things out of wood, rawhide, bark, at camp. Formerly titled Woodcraft. 295 illustrations. 580pp. 21951-8 Pa. $4.00

AN INTRODUCTION TO CHESS MOVES AND TACTICS SIMPLY EXPLAINED, Leonard Barden. Informal intermediate introduction: reasons for moves, tactics, openings, traps, positional play, endgame. Isolates patterns. 102pp. USO 21210-6 Pa. $1.35

LASKER'S MANUAL OF CHESS, Dr. Emanuel Lasker. Great world champion offers very thorough coverage of all aspects of chess. Combinations, position play, openings, endgame, aesthetics of chess, philosophy of struggle, much more. Filled with analyzed games. 390pp. 20640-8 Pa. $4.00

CATALOGUE OF DOVER BOOKS

DRIED FLOWERS, Sarah Whitlock and Martha Rankin. Concise, clear, practical guide to dehydration, glycerinizing, pressing plant material, and more. Covers use of silica gel. 12 drawings. Originally titled "New Techniques with Dried Flowers." 32pp. 21802-3 Pa. $1.00

ABC OF POULTRY RAISING, J.H. Florea. Poultry expert, editor tells how to raise chickens on home or small business basis. Breeds, feeding, housing, laying, etc. Very concrete, practical. 50 illustrations. 256pp. 23201-8 Pa. $3.00

HOW INDIANS USE WILD PLANTS FOR FOOD, MEDICINE & CRAFTS, Frances Densmore. Smithsonian, Bureau of American Ethnology report presents wealth of material on nearly 200 plants used by Chippewas of Minnesota and Wisconsin. 33 plates plus 122pp. of text. 6⅛ x 9¼. 23019-8 Pa. $2.50

THE HERBAL OR GENERAL HISTORY OF PLANTS, John Gerard. The 1633 edition revised and enlarged by Thomas Johnson. Containing almost 2850 plant descriptions and 2705 superb illustrations, Gerard's Herbal is a monumental work, the book all modern English herbals are derived from, and the one herbal every serious enthusiast should have in its entirety. Original editions are worth perhaps $750. 1678pp. 8½ x 12¼. 23147-X Clothbd. $50.00

A MODERN HERBAL, Margaret Grieve. Much the fullest, most exact, most useful compilation of herbal material. Gigantic alphabetical encyclopedia, from aconite to zedoary, gives botanical information, medical properties, folklore, economic uses, and much else. Indispensable to serious reader. 161 illustrations. 888pp. 6½ x 9¼. USO 22798-7, 22799-5 Pa., Two vol. set $10.00

HOW TO KNOW THE FERNS, Frances T. Parsons. Delightful classic. Identification, fern lore, for Eastern and Central U.S.A. Has introduced thousands to interesting life form. 99 illustrations. 215pp. 20740-4 Pa. $2.75

THE MUSHROOM HANDBOOK, Louis C.C. Krieger. Still the best popular handbook. Full descriptions of 259 species, extremely thorough text, habitats, luminescence, poisons, folklore, etc. 32 color plates; 126 other illustrations. 560pp. 21861-9 Pa. $4.50

HOW TO KNOW THE WILD FRUITS, Maude G. Peterson. Classic guide covers nearly 200 trees, shrubs, smaller plants of the U.S. arranged by color of fruit and then by family. Full text provides names, descriptions, edibility, uses. 80 illustrations. 400pp. 22943-2 Pa. $4.00

COMMON WEEDS OF THE UNITED STATES, U.S. Department of Agriculture. Covers 220 important weeds with illustration, maps, botanical information, plant lore for each. Over 225 illustrations. 463pp. 6⅛ x 9¼. 20504-5 Pa. $4.50

HOW TO KNOW THE WILD FLOWERS, Mrs. William S. Dana. Still best popular book for East and Central USA. Over 500 plants easily identified, with plant lore; arranged according to color and flowering time. 174 plates. 459pp. 20332-8 Pa. $3.50

DRIED FLOWERS, Sarah Whitlock and Martha Rankin. Concise, clear, practical guide to dehydration, glycerinizing, pressing plant material, and more. Covers use of silica gel. 12 drawings. Originally titled "New Techniques with Dried Flowers." 32pp. 21802-3 Pa. $1.00

ABC OF POULTRY RAISING, J.H. Florea. Poultry expert, editor tells how to raise chickens on home or small business basis. Breeds, feeding, housing, laying, etc. Very concrete, practical. 50 illustrations. 256pp. 23201-8 Pa. $3.00

HOW INDIANS USE WILD PLANTS FOR FOOD, MEDICINE & CRAFTS, Frances Densmore. Smithsonian, Bureau of American Ethnology report presents wealth of material on nearly 200 plants used by Chippewas of Minnesota and Wisconsin. 33 plates plus 122pp. of text. 6⅛ x 9¼. 23019-8 Pa. $2.50

THE HERBAL OR GENERAL HISTORY OF PLANTS, John Gerard. The 1633 edition revised and enlarged by Thomas Johnson. Containing almost 2850 plant descriptions and 2705 superb illustrations, Gerard's Herbal is a monumental work, the book all modern English herbals are derived from, and the one herbal every serious enthusiast should have in its entirety. Original editions are worth perhaps $750. 1678pp. 8½ x 12¼. 23147-X Clothbd. $50.00

A MODERN HERBAL, Margaret Grieve. Much the fullest, most exact, most useful compilation of herbal material. Gigantic alphabetical encyclopedia, from aconite to zedoary, gives botanical information, medical properties, folklore, economic uses, and much else. Indispensable to serious reader. 161 illustrations. 888pp. 6½ x 9¼. USO 22798-7, 22799-5 Pa., Two vol. set $10.00

HOW TO KNOW THE FERNS, Frances T. Parsons. Delightful classic. Identification, fern lore, for Eastern and Central U.S.A. Has introduced thousands to interesting life form. 99 illustrations. 215pp. 20740-4 Pa. $2.75

THE MUSHROOM HANDBOOK, Louis C.C. Krieger. Still the best popular handbook. Full descriptions of 259 species, extremely thorough text, habitats, luminescence, poisons, folklore, etc. 32 color plates; 126 other illustrations. 560pp. 21861-9 Pa. $4.50

HOW TO KNOW THE WILD FRUITS, Maude G. Peterson. Classic guide covers nearly 200 trees, shrubs, smaller plants of the U.S. arranged by color of fruit and then by family. Full text provides names, descriptions, edibility, uses. 80 illustrations. 400pp. 22943-2 Pa. $4.00

COMMON WEEDS OF THE UNITED STATES, U.S. Department of Agriculture. Covers 220 important weeds with illustration, maps, botanical information, plant lore for each. Over 225 illustrations. 463pp. 6⅛ x 9¼. 20504-5 Pa. $4.50

HOW TO KNOW THE WILD FLOWERS, Mrs. William S. Dana. Still best popular book for East and Central USA. Over 500 plants easily identified, with plant lore; arranged according to color and flowering time. 174 plates. 459pp. 20332-8 Pa. $3.50

THE STYLE OF PALESTRINA AND THE DISSONANCE, Knud Jeppesen. Standard analysis of rhythm, line, harmony, accented and unaccented dissonances. Also pre-Palestrina dissonances. 306pp.   22386-8 Pa. $4.50

DOVER OPERA GUIDE AND LIBRETTO SERIES prepared by Ellen H. Bleiler. Each volume contains everything needed for background, complete enjoyment: complete libretto, new English translation with all repeats, biography of composer and librettist, early performance history, musical lore, much else. All volumes lavishly illustrated with performance photos, portraits, similar material. Do not confuse with skimpy performance booklets.

CARMEN, Georges Bizet. 66 illustrations. 222pp.   22111-3 Pa. $3.00
DON GIOVANNI, Wolfgang A. Mozart. 92 illustrations. 209pp.   21134-7 Pa. $2.50
LA BOHÈME, Giacomo Puccini. 73 illustrations. 124pp.   USO 20404-9 Pa. $1.75
ÄIDA, Giuseppe Verdi. 76 illustrations. 181pp.   20405-7 Pa. $2.25
LUCIA DI LAMMERMOOR, Gaetano Donizetti. 44 illustrations. 186pp.
                                                               22110-5 Pa. $2.00

ANTONIO STRADIVARI: HIS LIFE AND WORK, W. H. Hill, et al. Great work of musicology. Construction methods, woods, varnishes, known instruments, types of instruments, life, special features. Introduction by Sydney Beck. 98 illustrations, plus 4 color plates. 315pp.   20425-1 Pa. $4.00

MUSIC FOR THE PIANO, James Friskin, Irwin Freundlich. Both famous, little-known compositions; 1500 to 1950's. Listing, description, classification, technical aspects for student, teacher, performer. Indispensable for enlarging repertory. 448pp.
                                                               22918-1 Pa. $4.00

PIANOS AND THEIR MAKERS, Alfred Dolge. Leading inventor offers full history of piano technology, earliest models to 1910. Types, makers, components, mechanisms, musical aspects. Very strong on offtrail models, inventions; also player pianos. 300 illustrations. 581pp.   22856-8 Pa. $5.00

KEYBOARD MUSIC, J.S. Bach. Bach-Gesellschaft edition. For harpsichord, piano, other keyboard instruments. English Suites, French Suites, Six Partitas, Goldberg Variations, Two-Part Inventions, Three-Part Sinfonias. 312pp. 8⅛ x 11.
                                                               22360-4 Pa. $5.00

COMPLETE STRING QUARTETS, Ludwig van Beethoven. Breitkopf and Härtel edition. 6 quartets of Opus 18; 3 quartets of Opus 59; Opera 74, 95, 127, 130, 131, 132, 135 and Grosse Fuge. Study score. 434pp. 9⅜ x 12¼.   22361-2 Pa. $7.95

COMPLETE PIANO SONATAS AND VARIATIONS FOR SOLO PIANO, Johannes Brahms. All sonatas, five variations on themes from Schumann, Paganini, Handel, etc. Vienna Gesellschaft der Musikfreunde edition. 178pp. 9 x 12.   22650-6 Pa. $4.50

PIANO MUSIC 1888-1905, Claude Debussy. Deux Arabesques, Suite Bergamesque, Masques, 1st series of Images, etc. 9 others, in corrected editions. 175pp. 9⅜ x 12¼.   22771-5 Pa. $4.00

INCIDENTS OF TRAVEL IN YUCATAN, John L. Stephens. Classic (1843) exploration of jungles of Yucatan, looking for evidences of Maya civilization. Travel adventures, Mexican and Indian culture, etc. Total of 669pp.
20926-1, 20927-X Pa., Two vol. set $6.00

LIVING MY LIFE, Emma Goldman. Candid, no holds barred account by foremost American anarchist: her own life, anarchist movement, famous contemporaries, ideas and their impact. Struggles and confrontations in America, plus deportation to U.S.S.R. Shocking inside account of persecution of anarchists under Lenin. 13 plates. Total of 944pp.
22543-7, 22544-5 Pa., Two vol. set $9.00

AMERICAN INDIANS, George Catlin. Classic account of life among Plains Indians: ceremonies, hunt, warfare, etc. Dover edition reproduces for first time all original paintings. 312 plates. 572pp. of text. 6⅛ x 9¼.
22118-0, 22119-9 Pa., Two vol. set $8.00
22140-7, 22144-X Clothbd., Two vol. set $16.00.

THE INDIANS' BOOK, Natalie Curtis. Lore, music, narratives, drawings by Indians, collected from cultures of U.S.A. 149 songs in full notation. 45 illustrations. 583pp. 6⅝ x 9⅜.
21939-9 Pa. $6.95

INDIAN BLANKETS AND THEIR MAKERS, George Wharton James. History, old style wool blankets, changes brought about by traders, symbolism of design and color, a Navajo weaver at work, outline blanket, Kachina blankets, more. Emphasis on Navajo. 130 illustrations, 32 in color. 230pp. 6⅛ x 9¼.
22996-3 Pa. $5.00
23068-6 Clothbd. $10.00

AN INTRODUCTION TO THE STUDY OF THE MAYA HIEROGLYPHS, Sylvanus Griswold Morley. Classic study by one of the truly great figures in hieroglyph research. Still the best introduction for the student for reading Maya hieroglyphs. New introduction by J. Eric S. Thompson. 117 illustrations. 284pp.
23108-9 Pa. $4.00

THE ANALECTS OF CONFUCIUS, THE GREAT LEARNING, DOCTRINE OF THE MEAN, Confucius. Edited by James Legge. Full Chinese text, standard English translation on same page, Chinese commentators, editor's annotations; dictionary of characters at rear, plus grammatical comment. Finest edition anywhere of one of world's greatest thinkers. 503pp.
22746-4 Pa. $5.00

THE I CHING (THE BOOK OF CHANGES), translated by James Legge. Complete translation of basic text plus appendices by Confucius, and Chinese commentary of most penetrating divination manual ever prepared. Indispensable to study of early Oriental civilizations, to modern inquiring reader. 448pp.
21062-6 Pa. $3.50

THE EGYPTIAN BOOK OF THE DEAD, E.A. Wallis Budge. Complete reproduction of Ani's papyrus, finest ever found. Full hieroglyphic text, interlinear transliteration, word for word translation, smooth translation. Basic work, for Egyptology, for modern study of psychic matters. Total of 533pp. 6½ x 9¼.
EBE 21866-X Pa. $4.95

BUILD YOUR OWN LOW-COST HOME, L.O. Anderson, H.F. Zornig. U.S. Dept. of Agriculture sets of plans, full, detailed, for 11 houses: A-Frame, circular, conventional. Also construction manual. Save hundreds of dollars. 204pp. 11 x 16.
21525-3 Pa. $6.00

HOW TO BUILD A WOOD-FRAME HOUSE, L.O. Anderson. Comprehensive, easy to follow U.S. Government manual: placement, foundations, framing, sheathing, roof, insulation, plaster, finishing — almost everything else. 179 illustrations. 223pp. 7⅞ x 10¾.
22954-8 Pa. $3.50

CONCRETE, MASONRY AND BRICKWORK, U.S. Department of the Army. Practical handbook for the home owner and small builder manual contains basic principles, techniques, and important background information on construction with concrete, concrete blocks, and brick. 177 figures, 37 tables. 200pp. 6½ x 9¼.
23203-4 Pa. $4.00

THE STANDARD BOOK OF QUILT MAKING AND COLLECTING, Marguerite Ickis. Full information, full-sized patterns for making 46 traditional quilts, also 150 other patterns. Quilted cloths, lamé, satin quilts, etc. 483 illustrations. 273pp. 6⅞ x 9⅝.
20582-7 Pa. $3.50

101 PATCHWORK PATTERNS, Ruby S. McKim. 101 beautiful, immediately useable patterns, full-size, modern and traditional. Also general information, estimating, quilt lore. 124pp. 7⅞ x 10¾.
20773-0 Pa. $2.50

KNIT YOUR OWN NORWEGIAN SWEATERS, Dale Yarn Company. Complete instructions for 50 authentic sweaters, hats, mittens, gloves, caps, etc. Thoroughly modern designs that command high prices in stores. 24 patterns, 24 color photographs. Nearly 100 charts and other illustrations. 58pp. 8⅜ x 11¼.
23031-7 Pa. $2.50

IRON-ON TRANSFER PATTERNS FOR CREWEL AND EMBROIDERY FROM EARLY AMERICAN SOURCES, edited by Rita Weiss. 75 designs, borders, alphabets, from traditional American sources printed on translucent paper in transfer ink. Reuseable. Instructions. Test patterns. 24pp. 8¼ x 11.
23162-3 Pa. $1.50

AMERICAN INDIAN NEEDLEPOINT DESIGNS FOR PILLOWS, BELTS, HANDBAGS AND OTHER PROJECTS, Roslyn Epstein. 37 authentic American Indian designs adapted for modern needlepoint projects. Grid backing makes designs easily transferable to canvas. 48pp. 8¼ x 11.
22973-4 Pa. $1.50

CHARTED FOLK DESIGNS FOR CROSS-STITCH EMBROIDERY, Maria Foris & Andreas Foris. 278 charted folk designs, most in 2 colors, from Danube region: florals, fantastic beasts, geometrics, traditional symbols, more. Border and central patterns. 77pp. 8¼ x 11.
USO 23191-7 Pa. $2.00

Prices subject to change without notice.
Available at your book dealer or write for free catalogue to Dept. GI, Dover Publications, Inc., 180 Varick St., N.Y., N.Y. 10014. Dover publishes more than 150 books each year on science, elementary and advanced mathematics, biology, music, art, literary history, social sciences and other areas.